JUNIOR COLLEGE DISTRICT
of St. Louis · St. Louis County
LIBRARY

7508 Forsyth Blvd.
St. Louis, Missouri 63105

PRINTED IN U.S.A.

ELECTRICAL ENGINEERING

STUDYING TO PASS
THE PROFESSIONAL ENGINEERS'
LICENSING EXAMINATION

Allan D. Kraus—Editor

DeRienzo: CHEMICAL ENGINEERING

Franklin: ELECTRICAL ENGINEERING

Kraus: STUDYING TO PASS THE PROFESSIONAL
ENGINEERS' LICENSING EXAMINATION

Naparstek: MECHANICAL ENGINEERING

Raphael: CIVIL ENGINEERING

Rosenthal: ENGINEERING ECONOMICS AND PRACTICE

JULIUS I. FRANKLIN, P.E.

Senior Engineer, Sperry Gyroscope Company

ELECTRICAL ENGINEERING

THE MACMILLAN COMPANY, NEW YORK
COLLIER-MACMILLAN LIMITED, LONDON

TO

MARLENE, STEVEN, AND SHARI

First Printing

Library of Congress catalog card number: 64-21963

The Macmillan Company, New York
Collier-Macmillan Canada, Ltd., Toronto, Ontario

Printed in the United States of America

᠊

DESIGN BY R. A. KASELER

PREFACE

This book is intended to aid the Engineer-in-Training to review for the Electrical Engineering portion of the Professional Engineering license examination. In the examination the applicant is required to prove his competence by demonstrating his ability to solve engineering problems. The subject matter has been developed based on typical examinations given throughout the United States. The text is an outgrowth of notes and lecture material used in P.E. license examination review courses taught by the author.

At the beginning let it be stated that no attempt has been made to teach Electrical Engineering, nor has every facet of the subject been discussed in this book. Such tasks are beyond the scope of this work. It is assumed that the reader has been exposed to at least part of this material in the past. Without such prior exposure, he may find difficulty understanding and applying the theory to the examination problems.

Because passing the examination requires problem-solving ability, the material in each chapter is directed toward this goal. Each topic is introduced by a statement of the basic theory along with the equations used to solve the problems. In a book of this type the amount of theoretical material that can be included is limited. For additional information on the theory or equations the reader is directed to more complete works, some of which are cited as references. The theory is then applied to sample problems selected from various examinations to illustrate methods and typical solutions. Finally problems, again from actual examinations, are presented for practice. Solutions to these practice problems are to be found at the back of the book. The sample problems develop problem-solving technique and increase the ability to obtain a rapid and accurate solution. It should be noted that not all symbols are included in the lists of symbols in each chapter. Certain special symbols and abbreviations are introduced and defined as required in the various problem solutions.

The material presented herein should be adequate to insure that when properly applied to the various problems, a passing grade will be obtained. It is left to the reader to decide how much further he wishes to pursue the various topics. The greater the depth of preparation and study and practice, the greater will be the probability of success.

Some hints for the examination:

1 — Take plenty of time to read thoroughly the entire examination before starting.
2 — Determine the average time per problem on the basis of examination time and the required number of problems.
3 — Where there is a choice and problems may be solved out of sequence, select the simplest problems and solve them first.
4 — Read each problem carefully. Make sure you know for what you are solving.
5 — Reduce each problem to its simplest concepts and build up from these.
6 — Keep all mathematics as simple as possible.
7 — Work carefully and neatly and explain briefly how you intend to solve the problem and what equations are to be used. In the event of a wrong answer or inability to complete the solution, part credit is usually allowed for understanding the problem and the method of solution.
8 — If a problem seems particularly difficult and a solution does not seem imminent, stop work on that problem.
9 — Keep track of the time.
10 — After working all the simple problems, take a fresh look at those problems which are troublesome.
11 — Do not drop a seemingly difficult problem too soon if you feel confident you are on the right track.
12 — If a choice is allowed, do not be afraid to look at problems outside your speciality. You may find additional simple problems.
13 — If an unusual or specially derived equation is used, state its source. If special data or handbook information relating to practice or empirical results is used, the source of this information should also be given.

The help of several people is gratefully acknowledged: Allan D. Kraus who edited the manuscript, checked the problem solutions, advised and acted as the all-around guiding spirit; Veronica McGee and Caroline Robert who helped type the manuscript; Edward Daley who prepared the illustrations; and most of all, to my dear wife Marlene who, in addition to typing the manuscript, provided the encouragement necessary to see me through this task.

Flushing, N.Y.   JULIUS I. FRANKLIN, P.E.

CONTENTS

TYPICAL GRAPHICAL SYMBOLS

Resistor, fixed

Resistor, variable

Capacitor, fixed

Capacitor, variable

Inductor

Transformer

Battery, d-c voltage source

Generator, d-c

Generator, a-c

Constant current source
   (arrow indicates current flow)

VACUUM TUBE ELEMENTS

⊥   plate

⎯ ⎯ ⎯   ⎯⎯⋀⋀⋁   grid

⌐   ⌐   ⌐   cathode, indirectly heated

∩   heater or directly heated cathode

⎯▶⎮⎯   Semiconductor diode

CHAPTER ONE

BASIC CIRCUITS

SYMBOLS

B	Susceptance, (imaginary part of admittance) mhos; also number of branches
C	Capacitance, farads
E	Electromotive force, volts (d-c value or magnitude of a sinusoid)
e	Electromotive force, volts (instantaneous value or time-varying quantity)
f	Frequency, cycles per second (cps)
G	Conductance (real part of admittance), mhos
I	Current, amperes (d-c value or magnitude of a sinusoid)
i	Current, amperes (instantaneous value or time-varying quantity)
j	The imaginary operator $\sqrt{-1}$
K	A multiplier denoting multiplication by 1000
L	Inductance, henrys; also number of loops
N	Number of nodes
n	An integer; integer values
P	Power, watts
pf	Power factor
Q	Quality factor
R	Resistance, ohms; also real part of impedance
t	Time, seconds
V	Electromotive force, volts (denotes a voltage drop)
X	Reactance (imaginary part of impedance), ohms
Y	Admittance, mhos
Z	Impedance, ohms
α, θ, ϕ	Vector angles or phase angles, radians or degrees
ω	Angular frequency, radians per second
Ω	A symbol denoting ohms
Σ	Summation of Quantities
$\angle$	A symbol denoting the angle of a vector
$\|\ \|$	A symbol denoting the magnitude of the quantity contained between the bars

1

Subscripts

C	Referring to a capacitor
eq.	Equivalent
G	Referring to a generator
L	Referring to a load, or to an inductor, or to a resistively-loaded circuit
max	The peak value of the amplitude of a sinusoid, also the maximum value of a variable
o	Referring to a resonance
oc	Open circuit
P	Parallel
Q	Quadrature
R	Resistive, in phase
r	Referring to resonance
S	Series
sc	Short circuit
T	Total
TH	Thévenin
u	Unloaded

1.1 ELEMENTS

The basic elements which comprise linear, passive, reciprocal electric networks are the resistor, inductor, capacitor, and transformer. The first three elements are considered in this chapter; the transformer is considered in Chapter 2.

The equations relating the voltage across and current through each of these three elements are presented in Table 1–1. The elements are assumed linear and constant.

TABLE 1–1
IDEAL ELEMENTS DEFINED IN TERMS OF VOLTAGE AND CURRENT

Element	Terminal Voltage	Line Current
Resistor	$V_R = i_R R$	$i_R = \dfrac{V_R}{R}$
Inductor	$V_L = L\dfrac{di_L}{dt}$	$i_L = \dfrac{1}{L}\int V_L dt$
Capacitor	$V_C = \dfrac{1}{C}\int i_C dt$	$i_C = C\dfrac{dV_C}{dt}$

The elements are assumed linear in that the values of resistance, inductance, and capacitance are independent of voltage or current;

and constant in that the values are independent of any other parameter.

Ideal power sources are catagorized by either constant voltage at the terminals independent of the current, or constant current independent of the voltage. Power sources are either independent of time (direct current), repetitive functions of time (such as a sinusoidal source), or random functions of time (noise). The most popular repetitive time function, usually referred to as the alternating current function, is the sinusoid.

1.2   IMPEDANCE AND ADMITTANCE

If the current through an element is sinusoidal, it can be represented mathematically as:

$$i = I_{max} \cos(\omega t + \theta) \tag{1-1}$$

where θ is an arbitrary phase angle.

This current can be substituted into the equations for terminal voltage in Table 1–1 yielding the following results when the indicated mathematical steps (differentiation or integration) are performed.

$$V_R = RI_{max} \cos(\omega t + \theta) = Ri \tag{1-2}$$
$$V_L = -\omega L I_{max} \sin(\omega t + \theta) = j\omega Li \tag{1-3}$$
$$V_C = \frac{1}{\omega C} I_{max} \sin(\omega t + \theta) = \frac{-j}{\omega C} i \tag{1-4}$$

These expressions are recognized as variations of Ohm's law which states that the voltage drop across an element is proportional to the current through the element.

The ratio of voltage drop across an element or combination of elements to the current through the element or combination is known as the impedance Z.

$$\frac{V}{i} = Z = R \pm jX \tag{1-5}$$

where the impedance may include both a real (resistive) and an imaginary (reactive) part.

The inverse of the impedance is known as the admittance Y which also may include a real (conductive) and an imaginary (susceptive) part.

$$\frac{i}{V} = \frac{1}{Z} = Y = G \pm jB \tag{1-6}$$

(Note that impedance and admittance have meaning only when the voltages and currents are sinusoidal quantities.)

The rules of complex numbers as points in complex Cartesian coordinates or as points represented by vectors in polar coordinates apply to Eqs. (1–5) and (1–6). These rules are summarized by [Kraus, *Studying* (4)].

1.3 COMBINATIONS OF IMPEDANCES AND ADMITTANCES

If several impedances are connected in series, an equivalent impedance may be found.

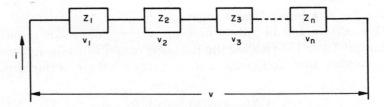

Figure 1–1. Impedances in series

A voltage V is assumed across the terminals of the circuit and a current i flows through the impedances. An equivalent impedance may be written as

$$Z_{eq} = \frac{V}{i} \tag{1-7}$$

But V is the sum of all the voltage drops in each of the elements

$$V = V_1 + V_2 + V_3 + \cdots + V_n$$
$$= i(Z_1 + Z_2 + Z_3 + \cdots + Z_n) \tag{1-8}$$

so that

$$Z_{eq} = \frac{i(Z_1 + Z_2 + Z_3 + \cdots + Z_n)}{i}$$
$$= Z_1 + Z_2 + Z_3 + \cdots + Z_n \tag{1-9}$$

and

$$Y_{eq} = \frac{i}{V} = \frac{1}{Z_1 + Z_2 + Z_3 + \cdots + Z_n} \tag{1-10}$$

Simply stated, the equivalent impedance of impedances in series is the sum of the individual impedances.

If several admittances are connected in parallel, an equivalent admittance may be found.

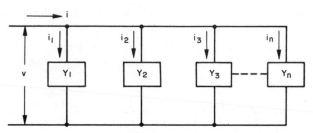

Figure 1–2. Admittances in parallel

Again a voltage V is assumed across the terminals of the circuit and a current i flows at the terminals. From Eq. (1–6).

$$Y_{eq} = \frac{i}{V} \tag{1-11}$$

But the total current i entering the junction of the elements equals the total current leaving the junction.

$$i = i_1 + i_2 + i_3 + \cdots + i_n = V(Y_1 + Y_2 + Y_3 + \cdots + Y_n) \tag{1-12}$$

so that

$$Y_{eq} = \frac{V(Y_1 + Y_2 + Y_3 + \cdots + Y_n)}{V} = Y_1 + Y_2 + Y_3 + \cdots + Y_n \tag{1-13}$$

and

$$Z_{eq} = \frac{V}{i} = \frac{1}{Y_1 + Y_2 + Y_3 + \cdots + Y_n} \tag{1-14}$$

Simply stated, the equivalent admittance of admittances in parallel is the sum of the individual admittances.

As a general rule it may be stated that if elements are connected in series, their impedances add to obtain an over-all equivalent impedance while for elements in parallel their admittances add to obtain an over-all equivalent admittance.

Now consider several admittances connected in series.

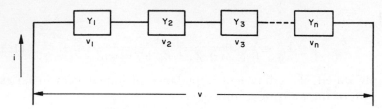

Figure 1–3. Admittances in series

Again the total voltage V equals the sum of the voltage drops.

$$V = V_1 + V_2 + V_3 + \cdots + V_n = i\left(\frac{1}{Y_1} + \frac{1}{Y_2} + \frac{1}{Y_3} + \cdots + \frac{1}{Y_n}\right)$$

Therefore,

$$Z_{eq} = \frac{V}{i} = \frac{1}{Y_1} + \frac{1}{Y_2} + \frac{1}{Y_3} + \cdots + \frac{1}{Y_n} \qquad (1\text{–}15)$$

and

$$Y_{eq} = \frac{i}{V} = \frac{1}{1/Y_1 + 1/Y_2 + 1/Y_3 + \cdots + 1/Y_n} \qquad (1\text{–}16)$$

Finally consider several impedances in parallel.

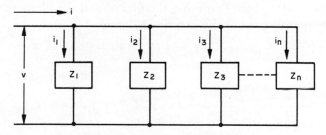

Figure 1–4. Impedances in parallel

As before, the total current i equals the sum of the individual element currents.

$$i = i_1 + i_2 + i_3 + \cdots + i_n = V\left(\frac{1}{Z_1} + \frac{1}{Z_2} + \frac{1}{Z_2} + \cdots + \frac{1}{Z_n}\right) \qquad (1\text{–}17)$$

Hence,

$$Y_{eq} = \frac{i}{V} = \left(\frac{1}{Z_1} + \frac{1}{Z_2} + \frac{1}{Z_3} + \cdots + \frac{1}{Z_n}\right) \qquad (1\text{–}18)$$

and

$$Z_{eq} = \frac{V}{i} = \frac{1}{1/Z_1 + 1/Z_2 + 1/Z_3 + \cdots + 1/Z_n} \qquad (1\text{--}19)$$

1.3.1   SAMPLE PROBLEM

What is the equivalent impedance between the terminals of the circuit shown?

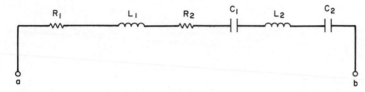

SOLUTION

Applying Eq. (1–9)

$$Z_{ab} = R_1 + j\omega L_1 + R_2 - \frac{j}{\omega C_1} + j\omega L_2 - \frac{j}{\omega C_2}$$

$$= (R_1 + R_2) + j\left(\omega L_1 + \omega L_2 - \frac{1}{\omega C_1} - \frac{1}{\omega C_2}\right)$$

or in polar form

$$Z_{ab} = \sqrt{(R_1 + R_2)^2 + \left(\omega L_1 + \omega L_2 - \frac{1}{\omega C_1} - \frac{1}{\omega C_2}\right)^2}$$

$$\underline{/\tan^{-1}} \frac{[(\omega L_1 + \omega L_2 - (1/\omega C_1) - (1/\omega C_2)]}{R_1 + R_2} \qquad \text{ANS.}$$

1.3.2   SAMPLE PROBLEM

What is the equivalent admittance between the terminals of the circuit shown?

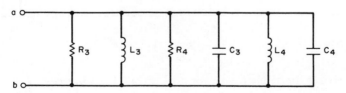

SOLUTION

Applying Eq. (1–13)

$$Y_{ab} = \frac{1}{R_3} - \frac{j}{\omega L_3} + \frac{1}{R_4} + j\omega C_3 - \frac{j}{\omega L_4} + j\omega C_4$$

$$= \left(\frac{1}{R_3} + \frac{1}{R_4}\right) + j\left(\omega C_3 + \omega C_4 - \frac{1}{\omega L_3} - \frac{1}{\omega L_4}\right)$$

or in polar form

$$Y_{ab} = \sqrt{\left(\frac{1}{R_3} + \frac{1}{R_4}\right)^2 + \left(\omega C_3 + \omega C_4 - \frac{1}{\omega L_3} - \frac{1}{\omega L_4}\right)^2}$$

$$\underline{/\tan^{-1}} \frac{[(\omega C_3 + \omega C_4 - (1/\omega L_3) - (1/\omega L_4)]}{(1/R_3 + 1/R_4)} \qquad \text{ANS.}$$

1.3.3   SAMPLE PROBLEM

A ladder network is formed of resistors as shown, and the resistances are indicated in ohms.

(a) What should be the resistance of load R so that the resistance at points c-d looking toward the right will also be R ohms?

(b) With a resistor of this value at R, what will be the resistance at the network terminals a-b?

(c) If each 4-ohm resistor is replaced by a pure reactor having an inductive reactance of 4 ohms, and each 20-ohm resistor is replaced by a capacitor having a capacitive reactance of 20 ohms, what should be the value of R for a match?

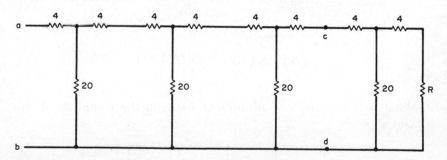

SOLUTION

(a) Using the rules for series and parallel resistances

$$R_{cd} = 4 + \frac{(R+4)20}{R+4+20} = R$$

or solving

$$4R + 96 + 20R + 80 = R^2 + 24R$$
$$R = \sqrt{176} = 13.28 \text{ ohms} \qquad \text{ANS.}$$

(b) This same value of R repeats itself at the junction of the 4-ohm resistors so that

$$R_{ab} = R = 13.28 \text{ ohms} \qquad \text{ANS.}$$

(c) Using the rules for series and parallel impedances

$$Z_{cd} = j4 + \frac{(R+j4)(-j20)}{R+j4-j20} = R$$
$$j4R + 64 - j20R + 80 = R^2 - j16R$$
$$R = \sqrt{144} = 12 \text{ ohms} \qquad \text{ANS.}$$

1.4   POWER FLOW

Figure 1–5 shows a battery (d-c source) of E volts connected to a network that has an equivalent input terminal resistance R_{eq}.

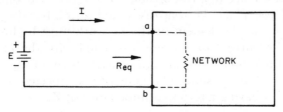

Figure 1–5. Battery connected to a network

Using Ohm's law, the current I that flows is

$$I = \frac{E}{R_{eq}} \qquad (1\text{–}20)$$

The voltage drop from a to b is

$$V_{ab} = IR_{eq} = E \qquad (1\text{–}21)$$

The convention for current flow is that V_{ab} is a positive voltage drop (that is, Terminal a is more positive than Terminal b) if the current flows from a to b through the network.

The power P delivered to the network by the battery is

$$P = IV_{ab} \text{ watts} \tag{1-22}$$

which is equal to the power delivered by the battery.

Power is delivered to a network or element if the current flows into the positive terminal and power is supplied by a network if the current flows out of the positive terminal. Thus in Fig. 1–5, the battery is delivering power and the network is absorbing power.

If the direction of current in Fig. 1–5 were reversed, the network would be supplying power and the battery would be absorbing power. In either case, the battery power (either absorbed or delivered) will be

$$P_{\text{battery}} = EI \text{ watts}$$

while the network power is

$$P_{\text{network}} = V_{ab}I \text{ watts}$$

Alternate expressions for Eq. (1–22) are

$$\begin{aligned} P &= IV_{ab} \\ &= EI \\ &= E^2/R_{\text{eq}} = I^2R_{\text{eq}} = E^2G_{\text{eq}} \end{aligned} \tag{1-23}$$

Note that so far the network has been considered as a single equivalent resistance R_{eq}, responsible for the power dissipation. The *total network power* may be that dissipated in R_{eq} but the power dissipated in any single element of the network must be found by determining the current or voltage associated with the element and computing the power using the appropriate form of Eq. (1–23).

Figure 1–6 shows a sinusoidal generator connected to a network of impedances having a terminal impedance of Z_{eq}.

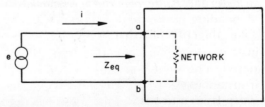

Figure 1–6. A-C generator connected to a network

Sinusoidal voltages and currents are characterized by their magnitudes and frequencies. (Phase angles are necessary when several sinusoids of identical frequency are related to each other.) The magnitudes of sinusoidal voltages and currents are stated and measured as root mean square (rms) or effective values which are $1/\sqrt{2}$ of the peak values of the sinusoid. Hence, a 100-v sinusoid has a peak value of 141 v.

In all further discussions, unless otherwise stated, the values of sinusoids will be stated as rms quantities.

In Fig. 1–6, let the generator e be represented as

$$e = E\underline{/\phi} \text{ (rms) volts}$$

and the equivalent terminal or input impedance Z_{eq} be

$$Z_{eq} = Z\underline{/\theta} \tag{1–24}$$

Then

$$i = I\underline{/\alpha} = \frac{E\underline{/\phi}}{Z\underline{/\theta}} = \frac{E}{Z}\underline{/\phi - \theta} \tag{1–25}$$

and the voltage drop V_{ab} is

$$V_{ab} = I\underline{/\alpha}\ Z\underline{/\theta} = E \tag{1–26}$$

In a-c circuits, the power delivered is

$$P = VI \text{ (power factor)} \tag{1–27}$$

where the power factor is the cosine of the phase angle between voltage and current.

In this example, the power factor angle is simply θ, the angle of the equivalent impedance and the power factor (pf) is $\cos \theta$.

As in the d-c case, there is the concept of power delivered by the generator to an external circuit or power delivered by a circuit to the generator depending upon the direction of current flow. In this case since both the generator polarity and current direction alternate cyclically, the instantaneous polarity and corresponding current flow must be considered. The same convention as used for the d-c case may be used: if instantaneously current flows from the positive generator terminal to the negative terminal, power is delivered by the generator to the circuit, and vice versa.

With this background, three simple series networks—resistor and inductor; resistor and capacitor; and resistor, inductor, and capacitor—connected to a sinusoidal generator of angular frequency ω will now be examined.

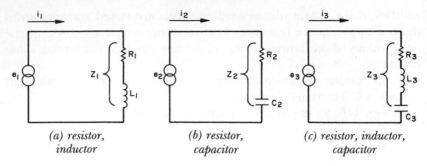

Figure 1–7. Generators connected to simple series networks

In Fig. 1–7, assume $e_1 = e_2 = e_3 = E\underline{/0}$

Then

$$i_1 = \frac{e_1}{Z_1} = \frac{E\underline{/0}}{Z_1\underline{/\theta_1}} \tag{1-28}$$

$$i_2 = \frac{e_2}{Z_2} = \frac{E\underline{/0}}{Z_2\underline{/\theta_2}} \tag{1-29}$$

$$i_3 = \frac{e_3}{Z_3} = \frac{E\underline{/0}}{Z_3\underline{/\theta_3}} \tag{1-30}$$

but,

$$Z_1 = R_1 + j\omega L_1 = \sqrt{R_1^2 + \omega^2 L_1^2} \ \underline{/\tan^{-1} \omega L_1/R_1} \tag{1-31}$$

$$Z_2 = R_2 - \frac{j}{\omega C_2} = \sqrt{R_2^2 + \frac{1}{\omega^2 C_2^2}} \ \underline{/-\tan^{-1} 1/\omega C_2 R_2} \tag{1-32}$$

$$Z_3 = R_3 + j(\omega L_3 - \frac{1}{\omega C_3})$$

$$= \sqrt{R_3^2 + (\omega L_3 - 1/\omega C_3)^2} \ \underline{/\tan^{-1} [\omega L_3 - 1/\omega C_3]/R_3} \tag{1-33}$$

So that

$$i_1 = \frac{E}{\sqrt{R_1^2 + \omega^2 L_1^2}} \ \underline{/-\tan^{-1} \omega L_1/R_1} \tag{1-34}$$

$$i_2 = \frac{E}{\sqrt{R_2^2 + 1/\omega^2 C_2^2}} \ \underline{/\tan^{-1} 1/\omega C_2 R_2} \tag{1-35}$$

$$i_3 = \frac{E}{\sqrt{R_3^2 + (\omega L_3 - 1/\omega C_3)^2}} \ \underline{/-\tan^{-1} [\omega L_3 - 1/\omega C_3]/R_3} \tag{1-36}$$

Thus in the inductive circuit (*a*) the current lags the applied voltage, in the capacitive circuit (*b*) the current leads the voltage, and in the series R, L, C circuit the current either leads or lags depending upon whether the circuit is net capacitive or inductive.

By its definition, the power factor may be seen to be simply the cosine of the impedance angle.

This is the source of the statement frequently heard that an inductive circuit operates at a lagging power factor and a capacitive circuit operates at a leading power factor.

The power delivered is

$$P = e_1 i_1 \cos \theta_1$$

$$= E \frac{E}{\sqrt{R_1^2 + \omega^2 L_1^2}} \cos \left(\tan^{-1} \omega L_1/R_1 \right)$$

$$= \frac{E^2}{\sqrt{R_1^2 + \omega^2 L_1^2}} \left(\frac{R_1}{\sqrt{R_1^2 + \omega^2 L_1^2}} \right)$$

$$= \frac{E^2 R_1}{(R_1^2 + \omega^2 L_1^2)} = |i_1|^2 R_1 \tag{1-37}$$

The power given by Eq. (1–37) may be alternately considered either as the square of the magnitude of the current multiplied by the resistive (real) part of the equivalent series impedance ($I^2 R$) or as the square of the voltage multiplied by the equivalent conductive (real) part of the equivalent shunt admittance ($E^2 G$).

1.5   RESONANCE

The condition of resonance may be defined in several different ways, all of which are essentially the same. Resonance is the particular combination of network elements or choice of operating frequency in which:

1. The equivalent terminal impedance or admittance is purely resistive or real; or
2. The reactive or susceptive portion of the equivalent terminal impedance or admittance is zero; or
3. The power factor is unity; or
4. The line current is in phase with the applied voltage.

In a large number of problems dealing with resonance and resonant circuits, Statement 2 is applied to determine either a resonant frequency or the value of a parameter for resonance. The impedance or admittance is expressed in terms of frequency or other variables; the imaginary portion is set equal to zero and the resulting equation solved for the desired values.

A simple series R, L, C circuit is shown in Fig. 1–8.

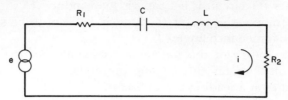

Figure 1–8. A simple series R-L-C circuit

The voltage generator e represents a constant amplitude variable frequency sinusoidal generator. The loop current i may be expressed as a function of the variable angular frequency ω.

$$i = \frac{e}{Z} = \frac{e}{R_1 + R_2 + j(\omega L - 1/\omega C)} \tag{1–38}$$

And if the voltage e can be represented as $E\underline{/0}$

$$i = \frac{E}{\sqrt{(R_1 + R_2)^2 + (\omega L - 1/\omega C)^2}} \underline{/-\tan^{-1} (\omega L - 1/\omega C)/(R_1 + R_2)} \tag{1–39}$$

Various quantities may be plotted as functions of the frequency variable ω. These are shown in Fig. 1–9.

The frequency of resonance ω_0 is the frequency at which

$$j\left(\omega_0 L - \frac{1}{\omega_0 C}\right) = 0 \tag{1–40}$$

or

$$\omega_0 = \frac{1}{\sqrt{LC}} \tag{1–41}$$

The magnitude of the current i may be written as

$$
\begin{aligned}
i &= \frac{E}{\sqrt{(R_1 + R_2)^2 + [\omega L(1 - 1/\omega^2 LC)]^2}} \\
&= \frac{E}{\sqrt{(R_1 + R_2)^2 + \omega_0^2 L^2 [(\omega/\omega_0) - (\omega_0/\omega)]^2}} \\
&= \frac{E}{(R_1 + R_2)\sqrt{1 + [\omega_0 L/(R_1 + R_2)]^2 [(\omega/\omega_0) - (\omega_0/\omega)]^2}}
\end{aligned} \tag{1–42}
$$

The parameter, $\omega_0 L/(R_1 + R_2)$, is called the quality factor or Q of the circuit and is related to the ratio of the energy stored to the power dissipated in the circuit. In this case Q is defined with respect

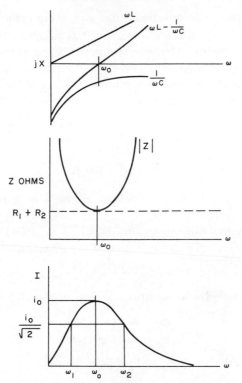

Figure 1–9. Variation of reactance, impedance, and current of a series R-L-C circuit with frequency as a variable

to the resonant angular frequency, ω_0. In general, Q may be defined at any frequency, not necessarily the resonant frequency. Thus Eq. (1–42) may be written as

$$i = \frac{E}{(R_1 + R_2)} \frac{1}{\sqrt{1 + Q^2 \left[(\omega/\omega_0) - (\omega_0/\omega)\right]^2}}$$

$$= i_0 \frac{1}{\sqrt{1 + Q^2 \left[(\omega/\omega_0) - (\omega_0/\omega)\right]^2}} \tag{1-43}$$

where i_0 is the current at resonance $E/(R_1 + R_2)$.

If R_2 is considered a load to which power is delivered, the power is

$$P_L = i^2 R_2. \tag{1-44}$$

This power will be a maximum where i has a maximum and will decrease as i decreases. The maximum power occurs at $\omega = \omega_0$ and is

$$P_{\max} = i_0^2 R_2 = \frac{E^2}{(R_1 + R_2)^2} R_2 \tag{1-45}$$

In the communications field, the two frequencies designated ω_1 and ω_2 in Fig. 1–9c where the current has fallen to $(1/\sqrt{2})i_0$ are very significant quantities. At these frequencies the power has fallen to $(P_{max}/2)$. The difference between these frequencies is also important. The two frequencies are often referred to as the half-power or 3-db frequencies while the difference between them is often called the half-power or 3-db bandwidth.

The decibel or db is defined as

$$db = 10 \log_{10} \frac{P_2}{P_1} \tag{1–46}$$

where P_2 is a power level which is referred to a reference power level P_1.

It can be seen from an examination of Eq. (1–43) that the half-power frequencies are those values of ω satisfying

$$Q[(\omega/\omega_0) - (\omega_0/\omega)] = \pm 1 \tag{1–47}$$

The resulting quadratic equations yield the positive roots

$$\omega_2 = \omega_0(1 + 1/2Q)$$
$$\omega_1 = \omega_0(1 - 1/2Q) \tag{1–48}$$

if it is assumed that $4Q^2 \gg 1$. Then the half-power bandwidth is

$$\Delta\omega = \omega_2 - \omega_1 = \omega_0/Q \tag{1–49}$$

or

$$\Delta f = f_2 - f_1 = f_0/Q \tag{1–50}$$

The above simply states that the half-power bandwidth is directly proportional to the resonant frequency and inversely proportional to the Q at resonance.

For the series resonant circuit the Q, at resonance, is

$$Q_{series} = \omega_0 L/R_S \tag{1–51}$$

where L represents the total equivalent series inductance and R_S represents the total equivalent series resistance. Using Eq. (1–41), an alternate expression for the Q is

$$Q_{series} = 1/\omega_0 C R_S \tag{1–52}$$

where C is the total equivalent series capacitance.

The resistors in the series circuit of Fig. 1–8 may be either actual circuit elements or may be the equivalent resistances associated with either the inductor or capacitor. If, for example, R_1 is the equivalent series resistance associated with the inductor whose equivalent series inductance is L, C represents an ideal capacitor having zero equivalent resistance, and R_2 represents a resistor added to the circuit; it is possible to consider two different values of Q for the circuit.

The unloaded Q, which will be designated Q_u, is that value of Q which is obtained by virtue of the resistive part of the circuit elements without any added resistive loading. Hence it is the Q of the elements themselves. For the circuit as defined above

$$Q_u = \omega_0 L/R_1 = 1/\omega_0 C R_1 \qquad (1\text{--}53)$$

The loaded Q, which will be designated Q_L, is that value of Q which results when resistance or resistive loading is added to the circuit. In the circuit under consideration

$$Q_L = \omega_0 L/(R_1 + R_2) = 1/\omega_0 C (R_1 + R_2) \qquad (1\text{--}54)$$

The unloaded Q is the largest Q-value that may be obtained from the combination of specific elements at a particular frequency.

It should be noted that the Q must be considered as a function of frequency because the equivalent resistive portion of element impedances may change with frequency as may the equivalent values of inductance and capacitance.

The shunt circuit of Fig. 1–10 may be analyzed in a manner similar to the series circuit of Fig. 1–8.

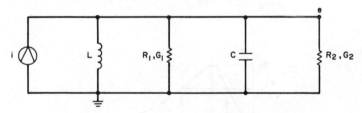

Figure 1–10. A simple parallel R-L-C circuit

The current generator i represents a constant amplitude variable frequency sinusoidal generator. The resistors are also designated by their equivalent conductances. The node voltage e may be expressed as a function of the variable angular frequency ω

$$e = iZ = \frac{i}{Y}$$

$$= \frac{i}{[1/R_1 + 1/R_2 + j(\omega C - 1/\omega L)]}$$

$$= \frac{i}{[G_1 + G_2 + j(\omega C - 1/\omega L)]} \qquad (1\text{--}55)$$

And if i can be represented as $I\underline{/0}$

$$e = \frac{I}{\sqrt{(G_1 + G_2)^2 + (\omega C - 1/\omega L)^2}} \underline{/-\tan^{-1} (\omega C - 1/\omega L)/(G_1 + G_2)}$$

$$(1-56)$$

As was done in the analysis of the series circuit, certain quantities may be plotted as functions of the variable ω.

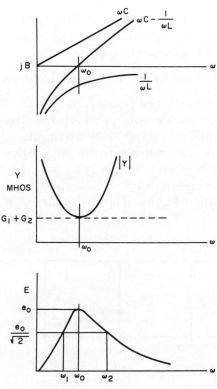

Figure 1–11. Variation of susceptance, admittance, and voltage of a parallel R-L-C circuit with frequency as a variable

The angular frequency of resonance ω_0 is the frequency at which the susceptance is zero.

$$j(\omega_0 C - 1/\omega_0 L) = 0 \qquad (1-57)$$

or

$$\omega_0 = \frac{1}{\sqrt{LC}} \qquad (1-58)$$

The magnitude of the voltage e may be written as

$$|e| = \frac{I}{\sqrt{(G_1 + G_2)^2 + [\omega C(1 - 1/\omega^2 LC)]^2}}$$

$$= \frac{I}{\sqrt{(G_1 + G_2)^2 + \omega_0^2 C^2 [(\omega/\omega_0) - (\omega_0/\omega)]^2}}$$

$$= \frac{I}{(G_1 + G_2)\sqrt{1 + [\omega_0 C/(G_1 + G_2)]^2 [(\omega/\omega_0) - (\omega_0/\omega)]^2}} \quad (1\text{-}59)$$

For this circuit, the Q may be defined as

$$Q = \frac{\omega_0 C}{G_1 + G_2} = \frac{1}{\omega_0 L(G_1 + G_2)} \quad (1\text{-}60)$$

so that Eq. (1–59) becomes

$$|e| = \frac{I}{G_1 + G_2} \frac{1}{\sqrt{1 + Q^2[(\omega/\omega_0) - (\omega_0/\omega)]^2}}$$

$$= e_0 \frac{1}{\sqrt{1 + Q^2[(\omega/\omega_0) - (\omega_0/\omega)]^2}} \quad (1\text{-}61)$$

where

$$e_0 = \frac{I}{G_1 + G_2} = \frac{I}{(1/R_1) + (1/R_2)} = \left(\frac{R_1 R_2}{R_1 + R_2}\right)I \quad (1\text{-}62)$$

If G_2 is a load to which power is delivered, the power is

$$P_L = e^2 G_2 \quad (1\text{-}63)$$

This power will be a maximum at the frequency at which e is a maximum, i.e. ω_0. The maximum power is

$$P_{\max} = \frac{I^2}{(G_1 + G_2)^2} G_2 = e_0^2 G_2 \quad (1\text{-}64)$$

At the half-power frequencies, the power has dropped to $P_{\max}/2$ and e has dropped to $e_0/\sqrt{2}$. These frequencies are indicated in Fig. 1–11c as ω_1 and ω_2. The half-power frequencies may be determined by using Eqs. (1–48) and (1–49) or (1–50).

Using Eq. (1–60), the Q for the parallel circuit at resonance may be written as

$$Q_{\text{parallel}} = \frac{\omega_0 C}{G_T} = \omega_0 C R_P \quad (1\text{-}65)$$

where C represents the total equivalent parallel capacitance, G_T, the total equivalent shunting conductance, and $R_P = 1/G_T$, the total equivalent shunting resistance. The parallel Q may also be written as

$$Q_{\text{parallel}} = R_P/\omega_0 L \qquad (1\text{-}66)$$

The various similarities and differences of the two circuits, series and parallel, may be noted.

In addition to its use in resonant circuit analysis, the concept of Q is often utilized to describe circuits consisting of resistance and one type of reactance. The Q is a particularly valuable quantity to describe a non-ideal reactance which has loss associated with it. Such loss may be due to the winding resistance associated with an inductor or the dielectric leakage associated with a capacitor. Table 1-2 shows the various combinations of resistance and reactance, either as actual elements or as simple equivalent circuits, and the Q expressions for these simple circuits.

TABLE 1-2
Q-EXPRESSIONS FOR VARIOUS SIMPLE CIRCUITS

CIRCUIT	Q EXPRESSION
L R	$\dfrac{\omega L}{R}$
C R	$\dfrac{1}{\omega C R}$
L / R	$\dfrac{R}{\omega L}$
C / R	$\omega C R$

Using the simple forms of Table 1-2, more complicated circuits may be developed.

1.5.1 SAMPLE PROBLEM

A parallel resonant circuit consists of a lossless capacitor in parallel with an inductor. The resonant frequency is 1000 kcs, the 3-db band-with is 10 kcs, and the resonant impedance is 50,000 ohms. Find the constants of the circuit.

SOLUTION

A lossless capacitor in parallel with a lossy inductor may be represented as shown on the following page.

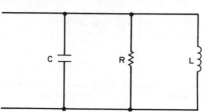

At resonance:

$$f_r = 1/2\pi\sqrt{LC} = 10^6 \text{ cps}$$
$$Z_r = R = 50{,}000 \text{ ohms}$$
$$Q = R/\omega L$$

The Q may be expressed as

$$Q = \frac{f_r}{\text{bandwidth}} = \frac{1000}{10} = 100$$

This is also the Q of the inductor.
Thus

$$L = \frac{R}{\omega Q}$$
$$= \frac{50{,}000}{2\pi(10^6)(100)} = 79.6 \times 10^{-6} \text{ henry with a } Q \text{ of } 100 \quad \text{ANS.}$$

and

$$C = \frac{1}{4\pi^2 f_r^2 L}$$
$$= \frac{1}{4\pi^2(10^6)^2(79.6)(10^{-6})} = 318 \times 10^{-12} \text{ farad} \qquad \text{ANS.}$$

1.6   POWER FACTOR CORRECTION

In a power distribution system, two major reasons for maintaining the highest possible power factor are to maximize the system efficiency and reduce voltage fluctuations with changing load (improved system regulation). To appreciate this, consider the simplified power system shown in Fig. 1–12.

The equivalent impedance of the generator consists of the conductor resistance and inductive reactance of the machine coils. The line equivalent impedance is shown as resistance and inductive reactance. The line may have shunt capacitance but generally the inductance

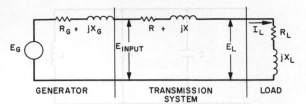

Figure 1–12. A simplified power transmission system

predominates. The load also is shown as having inductive reactance. This is characteristic of virtually all commercial or residential loads unless deliberate steps are taken by the addition of equivalent capacitive reactance to change the nature of the total load. Fluorescent lights, all motor-driven appliances and inductive-motor loads are typical examples of loads having inductive reactance.

The power delivered to the load is

$$P_L = E_L I_L \cos \theta$$
$$= E_L I_L \frac{R_L}{\sqrt{R_L{}^2 + X_L{}^2}}$$
$$= I_L{}^2 R_L \tag{1-67}$$

or the line current is

$$I_L = \frac{P_L}{E_L \cos \theta} = \frac{P_L}{E_L(pf)} \tag{1-68}$$

But the load voltage is

$$E_L = E_G - I_L[R_G + R + j(X_G + X)] \tag{1-69}$$

And the power lost in the generator and transmission system is

$$P_{\text{losses}} = I_L{}^2(R_G + R) \tag{1-70}$$

From Eqs. (1–68) and (1–70) it may be seen that for a given load power, the lower the power factor the greater will be the magnitude of line current and the greater will be the system losses. Also from Eqs. (1–68) and (1–69) if a load fluctuates from zero to some value, the lower the power factor, the greater will be the line current and the greater will be the variation in load voltage. These factors make themselves felt directly by the system changes and indirectly in the case of the industrial consumer by a higher power cost for a low power factor.

The simplest method of power factor correction for an inductive load is to connect a capacitor across the line terminals. If the power factor is to be corrected to unity, the analysis of the problem becomes that of a resonant circuit. If the ultimate power factor is not unity (i.e., 0.8 lagging power factor to be corrected to 0.9) the problem becomes that of a resonant circuit off-resonance. A current-voltage vector diagram becomes helpful. A simple circuit is shown in Fig. 1–13a and the current-voltage vector diagram in Fig. 1–13b. In the vector diagram, cos θ_2 is the load power factor while cos θ_1 is the corrected power factor.

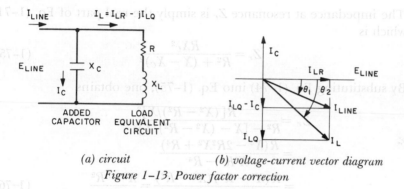

(a) circuit   (b) voltage-current vector diagram

Figure 1–13. Power factor correction

This problem can also be solved by operating on the expression for the power factor angle obtained from the impedance expression. The statement of the problem often will give a clue as to which method of solution requires less effort.

As an example, the circuit of Fig. 1–13a will be examined mathematically. The circuit consists of a capacitor connected in parallel with the series combination of a resistor and an inductor. The total impedance presented to the line by this combination is obtained using the rules for series and parallel impedance. Thus

$$Z_T = \frac{1}{1/(R+jX) + 1/-jX_C}$$

$$= \frac{(R+jX)(-jX_C)}{R+j(X-X_C)}$$

$$= \frac{[XX_C - jRX_C][R - j(X-X_C)]}{[R+j(X-X_C)][R-j(X-X_C)]}$$

$$= \frac{RX_C^2 - j(R^2X_C - X^2X_C + XX_C^2)}{R^2 + (X-X_C)^2} \qquad (1\text{--}71)$$

For resonance or unity power factor the imaginary part of Eq. (1–71) is equated to zero

$$(R^2X_C - X^2X_C + XX_C^2) = 0 \qquad (1\text{--}72)$$

If the value of X_C is desired

$$X_C(R^2 - X^2 + XX_C) = 0 \qquad (1\text{-}73)$$

So there are two possible values

$$X_C = 0 \text{ or } X_C = \frac{X^2 - R^2}{X} \qquad (1\text{-}74)$$

with the value $X_C = 0$ being trivial.

The impedance at resonance Z_r is simply the real part of Eq. (1–71) which is

$$Z_r = \frac{RX_C^2}{R^2 + (X - X_C)^2} \qquad (1\text{-}75)$$

By substituting Eq. (1–74) into Eq. (1–75), one obtains

$$\begin{aligned}
Z_r &= \frac{R[(X^2 - R^2)/X]^2}{R^2 - [X - (X^2 - R^2)/X]^2} \\
&= \frac{R(X^4 - 2R^2X^2 + R^4)}{X^2R^2 - R^4} \\
&= \frac{R(X^2 - R^2)(X^2 - R^2)}{R^2(X^2 - R^2)} = \frac{X^2 - R^2}{R}
\end{aligned} \qquad (1\text{-}76)$$

Using the Q of the load defined as X/R, Eq. (1–76) becomes

$$\begin{aligned}
Z_r &= R\left(\frac{X^2 - R^2}{R^2}\right) \\
&= R\left(\frac{X^2}{R^2} - 1\right) = R(Q^2 - 1)
\end{aligned} \qquad (1\text{-}77)$$

If some value of power factor other than unity is desired, the mathematics, while not difficult, becomes cumbersome. The graphical method or a variation thereof generally provides the most direct method of solution.

1.7 NETWORK ANALYSIS

Up to this point, the discussion has been concerned only with two-terminal networks; that is, combinations of elements which can be reduced to a single equivalent impedance between a pair of terminals where current, voltage, power, etc. are to be determined. More complicated networks require the application of rules such as Kirchhoff's laws as an aid to analysis.

Gustav Robert Kirchhoff first formulated two rules which considerably simplified the mathematical solutions for complicated networks. His two rules are:

1. *Node rule.* The algebraic sum of currents directed toward (or away from) a node is zero. Mathematically

$$\Sigma i = 0 \qquad (1\text{--}78)$$

A node is defined as the junction of two or more elements or conductors.

Another way to stating this rule is that the sum of currents entering a node equals the sum of currents leaving the node. In the case of sinusoids this is a vector summation.

2. *Loop Rule.* The algebraic sum of voltage sources in a loop equals the sum of the voltage drops taken around the loop. Mathematically

$$\Sigma E = \Sigma Z i \qquad (1\text{--}79)$$

A loop is defined as any closed conducting path encompassing several elements in a network. This rule might also be stated as the sum of voltage drops around a loop is zero if voltage sources are considered as negative voltage drops.

It should be noted that in Eq. (1–79) each Zi term is the product of the impedance and the total current flowing through that impedance. In the case of sinusoids, Eq. (1–79) represents a vector summation.

Equation (1–78) may be written in a form similar to Eq. (1–79) by expressing current as the product of admittance and the voltage across that admittance.

1.7.1   NETWORK ANALYSIS BY THE LOOP METHOD

A circuit to be analyzed by the loop method is shown in Fig. 1–14. The complex impedances are arbitrarily represented by resistor symbols.

In this circuit, the voltages and impedances are known. It is desired to determine the current flowing in each impedance. The voltage sources have identically the same frequencies.

For analysis, the circuit is divided into loops so that all the elements are included in at least one loop. An unknown current is assumed to flow in each of the loops; it is these currents which are determined. Application of the loop rule results in as many equations as there are unknowns.

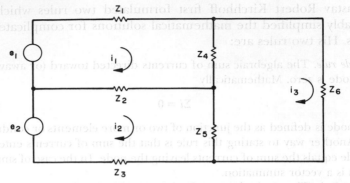

Figure 1–14. A circuit to be analyzed by the loop method

The three unknown currents which have been assumed are shown in the diagram as i_1, i_2, and i_3. The three loop equations are written by inspection in the general form:

$$e_1 = Z_{11}i_1 + Z_{12}i_2 + Z_{13}i_3 \qquad (1\text{–}80)$$
$$e_2 = Z_{21}i_1 + Z_{22}i_2 + Z_{23}i_3 \qquad (1\text{–}81)$$
$$0 = Z_{31}i_1 + Z_{32}i_2 + Z_{33}i_3 \qquad (1\text{–}82)$$

There are two types of impedance terms: the Z_{XX} and the Z_{XY} terms. The Z_{XX} terms represent the total impedance in loop X to the current i_X and are called the loop self-impedances. The Z_{XY} terms represent the impedance in loop X common to loop Y and are called mutual impedances.

The Zi voltage drops are positive when the loop is traversed in the direction of the current. Hence the mutual impedance will have a negative sign if the current in loop Y is opposite to the direction in which loop X is being traversed. The sign of the mutual impedance is independent of any sign associated with the impedance itself such as a negative reactance term. It should be noted that for linear reciprocal elements, $Z_{XY} = Z_{YX}$.

By inspection, then, the three loop equations are:

$$e_1 = (Z_1 + Z_2 + Z_4)i_1 \qquad\qquad -Z_2i_2 \qquad\qquad -Z_4i_3 \quad (1\text{–}83)$$
$$e_2 = \qquad -Z_2i_1 + (Z_2 + Z_3 + Z_5)i_2 \qquad\qquad -Z_5i_3 \quad (1\text{–}84)$$
$$0 = \qquad -Z_4i_1 \qquad\qquad -Z_5i_2 + (Z_4 + Z_5 + Z_6)i_3 \quad (1\text{–}85)$$

These simultaneous equations may be solved either by substitution or by determinants. The solution by determinants in accordance with Cramer's Rule may be found in [Kraus, *Studying* (4)]

Note that various other loops might have been chosen leading to a different set of simultaneous equations. However, the total current in any element will be the same regardless of the loops chosen.

In certain simple networks, the number of loop equations is obvious by inspection; in more complex networks it may not be so obvious. The following rule may be helpful: If B represents the number of branches (elements between nodes) and N represents the number of nodes, the number of loop equations L will be

$$L = B - N + 1 \tag{1–86}$$

This rule applied to the circuit of Fig. 1–14 yields the following: there are six nodes, eight branches and hence three loop equations.

1.7.1.1   SAMPLE PROBLEM

The unbalanced bridge network shown is supplied with power from a 100-v generator. The values of the bridge arms are expressed in ohms, as shown. Calculate the current in the detector connected across b-d.

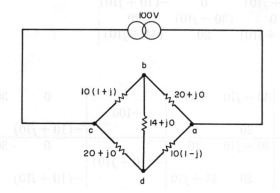

SOLUTION

Solve as a three-loop circuit. Pick three loops so that only one current flows through b-d. The loop equations are:

$$100 = (30 + j10)i_1 \qquad\qquad + 0i_2 - (10 + j10)i_3$$
$$100 = \qquad\qquad 0i_1 + (30 - j10)i_2 \qquad + 20i_3$$
$$0 = -(10 + j10)i_1 \qquad\qquad + 20i_2 + (44 + j10)i_3$$

The foregoing equations are solved by Cramer's rule. In this case, reduction of the determinant will be utilized.

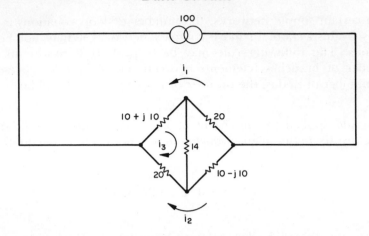

$$i_3 = \frac{\begin{vmatrix} (30+j10) & 0 & 100 \\ 0 & (30-j10) & 100 \\ -(10+j10) & 20 & 0 \end{vmatrix}}{\begin{vmatrix} (30+j10) & 0 & -(10+j10) \\ 0 & (30-j10) & 20 \\ -(10+j10) & 20 & (44+j10) \end{vmatrix}}$$

$$= \frac{(30+j10)\begin{vmatrix} 30-j10 & 100 \\ 20 & 0 \end{vmatrix} +100\begin{vmatrix} 0 & 30-j10 \\ -(10+j10) & 20 \end{vmatrix}}{(30+j10)\begin{vmatrix} 30-j10 & 20 \\ 20 & 44+j10 \end{vmatrix} -(10+j10)\begin{vmatrix} 0 & 30-j10 \\ -(10+j10) & 20 \end{vmatrix}}$$

$$= \frac{(30+j10)(-2000) + 100(30-j10)(10+j10)}{(30+j10)(30-j10)(44+j10) - (30+j10)(400)}$$
$$- (10+j10)(30-j10)(10+j10)$$

$$= \frac{31.6\underline{/18.4}(-2000) + 100(31.6\underline{/-18.4})(14.1\underline{/45})}{(31.6\underline{/18.4})(31.6\underline{/-18.4})(45\underline{/12.8}) - (31.6\underline{/18.4})(400)}$$
$$- (14.1\underline{/45})(31.6\underline{/-18.4})(14.1\underline{/45})$$

$$= \frac{-60,000 - j20,000 + 44,600\underline{/26.6}}{45,000\underline{/12.8} - 12,000 - j4000 - 6320\underline{/71.6}}$$

$$= \frac{-60,000 - j20,000 + 40,000 + j20,000}{44,000 + j10,000 - 12,000 - j4000 - 2000 - j6000}$$

$$= \frac{-20,000}{30,000}$$

$$|i_3| = \frac{2}{3} \text{ amp} \qquad\qquad\qquad\qquad\qquad\qquad \text{ANS.}$$

1.8   THÉVENIN'S THEOREM

Very often a particular problem can be solved by determining the current in a single element or branch of a network. Under these conditions, the loops should be chosen so that only one unknown current flows through the element in question. In this way the simultaneous equations need be solved only once.

An alternative to this method is the application of Thévenin's Theorem which states that a network of generators and impedances seen looking into the network from any two points in the network may be replaced by a single voltage source in series with a single impedance. This means that if the current or voltage of a single element or branch of a network is desired, no matter how involved the rest of the network may be, in theory at least it can be reduced to a voltage source in series with an impedance. The analysis is then performed on a single simple loop. The reduced network is sometimes referred to as a Thévenin's equivalent circuit.

The values of the elements of a Thévenin's equivalent are as follows:

• The emf of the voltage source is the voltage existing across the terminals of the branch in question with the branch removed (the open-circuit voltage at the terminals).
• The series impedance is that total impedance between the terminals of the branch in question with the branch removed and all voltage sources replaced by short circuits and current sources replaced by open circuits except for the internal impedance of sources which remain.

The determination of the Thévenin voltage (open-circuit voltage) requires the solution of $(n - 1)$ simultaneous equations where n is the number of equations to be solved in the original network.

The dual of the Thévenin's equivalent circuit is the Norton's equivalent circuit. This consists of a constant-current generator in parallel with an admittance. The magnitude of the current is the short-circuit current at the terminals in question, and the admittance has a value equal to the total admittance seen looking into the network at the terminals with all generators removed and replaced by short-circuits in the case of voltage generators and open-circuits in the case of current generators.

1.8.1 SAMPLE PROBLEM

(This is the same as Problem 1.7.1.1 solved in a different manner.)

The unbalanced bridge network shown is supplied with power from a 100-v generator. The values of the bridge arms are expressed in ohms, as shown. Calculate the current in the detector connected across *b-d*.

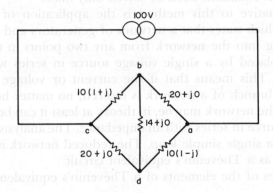

SOLUTION

Make a Thévenin's equivalent circuit for the network excluding the branch *b-d*.

The open-circuit voltage may be determined by considering the branches *a-b-c* and *a-d-c* as voltage dividers.

$$E_{bd_{oc}} = E_{bc} - E_{dc} = 100 \frac{10 + j10}{30 + j10} - 100 \frac{20}{30 - j10}$$

$$= 100 \left[\frac{(10 + j10)(30 - j10) - 20(30 + j10)}{(30 + j10)(30 - j10)} \right]$$

$$= 100 \left[\frac{300 + 100 + j300 - j100 - 600 - j200}{900 + 100} \right]$$

$$= 100 \left(\frac{-200 + j0}{1000} \right) = -20 \text{ v.}$$

The Thévenin's impedance is found from the modified circuit.

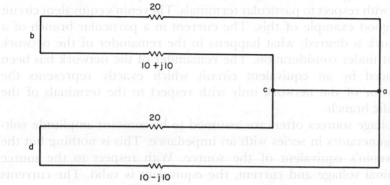

$$Z_{TH} = Z_{bd_{sc}} = \frac{20(10 + j10)}{30 + j10} + \frac{20(10 - j10)}{30 - j10}$$

$$= \frac{(200 + j200)(30 - j10) + (200 - j200)(30 + j10)}{(30 + j10)(30 - j10)}$$

$$= \frac{200}{1000}[30 - j10 + j30 + 10 + 30 + j10 - j30 + 10]$$

$$= \frac{80}{5} = 16 \text{ ohms}$$

Then the total equivalent circuit is obtained by adding the impedance of branch *b-d* to the Thévenin's equivalent as shown.

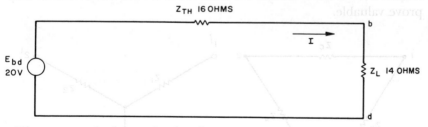

The current is determined to be

$$I = \frac{E_{bd}}{Z_{TH} + Z_L}$$

$$= \frac{20}{16 + 14} = \frac{2}{3} \text{ amp.} \qquad\qquad \text{ANS.}$$

1.9 EQUIVALENCE AND EQUIVALENT CIRCUITS

The concept of equivalence and equivalent circuits has been mentioned several times previously and is quite important in Electrical Engineering. In its most general sense, an equivalent circuit is valid only with respect to particular terminals. Thévenin's equivalent circuit is a good example of this. The current in a particular branch of a network is desired; what happens in the remainder of the network is not under consideration. The remainder of the network has been replaced by an equivalent circuit which exactly represents the behavior of the network only with respect to the terminals of the specific branch.

Voltage sources often are assumed to be constant amplitude voltage generators in series with an impedance. This is nothing but the Thévenin's equivalent of the source. With respect to the source terminal voltage and current, the equivalent is valid. The currents and voltages within the source network cannot be determined from its equivalent.

1.9.1 WYE TO DELTA TRANSFORMATION

In the reduction of a network to its simplest equivalent impedance, a configuration of elements may be encountered that cannot be reduced by means of the rules of series or parallel elements. In this situation the WYE to DELTA or DELTA to WYE transformation may prove valuable.

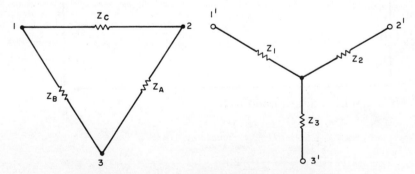

Figure 1–15 Delta and wye connections of impedances

Figure 1–15 illustrates these two connections of impedances. The two networks are equivalent if the impedance between corresponding terminal pairs is the same. The transformation expressions are as follows:

$$Z_1 = \frac{Z_B Z_C}{Z_A + Z_B + Z_C} \tag{1-87}$$

$$Z_2 = \frac{Z_A Z_C}{Z_A + Z_B + Z_C} \tag{1-88}$$

$$Z_3 = \frac{Z_A Z_B}{Z_A + Z_B + Z_C} \tag{1-89}$$

$$Z_A = \frac{Z_1 Z_2 + Z_2 Z_3 + Z_1 Z_3}{Z_1} \tag{1-90}$$

$$Z_B = \frac{Z_1 Z_2 + Z_2 Z_3 + Z_1 Z_3}{Z_2} \tag{1-91}$$

$$Z_C = \frac{Z_1 Z_2 + Z_2 Z_3 + Z_1 Z_3}{Z_3} \tag{1-92}$$

1.10   THE BRIDGE CIRCUIT

The circuit shown in Fig. 1–16 is a typical bridge circuit that finds a number of applications in measuring equipment and electronic devices. It will be analyzed by simultaneous equations to demonstrate the method and to illustrate a feature of the circuit. The problem is to determine the current in the detector Z_D. The three loops have been chosen so that only one current flows through the detector.

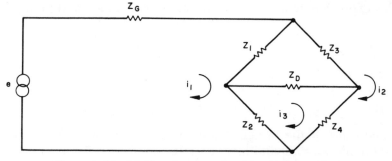

Figure 1–16 A bridge circuit analyzed by the loop method

The three loop equations are

$$e = (Z_1 + Z_2 + Z_G)i_1 \qquad + Z_G i_2 \qquad - Z_2 i_3 \qquad (1\text{--}93)$$

$$e = \qquad Z_G i_1 \qquad + (Z_3 + Z_4 + Z_G)i_2 \qquad + Z_4 i_3 \qquad (1\text{--}94)$$

$$0 = \qquad - Z_2 i_1 \qquad + Z_4 i_2 \qquad (Z_2 + Z_4 + Z_D)i_3 \qquad (1\text{--}95)$$

By Cramer's rule the solution for i_3 is

$$i_3 = \frac{\begin{vmatrix} (Z_1 + Z_2 + Z_G) & Z_G & e \\ Z_G & (Z_3 + Z_4 + Z_G) & e \\ -Z_2 & Z_4 & 0 \end{vmatrix}}{\begin{vmatrix} (Z_1 + Z_2 + Z_G) & Z_G & -Z_2 \\ Z_G & (Z_3 + Z_4 + Z_G) & Z_4 \\ -Z_2 & Z_4 & (Z_2 + Z_4 + Z_D) \end{vmatrix}}$$

$$= \frac{\begin{aligned} &e(Z_G Z_4 + Z_2 Z_3 + Z_2 Z_4 + Z_2 Z_G) \\ &-e(Z_1 Z_4 + Z_2 Z_4 + Z_4 Z_G + Z_2 Z_G) \end{aligned}}{\begin{aligned} &(Z_1 + Z_2 + Z_G)[(Z_3 + Z_4 + Z_G)(Z_2 + Z_4 + Z_D) - Z_4^2] \\ &-Z_G[Z_G Z_2 + Z_G Z_4 + Z_G Z_D + Z_2 Z_4] - Z_2[Z_G Z_4 + Z_2 Z_3 + Z_2 Z_4 + Z_2 Z_G] \end{aligned}}$$

$$= \frac{e(Z_2 Z_3 - Z_1 Z_4)}{\begin{aligned} &Z_G Z_D(Z_1 + Z_2 + Z_3 + Z_4) + Z_D(Z_1 + Z_2)(Z_3 + Z_4) \\ &+ Z_G(Z_1 + Z_3)(Z_2 + Z_4) + Z_1 Z_2(Z_3 + Z_4) + Z_3 Z_4(Z_1 + Z_2) \end{aligned}}$$

$$(1\text{--}96)$$

The bridge is balanced when the detector current is zero. For this condition to occur, the numerator of Eq. (1–96) is zero.

$$Z_2 Z_3 - Z_1 Z_4 = 0 \qquad (1\text{--}97)$$

or

$$\frac{Z_1}{Z_2} = \frac{Z_3}{Z_4} \qquad (1\text{--}98)$$

This expression must be satisfied in both magnitude and phase.

1.10.1 SAMPLE PROBLEM

The arms of the bridge shown have the following values: $R_1 = 1000$ ohms, $R_2 = 5000$ ohms, $R_3 = 10^4$ ohms, and $C = 0.100$ microfarads, the bridge is balanced at 60 cps. Compute the values of R_x and L_x.

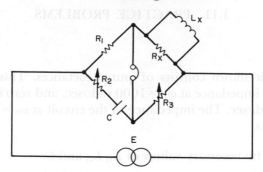

SOLUTION

Denote R_1 as Z_1, R_x and L_x as Z_2, R_2 and C as Z_3 and R_3 as Z_4. If the bridge is balanced

$$\frac{Z_1}{Z_2} = \frac{Z_3}{Z_4}$$

or

$$\frac{R_1}{jR_x\omega L_x/(R_x + j\omega L_x)} = \frac{R_2 - j/\omega C}{R_3}$$

$$\frac{R_2 - j/\omega C}{R_1 R_3} = \frac{R_x - j\omega L_x}{j\omega R_x L_x} = \frac{\omega L_x - jR_x}{\omega R_x L_x}$$

Equating the real parts.

$$\frac{R_2}{R_1 R_3} = \frac{\omega L_x}{\omega R_x L_x} = \frac{1}{R_x}$$

Hence

$$R_x = \frac{R_1 R_3}{R_2}$$

$$= \frac{(10^3)(10^4)}{5 \times 10^3} = 2 \times 10^3 \text{ ohms} \qquad\qquad \text{ANS.}$$

Equating the imaginary parts:

$$\frac{-j}{\omega C R_1 R_3} = \frac{-jR_x}{\omega R_x L_x}$$

$$\frac{1}{C R_1 R_3} = \frac{1}{L_x}$$

Hence

$$L_x = C R_1 R_3$$

$$= (0.1 \times 10^{-6})(10^3)(10^4)$$

$$= 1 \text{ henry} \qquad\qquad\qquad\qquad \text{ANS.}$$

1.11 PRACTICE PROBLEMS

1–1

The circuit shown consists of pure reactances. This circuit is to yield infinite impedance at $\omega_1 = 1000$ rad./sec. and zero impedance at $\omega_2 = 3000$ rad./sec. The impedance of the circuit at $\omega_3 = 500$ rad./sec. is $j1000$ ohms.

Calculate the necessary values of L_1, L_2, and C.

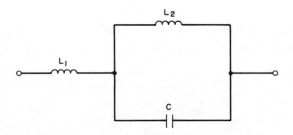

1–2

The circuit shown is to be adjusted to unity power factor by the variation of the inductance L. Calculate

  (a) The value of R which will result in only one condition of unity power factor as L is varied,

  (b) The value of Z at unity power factor under the conditions of (a).

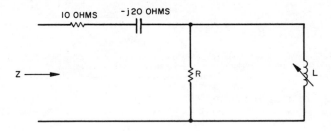

1–3

In the circuit shown, the generator has an internal impedance of $1000(1 + j)$ ohms and an internal emf of 100 v., both at a frequency of $10^4/2\pi$ cps. This generator is matched to the 500-ohm load by means of L and C.

Calculate the necessary values of L and C which will yield maximum power in the 500-ohm load.

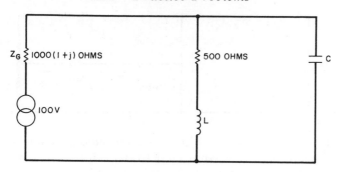

1-4

It is required to adjust a series circuit so that it will resonate at 10^6 cps and have a fractional bandwidth at the half-power points of 0.10. A coil of 125 microhenrys and a Q-factor of 20 is to be used in conjunction with a variable capacitor of negligible loss. State how the circuit is to be adjusted to meet the requirements.

1-5

The circuit shown represents a direct-current 3-wire system obtained by using a balancer set B_1, B_2 in conjunction with the generator G. For the purposes of this problem, the losses in the balancer set may be neglected, and both armatures may be considered as batteries of equal voltage. Each line wire has a resistance of 0.3 ohm, the generator voltage is 240, and the loads are 4.2 and 6.3 ohms.

Calculate the currents in each line, and in the machines G, B_1, and B_2.

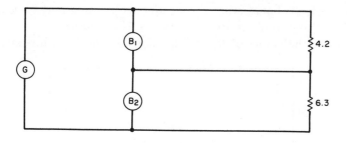

1-6

A source of constant current delivers 10 amp to the network shown. Calculate

(a) The value of R which will absorb maximum power from the circuit

(b) The value of this maximum power.

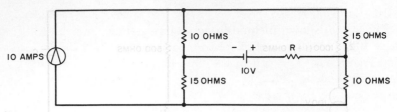

1-7

Three resistors, each of 1 ohm, are connected in delta. Inside the delta, a 1-ohm resistor is connected from each corner to a common point, thus forming a wye inside the delta. Six batteries, each of a different unknown emf and negligible internal resistance, are inserted into the network, one in each of the six branches. The current in one of the delta resistors is found to be 5 amp. Now an additional resistance of 2 ohms is inserted in the branch which was carrying 5 amp, making a total of 3 ohms in this branch under the new condition. What is the new current in this branch?

1-8

The open-circuit emf and short-circuit current of an audio oscillator are 50 v. and 0.447 amp, respectively. When a 50-ohm resistance is connected to this oscillator, the terminal potential difference is 17.65 v. What is the absolute value of the internal impedance of this generator?

1-9

The bridge shown receives power from the generator G at 1000 cps. This bridge is first balanced with S_1 at 1 and S_2 open. This balance yields $R = 10$ ohms and $C_s = 1200 \times 10^{-12}$ farad.

The bridge is balanced a second time with S_1 at 2 and S_2 closed. In this case, $R = 100$ ohms and $C_s = 900 \times 10^{-12}$ farad.

Calculate the values of R_x and C_x, considering C_s as lossless.

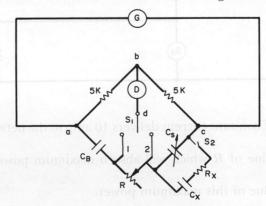

1-10

The circuit shown includes a generator with an internal resistance $R_G = 1000$ ohms; an emf of constant magnitude $E = 150$ v.; and variable frequency. The coil in the tank circuit has an inductance, $L = 200$ microhenrys, and a Q-factor, $Q = 10$, which may be considered constant. The tuning capacitor is fixed at $C = 10^{-10}$ farad. Calculate

(a) The frequency of parallel resonance,

(b) The voltage E_0 across the tank at parallel resonance,

(c) The power delivered to the tank coil at parallel resonance.

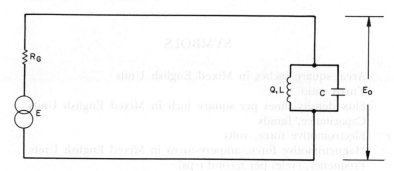

CHAPTER TWO

TRANSFORMERS

SYMBOLS

A	Area, square inches in Mixed English Units
a	Turns ratio
B	Flux density, lines per square inch in Mixed English Units
C	Capacitance, farads
E, e	Electromotive force, volts
F	Magnetomotive force, ampere-turns in Mixed English Units
f	Frequency, cycles per second (cps)
H	Magnetic field intensity, ampere-turns/inch in Mixed English Units
I, i	Current, amperes
j	The imaginary operator $\sqrt{-1}$
K	A multiplier; also the coefficient of coupling
kva	Kilovolt-amperes
kw	Kilowatts
L	Inductance, henrys
l	Length, inches in Mixed English Units
M	Mutual inductance, henrys
N	Number of turns
n	A numeric, the Steinmetz exponent
P	Power, watts
Q	Quality factor
R	Resistance, ohms
$\Re$	Reluctance, ampere-turns/line in Mixed English Units
t	Time, seconds
V, v	Voltage drop, volts
va	Volt-amperes
X	Reactance, ohms
Y	Admittance, mhos
Z	Impedance, ohms
CGS	Centimeter-gram-second system of units
MKS	Meter-kilogram-second system of units
η	Efficiency, per unit or per cent
ϕ	Flux, lines in the Mixed English Units

40

ω	Angular frequency, radians per second (rad/sec)
μ	Permeability of magnetic material, lines/ampere-turn-inch in Mixed English Units
μ_0	Permeability of free space, 3.192 in Mixed English Units

Subscripts

b	Referring to base quantities
c	Referring to core; also denotes critical value
e	Excitation
e	Eddy-current
G	Generator
h	Hysteresis
i, in	Input
L	Load
l	Leakage
M	Referring to mutual inductance
max	Peak or maximum value
o	Referring to resonant conditions
o	Output
p	Primary
s	Secondary
T	Total
TH	Thévenin
φ	Magnetization

2.1   THE MAGNETIC CIRCUIT

A direct analogy can be made between the electric circuit and the magnetic circuit. In a simple d-c series circuit an electromotive force causes a current to flow opposed by the circuit resistance. In the analogous magnetic circuit a magnetomotive force causes a magnetic flux to flow opposed by the magnetic circuit reluctance. Table 2–1 lists some of the magnetic circuit parameters and their units. Several different systems of units may be used. Three of these are presented in the table.

TABLE 2–1
MAGNETIC CIRCUIT PARAMETERS

Parameter	*MKS Unit*	*CGS Unit*	*Mixed English Unit*
Magnetomotive Force (*F*)	Ampere-turn	Gilbert	Ampere-turn
Magnetic Field Intensity (*H*)	Amp-turn/meter	Oersted	Amp-turn/inch
Flux (φ)	Weber	Maxwell	Line
Flux density (*B*)	Weber/m²	Gauss	Line/in²

The magnetic circuit reluctance is defined as

$$\Re \equiv \frac{F}{\phi} \qquad (2\text{--}1)$$

or alternately

$$\Re = \frac{l}{\mu A} \qquad (2\text{--}2)$$

The permeability is obtained from the relation

$$B = \mu H \qquad (2\text{--}3)$$

A typical *B-H* curve for magnetic material is shown in Fig. 2–1.

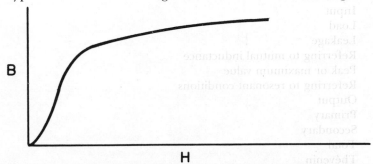

Figure 2–1 Typical B-H curve for magnetic material

The leveling out with increasing field intensity is characteristic of magnetic material saturation. In fact, the *B-H* curve is often called the saturation curve. From this it may be seen that because of saturation, the value of the permeability changes greatly with *B* or *H*. It is typical of magnetic materials that the unsaturated permeability may be several thousand times that of air or free space.

The permeability of air or free space (μ_0) in the Mixed English system of units is 3.192 lines/ampere-turn-inch.

The total flux ϕ is given by

$$\phi = \int B dA \qquad (2\text{--}4)$$

If *B* is constant over the area *A*,

$$\phi = BA \qquad (2\text{--}5)$$

so that

$$\frac{d\phi}{dt} = A \frac{dB}{dt} \qquad (2\text{--}6)$$

if the area is constant.

If the voltage is sinusoidal then B is also sinusoidal. Because H is proportional to current, if the magnetic material is operated into saturation, the necessary excitation current to provide the magnetization will have a peaked shape. This indicates the presence of harmonics in the current similar to those shown in Fig. 2–2.

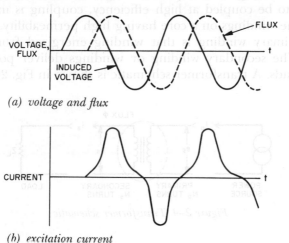

(a) voltage and flux

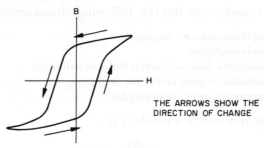

(b) excitation current

Figure 2–2 *Typical voltage, flux, and current waveshapes for magnetic material operated into the region of saturation*

The so-called hysteresis curve is similar to the saturation curve and is shown in Fig. 2–3.

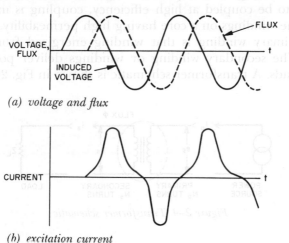

Figure 2–3 *Typical hysteresis loop for iron material*

2.2   TRANSFORMERS

A transformer is a device for coupling electrical energy from one circuit to another by means of a magnetic field. In a transformer, the current flowing in a winding induces a magnetic flux which, in turn, induces a voltage due to the time rate of change of this flux $d\phi/dt$. Because a time rate of change of flux is necessary the transformer cannot operate as a d-c device.

The structure of a transformer consists of two or more windings arranged so that their respective magnetic fie⟋⟍ct. Where power is to be coupled at high efficiency, coupling is increased by placing the windings on a core having high permeability.

The primary winding is that winding energized from a power source. The secondary winding or windings deliver power to the load of loads. A transformer schematic is shown in Fig. 2–4.

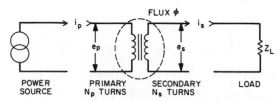

Figure 2–4 Transformer schematic

2.3 IDEAL TRANSFORMERS

The ideal transformer has the following characteristics:

a. The winding resistances are negligible
b. The core loss is negligible
c. The entire magnetic flux completely links all windings
d. The core excitation requirements are negligible
e. The winding capacitances are negligible.

The voltage induced in a winding is

$$e = N\frac{d\phi}{dt} \times 10^{-8} \tag{2-7}$$

Because the entire flux completely links all windings

$$\frac{e_p}{N_p} = \frac{e_s}{N_s} \tag{2-8}$$

or

$$\frac{e_p}{e_s} = \frac{N_p}{N_s} = a \tag{2-9}$$

where a is the primary to secondary turns ratio

$$a \equiv \frac{N_p}{N_s} \tag{2-10}$$

The flux produced is a function of the magnetizing force denoted as ampere-turns (Ni). Because the core requires no magnetization

$$N_p i_p = N_s i_s \tag{2-11}$$

and one obtains using Eq. (2–4)

$$\frac{i_p}{i_s} = \frac{N_s}{N_p} = \frac{1}{a} \tag{2-12}$$

In Fig. 2–4 the load impedance Z_L is the ratio of the voltage to the current

$$Z_L = \frac{e_s}{i_s} \tag{2-13}$$

An equivalent input impedance Z_i may be written as

$$Z_i = \frac{e_p}{i_p} \tag{2-14}$$

and using Eqs. (2–9) and (2–12)

$$Z_i = \frac{a e_s}{i_s/a} = a^2 \frac{e_s}{i_s} = a^2 Z_L \tag{2-15}$$

Equations (2–9), (2–12), and (2–15) are three important defining expressions for the ideal transformer.

2.3.1   SAMPLE PROBLEM

The transformer supplies the loads shown and may be considered as ideal.

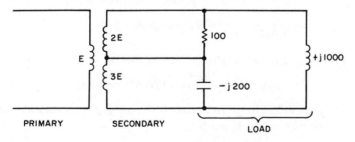

(a) Calculate the impedance reflected by the three loads into the primary winding.

(b) Calculate the power factor of this impedance and state whether it is leading or lagging.

SOLUTION

(a) The secondary impedances reflect into the primary winding with a value equal to the impedance multiplied by the turns-ratio squared. The turns ratio equals the primary-to-secondary voltage ratio.

Assume the voltages on the secondary are additive (the total voltage is $5E$).

The 100-ohm resistor reflects as $100(\frac{1}{2})^2$ $= 25$ ohms
the $-j200$-ohm reactance reflects as $-j200(\frac{1}{3})^2 = -j22\frac{2}{9}$ ohms
the $j1000$-ohm reactance reflects as $j1000(\frac{1}{5})^2 = j40$ ohms

These three are effectively in parallel across the primary terminals and are as shown

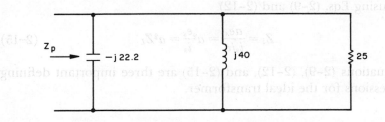

The total impedance Z_p, is

$$Z_p = \cfrac{1}{1/25 + 1/j40 + 1/-j22.2}$$

$$= \frac{1}{0.04 - j0.025 + j0.045} = \frac{1}{0.040 + j0.020}$$

$$= \frac{1}{0.0447 \underline{/26.6}} = 22.3 \underline{/-26.6} \qquad \text{ANS.}$$

(b) The power factor is the cosine of the impedance angle

$$\text{power factor} = \cos(26.6°) = 0.895 \qquad \text{ANS.}$$

The impedance angle is negative indicating a capacitance circuit, hence the power factor is leading. ANS.

2.3.2   SAMPLE PROBLEM

An ideal transformer has a primary coil P and two secondaries S_1 and S_2. The turns-ratio between P and S_1 is 10:1, while that between P and S_2 is 5:4. Across S_2 is connected a parallel combination of R and C. Across S_1 is connected an impedance $Z_1 = 10 + j20$ ohms.

What must be the value of R and the reactance of C in order that the impedance, seen when looking into P is $500 + j0$ ohms?

SOLUTION

The circuit is as shown below.

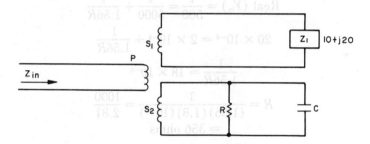

The impedances reflect in parallel across the primary. The problem may be solved by equating the reflected admittance to the required value

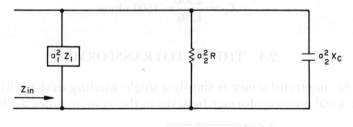

$$Y_{in} = \frac{1}{Z_{in}} = \frac{1}{500} \text{ mhos}$$

The turns-ratio, P to S_1 is designated a_1 and P to S_2 is designated a_2.

$$Y_{in} = \frac{1}{500} = \frac{1}{a_1^2 Z_1} + \frac{1}{a_2^2 R} + \frac{1}{-ja_2^2 X_C}$$

But

$$a_1{}^2Z_1 = (10)^2(10 + j20) = 1000 + j2000$$
$$a_2{}^2R = (1.25)^2R = 1.56R$$
$$-ja_2{}^2X_C = -j(1.25)^2X_C = -j1.56X_C$$

and

$$\frac{1}{a_1{}^2Z_1} = \frac{1}{1000 + j2000}$$

$$= \frac{1}{1000(1 + j2)} \frac{(1 - j2)}{(1 - j2)}$$

$$= \frac{1 - j2}{1000(1 + 4)} = \frac{1}{5000} - \frac{j}{2500}$$

The value of R may be found from the real portion of Y_{in}.

$$\text{Real } (Y_{in}) = \frac{1}{500} = \frac{1}{5000} + \frac{1}{1.56R}$$

$$20 \times 10^{-4} = 2 \times 10^{-4} + \frac{1}{1.56R}$$

$$\frac{1}{1.56R} = 18 \times 10^{-4}$$

$$R = \frac{1}{(1.56)(1.8)(10^{-3})} = \frac{1000}{2.81}$$
$$= 356 \text{ ohms} \qquad \text{ANS.}$$

The value of X_C may be found from the imaginary portion of Y_{in}.

$$\text{Imag } (Y_{in}) = 0 = \frac{-j}{2500} + \frac{j}{1.56X_C}$$

$$X_C = \frac{2500}{1.56} = 1600 \text{ ohms} \qquad \text{ANS.}$$

2.4   THE AUTOTRANSFORMER

The autotransformer is simply a single winding device with a tap. The ideal autotransformer behaves in the same manner as the ideal

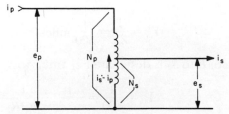

Figure 2–5 A voltage step-down transformer

transformer if the proper turns ratio is used. Fig. 2–5 shows schematically one form of autotransformer (voltage step down) with certain terms defined.

2.4.1   SAMPLE PROBLEM

A transformer with two coils, *A-B* and *C-D*, is connected as an autotransformer. The turns-ratio of coil *C-D* to coil *A-B* is 1.5:1. Terminals *B* and *C* are connected together so that the voltages in the two coils will aid each other. A resistive load of 10 ohms is connected across the terminals *C-D*, and a capacitive load of 10 ohms is connected across terminals *A-D*. Neglect the losses in the transformer, and calculate the current in each coil when 120 v. are impressed at terminals *A-B*.

SOLUTION

The circuit is as shown. Assume the polarities as shown.

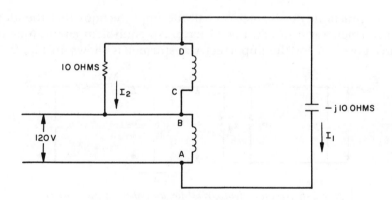

From the definition of turns-ratio

$$E_{DC} = 1.5E_{BA} = 1.5(120) = 180 \text{ v.}$$

and

$$E_{DA} = E_{BA} + E_{DC} = 120 + 180 = 300 \text{ v.}$$

But

$$I_1 = \frac{E_{DA}}{Z_{DA}} = \frac{300\ \underline{/0}}{10\ \underline{/-90}} = 30\ \underline{/90} \text{ amp}$$

and

$$I_2 = \frac{E_{DC}}{Z_{DC}} = \frac{180\ \underline{/0}}{10\ \underline{/0}} = 18\ \underline{/0}\ \text{amp}$$

But

$$I_{CD} = I_1 + I_2$$
$$= 18 + j30\ \text{amp}$$
$$|I_{CD}| = \sqrt{(18)^2 + (30)^2} = \sqrt{324 + 900} = \sqrt{1224} = 35\ \text{amp}\ \text{ANS.}$$

and

$$\frac{I_{CD}}{I_{AB}} = \frac{1}{1.5}$$

Thus

$$I_{AB} = 1.5 I_{CD} = 27 + j45\ \text{amp}$$

$$|I_{AB}| = \sqrt{(27)^2 + (45)^2} = 52.5\ \text{amp}\ \qquad \text{ANS.}$$

2.5   PRACTICAL TRANSFORMERS

The practical transformer has all the imperfections that the ideal transformer was assumed not to have. An equivalent circuit (one of many possible) for the imperfect transformer is shown in Fig. 2–6.

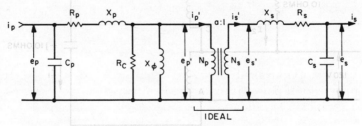

Figure 2–6 An equivalent circuit for an imperfect transformer

The imperfections have been lumped together to convert an ideal to a non-ideal transformer. The ideal portion of the circuit is still governed by the rules stated in Sec. 2.3. The symbols are as follows:

R_p and R_s represent the equivalent winding resistances; X_p and X_s, the equivalent leakage reactances; and C_p and C_s, the equivalent winding capacitances. The equivalent core loss resistance is R_c and the core magnetizing reactance is X_ϕ. The core components are shown referred to the primary side.

The equivalent circuit parameters may be evaluated from measured data. A measurement of input voltage, current, and power with the secondary open circuited yields very nearly the core loss resistance and magnetizing reactance at operating voltage. Often a simple evaluation of the vector exciting current will satisfy the needs of the problem. Thus, if I_e represents the total exciting current

$$I_e = I_p \; /\!\!-\cos^{-1} P_p/E_p I_p \tag{2-16}$$

The winding resistance and reactance referred to either winding may be evaluated from input voltage, current, and power measurements with the secondary short circuited. This is performed at reduced voltage but approximately rated current and assumes negligible effects from excitation current. Thus on the primary side

$$\frac{E_p}{I_p} = Z_p = R_p + a^2 R_s + j(X_p + a^2 X_s) \tag{2-17}$$

$$R_p + a^2 R_s = Z_p \cos \theta = Z_p \left(\frac{P_p}{E_p I_p}\right) = \frac{P_p}{I_p^2} \tag{2-18}$$

$$X_p + a^2 X_s = \sqrt{Z_p^2 - (R_p + a^2 R_s)^2} \tag{2-19}$$

where a is the voltage transformation ratio.

These qualities may also be evaluated with respect to the secondary side.

The effects of the winding capacitances are generally negligible at power line and lower audio frequencies. The current through the magnetizing reactance is generally insignificant at full load and usually is non-sinusoidal for sinusoidal excitation voltage. The equivalent core loss resistance can be computed from the dissipated power. This will be discussed in Sec. 2.6.

A simplified equivalent circuit that can be applied to the steady-state analysis of a power transformer completely neglects R_c, X_ϕ and the capacitances. Transient analyses become more involved.

2.6   CORE LOSS

The transformer core loss is the result of properties of the iron and consists of Eddy-current loss and Hysteresis loss. That is

$$P_c = P_e + P_h \tag{2-20}$$

Eddy-current loss results from circulating currents in the core which give rise to power loss. This loss is reduced by constructing the core of thin insulated laminations, (the thinner the better) and by increasing the core resistivity. An expression for Eddy-current loss is

$$P_e = K_e f^2 (B_{max})^2 \text{ watts} \tag{2-21}$$

Hysteresis loss is the result of the alternating magnetization and demagnetization of the core material in an alternating field. The power loss is directly proportional to the area within the hysteresis loop. This is a property of the material.

Empirically Steinmetz in 1892 determined that the following expression was valid

$$P_h = K_h f (B_{max})^n \text{ watts} \tag{2-22}$$

For the materials then in general use, Steinmetz determined that $n = 1.6$ was a good number over a wide range of flux densities. More recently it has been determined that the value of n may vary from 1.5 to 2.5, or more, and may not be constant for a given material.

If the applied or induced voltage in a magnetic device is sinusoidal, then

$$B_{max} = \frac{E}{4.44 f N A \times 10^{-8}} \tag{2-23}$$

where E is the rms value of the sinusoidal voltage. Using Eq. (2–23), then Eqs. (2–21) and (2–22) may be rewritten as

$$P_e = K'_e E^2 \tag{2-24}$$

and

$$P_h = K'_h \frac{E^n}{f^{(n-1)}} \tag{2-25}$$

where K'_e and K'_h are constant for the structure and material.

2.6.1 SAMPLE PROBLEM

A test of the core losses of a transformer yields the following data:
The core loss at 60 cps is 240 watts when 120 v. is applied to the primary winding.
The core loss at 25 cps is 50 watts when 50 v. is applied to the primary winding.

Calculate the Eddy-current loss for this transformer when 240 v. at 60 cps is applied to the primary winding.

SOLUTION

Use the expressions for Hysteresis and Eddy-current losses to divide the total loss into its components, and evaluate as required.
Total loss = Eddy-current loss + Hysteresis loss = $P_e + P_h$.
Assuming rms sinusoidal voltage

$$P_h = K'_h \frac{E^n}{f^{(n-1)}} = K'_h E^n f^{(1-n)}$$

and

$$P_e = K'_e E^2$$

At 60 cps the total loss is

$$240 = K'_h (120)^n (60)^{(1-n)} + K'_e (120)^2$$
$$= K'_h 120 \frac{(120)^{(n-1)}}{(60)^{(n-1)}} + K'_e (120)^2$$
$$= K'_h 120 (2)^{(n-1)} + K'_e (120)^2$$

And at 25 cps the total loss is

$$50 = K'_h (50)^n (25)^{(1-n)} + K'_e (50)^2$$
$$= K'_h 50 \frac{(50)^{(n-1)}}{(25)^{(n-1)}} + K'_e (50)^2$$
$$= K'_h 50 (2)^{(n-1)} + K'_e (50)^2$$

The two equations can be solved simultaneously for K'_e

$$(240)(50) = K'_h (120)(2)^{(n-1)}(50) + K'_e (120)^2 (50)$$
$$\underline{-(50)(120) = -K'_h (50)(2)^{(n-1)}(120) - K'_e (50)^2 (120)}$$
$$(120)(50) = K'_e [(120)^2 (50) - (50)^2 (120)]$$

or

$$1 = K'_e [120 - 50]$$
$$K'_e = \frac{1}{70}$$

Thus at 60 cps with 240 v. applied, the Eddy-current loss is

$$P_e = \frac{1}{70}(240)^2 = 823 \text{ watts} \qquad\qquad \text{ANS.}$$

2.7 THE TRANSFORMER AS A NETWORK ELEMENT

An alternate form of transformer equivalent circuit which neglects the core loss is often employed [cf. Kraus, *Studying*, (4) p. 319]. This allows the transformer to be treated as a simple circuit coupling element. Figure 2–7 shows such an equivalent circuit.

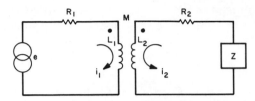

Figure 2–7 An alternate transformer equivalent circuit

The loop equations are

$$e = (R_1 + j\omega L_1)i_1 + j\omega M i_2 \qquad (2\text{--}26)$$

$$0 = j\omega M i_1 + (R_2 + Z + j\omega L_2)i_2 \qquad (2\text{--}27)$$

The coefficient of coupling K is defined as

$$K \equiv \frac{M}{\sqrt{L_1 L_2}} \qquad (2\text{--}28)$$

and the permitted values of K are

$$0 \leq K \leq 1 \qquad (2\text{--}29)$$

Figure 2–8 shows an equivalent form of the transformer equivalent circuit shown in Fig. 2–7. The equivalence can easily be verified by writing the loop equations. If correctly written, they will be indentical to Eqs. (2–26) and (2–27).

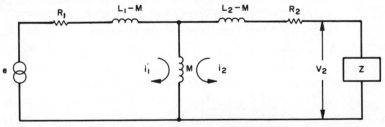

Figure 2–8 A transformer tee equivalent circuit

A useful relation, derived in [M.I.T Staff, *Transformers*, (9) Chap. 17] is that the square root of the ratio of the self inductances of an iron-core transformer very nearly equals the turns ratio. Mathematically

$$\sqrt{L_1/L_2} = N_1/N_2 \qquad (2\text{–}30)$$

The equivalent circuit of Fig. 2–7 or Fig. 2–8 may be modified by using the transformation equations to obtain the equivalent circuit shown in Fig. 2–9. This circuit is derived by transforming the total secondary impedance into the primary by multiplication by the square of the turns ratio. The new value of mutual impedance is obtained from Eq. (2–28) by substituting the transformed secondary inductance and maintaining the same coupling. A similar circuit could be derived by transforming into the secondary side.

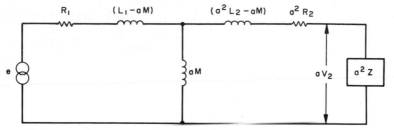

Figure 2–9 *Transformer tee equivalent circuit with the secondary transformed to the primary side*

2.7.1   SAMPLE PROBLEM

A transformer has the following constants:

Primary resistance	10 ohms
Primary reactance	40 ohms
Secondary resistance	2 ohms
Secondary reactance	10 ohms
Coefficient of coupling	0.5

The applied voltage is a sinusoid having a peak value of 100 volts at an angular frequency of 100 radians per second.

(a) With the secondary terminals short-circuited, what value of capacitance should be placed across the primary terminals in order that a unity power factor load is presented to the generator?

(b) With no capacitance connected across the primary terminals, what should the secondary load impedance be in order that maximum power be delivered to the load?

SOLUTION

(a) If the input admittance of the transformer is determined under the stated conditions, the susceptance of the added capacitor equals the (inductive) susceptive portion of the admittance. The input admittance may be found from the equivalent circuits.

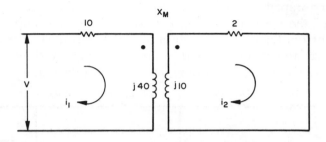

The input admittance is

$$Y_{\text{in}} = \frac{i_1}{v}$$

The mutual reactance X_M is

$$X_M = K\sqrt{X_p X_s}$$

$$= 0.5\sqrt{(j40)(j10)} = j10 \text{ ohms}$$

The loop equations from which i_1 is determined are

$$v = (10 + j40)i_1 - j10i_2$$
$$0 = -j10i_1 + (2 + j10)i_2$$

Solving

$$i_1 = \frac{\begin{vmatrix} v & -j10 \\ 0 & (2+j10) \end{vmatrix}}{\begin{vmatrix} (10+j40) & -j10 \\ -j10 & (2+j10) \end{vmatrix}} = \frac{v(2+j10)}{(10+j40)(2+j10) + 100}$$

so that

$$Y_{\text{in}} = \frac{i_1}{v} = \frac{(2+j10)}{20 - 400 + j80 + j100 + 100}$$

$$= \frac{2 + j10}{-280 + j180}$$

$$= \frac{10.2 \,\underline{/78.7}}{333 \,\underline{/147.3}} = 0.0307 \,\underline{/-68.6} = 0.0112 - j0.0285$$

The capacitive susceptance ωC equals the inductive susceptance or

$$C = \frac{0.0285}{\omega}$$

$$= \frac{0.0285}{100} = 0.000285 \text{ farads}$$
$$= 285 \text{ microfarads} \qquad \text{ANS.}$$

(b) The load for maximum power equals the conjugate of the Thévenin impedance. The source generator is assumed to have zero impedance. The Thévenin impedance seen by the load impedance may be determined from the equivalent circuit shown below.

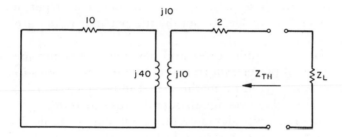

An alternate form of the equivalent circuit is shown below.

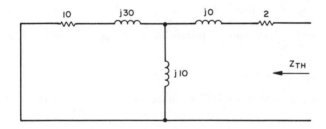

The impedance Z_{TH} is

$$Z_{TH} = 2 + \frac{(j10)\,(10 + j30)}{10 + j40}$$

$$= 2 + \frac{(-300 + j100)\,(1 - j4)}{(10 + j40)\,(1 - j4)}$$

$$= 2 + \frac{-30 + 40 + j10 + j120}{1 + 16}$$

$$= 2 + \frac{10 + j130}{17}$$

$$= 2 + 0.59 + j7.64$$

$$= 2.59 + j7.64$$

Thus the load impedance is the complex conjugate of Z_{TH} or

$$Z_L = 2.59 - j7.64$$ ANS.

2.8   PER CENT AND PER UNIT QUANTITIES

It is common practice to express voltages and currents as a per cent or a fraction of their nominal full-load values. The actual current, voltage or voltage drop (in an impedance) expressed as a per cent or fraction of this base value becomes the per cent or per unit value of the current or voltage. Generally the per unit values are simpler to use.

Similarly the per unit power and per unit impedance are respectively the actual power as a fraction of base volt-amperes (base voltage times base current) and the actual impedance as a fraction of base impedance (base voltage divided by base current).

This system of units allows certain computations to be made very simply using the per unit system instead of the actual values.

For example assume a 1200/120-v. 12-kva transformer. The base current and impedance may be simply computed. On the high voltage side the base current is

Base Current = base volt-amperes/base voltage = 12000/1200 = 10 amp
$$(2\text{-}31)$$

and the base impedance is

Base Impedance = base voltage/base current = 1200/10 = 120 ohms
$$(2\text{-}32)$$

On the low voltage side the base current is

Base Current = 12000/120 = 100 amp $(2\text{-}33)$

and the base impedance is

Base Impedance = 120/100 = 1.20 ohms $(2\text{-}34)$

Thus, if the transformer has 2% series resistance and 3% series reactance this represents (0.02)(120) ohms or 2.4 ohms resistance and (0.03)(120) or 3.6 ohms reactance referred to the high voltage side and 0.024 ohms resistance and 0.036 ohms reactance referred to the low voltage side. If full load current (1.0 p.u.) is drawn, the series resistance power loss would be $(0.02)(1.0)^2$ or 0.02 p.u. power while if 0.8 p.u. current is drawn, the power loss becomes $(0.02)(0.8)^2$ or 0.0128 p.u. power.

2.8.1   SAMPLE PROBLEM

A 500-kva, 13200/2400-v., 60 cycle, single-phase transformer has a 4.0% reactance and a 1.0% resistance. The leakage reactance and the resistance of the low-voltage winding are 0.250 and 0.055 ohm, respectively. The core loss under rated conditions is 1800 watts.

(a) Calculate the leakage reactance and the resistance of the high-voltage winding, in ohms.

(b) Calculate the efficiency of this transformer at full load and 85% power factor.

SOLUTION

(a) The steps in the calculation of the winding impedance are: The base impedance is given by

$$Z_b = (\text{voltage})^2/\text{volt-amps}$$

On the high-voltage side

$$Z_b = (13200)^2/500,000 = 348 \text{ ohms}$$

The turns-ratio, high to low voltage, is equal to the voltage ratio

$$a = 13,200/2400 = 5.5$$

The total reactance on the high-voltage side is 4% or

$$X_T = 0.04(348) = 13.9 \text{ ohms}$$

The reflected low-voltage winding reactance is

$$X_L' = (5.5)^2(0.250) = 7.6 \text{ ohms}$$

The reactance of the high-voltage winding is the difference

$$X_H = X_T - X_L'$$
$$= 13.9 - 7.6 = 6.3 \text{ ohms} \qquad \text{ANS.}$$

Similarly the total resistance on the high-voltage side is 1% or

$$R_T = 0.01(348) = 3.48 \text{ ohms}$$

The reflected low-voltage winding resistance is

$$R_L' = (5.5)^2(0.055) = 1.66 \text{ ohms}$$

The resistance of the high-voltage winding is the difference

$$R_H = R_T - R_L'$$
$$= 3.48 - 1.66 = 1.82 \text{ ohms} \qquad \text{ANS.}$$

(b) The efficiency η may be found from

$$\eta = \text{output/output plus losses}$$

Assuming full kva load, the output is

$$P_O = (\text{v.a.})(\text{power factor})$$
$$= 500,000(0.85) = 425,000$$

The losses are the sum of core loss plus winding resistance loss. At full load, the total resistance loss is 1% of the output volt-amperes or

$$P_R = 0.01(500,000) = 5000 \text{ watts.}$$

The core loss is given as 1800 watts, thus

$$\eta = \frac{(425,000)100\%}{(431,800)} = 98.4\% \qquad \text{ANS.}$$

2.9   R.F. TRANSFORMERS

At radio frequencies, the transformer is used in conjunction with vacuum tube amplifier circuits to provide frequency selective amplification. In this situation the transmission of power is not significant. Frequency selection is provided by resonating the primary and/or secondary inductances with capacitors. Typical equivalent circuits are shown in Fig. 2–10.

The analysis of these circuits appears in practically every modern text on electronics and electronics handbook.

Typical frequency response curves for the double tuned circuit for different values of coupling are shown in Fig. 2–11.

The coefficient of coupling K is as defined by Eq. (2–28). The critical coupling value K_c is

$$K_c = 1/\sqrt{Q_1 Q_2} \qquad (2\text{–}35)$$

where

$$Q_1 = \omega_0 L_1/R_1$$

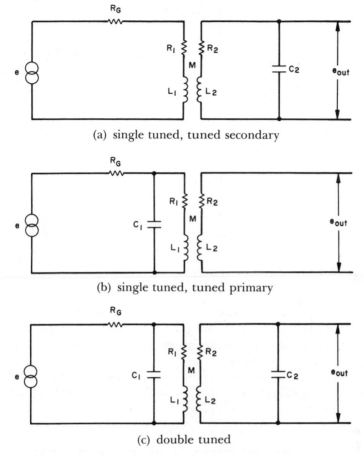

(a) single tuned, tuned secondary

(b) single tuned, tuned primary

(c) double tuned

Figure 2–10 Various tuned transformer circuits

and

$$Q_2 = \omega_0 L_2 / R_2$$

The circuits are adjusted such that

$$\omega_0 = 1/\sqrt{L_1 C_1} = 1/\sqrt{L_2 C_2} \qquad (2\text{–}36)$$

For K less than or equal to K_c, only one peak occurs in the frequency response. For K greater than K_c, two peaks occur on either side of a dip at ω_0. The frequencies of the peaks are ω_1 and ω_2 and are given by Eqs. (2–37) and (2–38)*

* From John D. Ryder, *Networks, Lines, and Fields,* second edition, copyright 1955. Used by permission of Prentice-Hall, Inc., Englewood Cliffs, N.J.

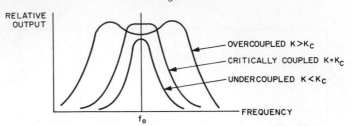

Figure 2–11 Response curves for the double-tuned transformer

$$\omega_1 = \omega_0\left(1 + \frac{K_c}{2}\sqrt{\frac{K^2}{K_c^2} - 1}\right) = \omega_0\left(1 + \sqrt{\frac{K^2}{4} - \frac{K_c^2}{4}}\right) \qquad (2\text{–}37)$$

$$\omega_2 = \omega_0\left(1 - \frac{K_c}{2}\sqrt{\frac{K^2}{K_c^2} - 1}\right) = \omega_0\left(1 - \sqrt{\frac{K^2}{4} - \frac{K_c^2}{4}}\right) \qquad (2\text{–}38)$$

2.9.1 SAMPLE PROBLEM

The circuit shown is the simplification of an intermediate-frequency, tuned transformer in which the elements are of such high quality (high Q) as to make the resistance components negligible for the purposes of this problem.

When $L_1C_1 = L_2C_2 = LC$ determine the product of LC and the coefficient of coupling K necessary in order that V will have peaks at 450 kc and 460 kc and a valley at 455 kc.

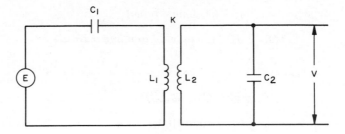

SOLUTION

See [*Data* (17) pp. 236–246]. The center angular frequency ω_0 is given by

$$\omega_0 = \frac{1}{\sqrt{L_1C_1}} = \frac{1}{\sqrt{L_2C_2}} = 2\pi(455 \text{ kc})$$

thus

$$LC = \frac{1}{4\pi^2(455 \times 10^3)^2} = 0.122 \times 10^{-12} \qquad \text{ANS.}$$

The frequencies at which V has peaks are given by

$$\omega_p = \omega_0\left(1 \pm \sqrt{\frac{K^2}{4} - \frac{K_c^2}{4}}\right)$$

where K_c is the value of critical coupling given by

$$K_c = \frac{1}{\sqrt{Q_1 Q_2}}$$

Under the conditions of this problem, $K_c = 0$. Thus

$$\frac{\omega_p}{\omega_0} = 1 \pm \frac{K}{2}$$

Substituting values

$$\omega_p/\omega_0 = 2\pi(460{,}000)/2\pi(455{,}000) = 1 \pm K/2$$

or

$$K/2 = (460 - 455)/455$$
$$K = 2(460 - 455)/455 = 0.022 \qquad \text{ANS.}$$

As a check use the other values

$$1 - \frac{K}{2} = \frac{450}{455}$$

or

$$\frac{K}{2} = \frac{455 - 450}{455}$$
$$K = \frac{2(455 - 450)}{455} = 0.022$$

2.10 IMPEDANCE TRANSFORMATION

In addition to magnetically coupled circuits for impedance transformation, it is possible to employ reactive networks for this purpose. In general these networks tend to be narrow band because of the arrangement of elements to form resonant circuits.

One form of impedance matching between a source having an equivalent internal impedance which is purely resistive and a resistive load is shown in Fig. 2–12.

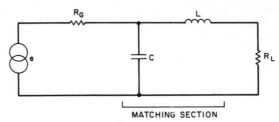

MATCHING SECTION

Figure 2–12 A reactive impedance matching section ($R_L < R_G$)

This section is applicable if $R_L < R_G$. The conditions of perfect impedance match require that the generator equivalent load impedance be the complex conjugate of the generator internal impedance (in this case simply R_G) and the equivalent source impedance for the load be its complex conjugate impedance which is simply R_L. For these conditions to be met

$$C = \frac{1}{\omega R_G}\sqrt{\frac{R_G}{R_L} - 1} \qquad (2\text{–}39)*$$

and

$$L = \frac{R_L}{\omega}\sqrt{\frac{R_G}{R_L} - 1} \qquad (2\text{–}40)$$

These equations were derived from the resonant frequency equation

$$\omega = \sqrt{\frac{1}{LC} - \frac{R_L^2}{L^2}} \qquad (2\text{–}41)$$

and the equation for the impedance seen by the generator at resonance which is

$$R_{\text{res}} = R_G = \frac{L}{CR_L} \qquad (2\text{–}42)$$

For the case of $R_L > R_G$, the network is reversed as shown in Fig. 2–13.

---

* Equations 2–39 through 2–46 taken from John D. Ryder, *Networks, Lines, and Fields,* second edition, copyright 1955, by permission of Prentice-Hall, Inc., Englewood Cliffs, N.J.

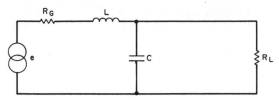

Figure 2–13 A reactive impedance matching section ($R_L > R_G$)

In this case the design equations are

$$C = \frac{1}{\omega R_L}\sqrt{\frac{R_L}{R_G} - 1} \qquad (2\text{--}43)$$

and

$$L = \frac{R_G}{\omega}\sqrt{\frac{R_L}{R_G} - 1} \qquad (2\text{--}44)$$

If either the generator or load have reactive portions these may be resonated initially by an appropriate series element which may be included in, or added to, the matching section.

A more versatile matching section may be built around a Tee section which may, if desired, be converted to an equivalent Pi network by the use of the appropriate transformation equations given in Chapter 1. The Tee matching network is illustrated in Fig. 2–14.

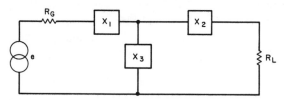

Figure 2–14 A reactive tee impedance matching section

The impedance seen by the generator is to be equal to R_G while the source impedance to the load is to be equal to R_L. The three elements of the Tee—X_1, X_2, and X_3—are assumed pure reactances. In order to satisfy the impedance match conditions it is necessary that one of the three reactances be opposite in sign to the other two. Hence the Tee will consist of either two inductances and one capacitance or two capacitances and one inductance. If it is necessary to resonate reactive portions of either the generator or load, these resonating elements may be combined with the values of X_1 and X_2 as required.

The design equations are:

$$X_2 = \pm\sqrt{\frac{R_L}{R_G}(X_3{}^2 - R_G R_L)} - X_3 \qquad (2\text{--}45)$$

and

$$X_1 = \pm\sqrt{\frac{R_G}{R_L}(X_3{}^2 - R_G R_L)} - X_3 \qquad (2\text{--}46)$$

The design of such a network requires the arbitrary choice of value for one element which then determines the other two.

In order to insure maximum power transfer it is necessary that $X_3{}^2 \geqq R_G R_L$. If $X_3{}^2 < R_G R_L$, the coupling is said to be insufficient. If $X_3{}^2 = R_G R_L$, the circuit is said to have critical coupling and only one possible network may be designed. If $X_3{}^2 > R_G R_L$, there are two possible networks.

As stated earlier, reactive portions of generator or load require resonating elements which may be combined with X_1 or X_2 to make the series arm on one side equal to zero eliminating one element even though electrically the element is still present in the network.

2.10.1 SAMPLE PROBLEM

It is desired to match a 500-ohm resistor to a 5000-ohm generator at a frequency of $10,000/2\pi$ cps. This is to be done by means of a coil and capacitor, each of which has negligible loss. Give the circuit to be used and calculate the values of the inductance and capacitance required.

SOLUTION

Ref: [Ryder, *Networks* (19), Chap. 3].
The generator resistance is greater than the load resistance so the following matching network is applicable.

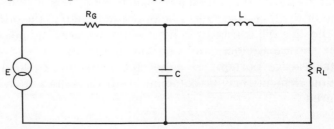

The values of L and C are

$$L = \frac{R_L}{\omega}\sqrt{\frac{R_G}{R_L} - 1}$$

$$C = \frac{1}{\omega R_G}\sqrt{\frac{R_G}{R_L} - 1}$$

where

$$\omega = 2\pi f = 2\pi\frac{10^4}{2\pi} = 10^4 \text{ rad/sec.}$$

$$R_G = 5 \times 10^3$$
$$R_L = 5 \times 10^2$$

Substituting values

$$L = \frac{5 \times 10^2}{10^4}\sqrt{\frac{5 \times 10^3}{5 \times 10^2} - 1}$$

$$= 5 \times 10^{-2}\sqrt{10 - 1} = 0.150 \text{ henry} \qquad \text{ANS.}$$

$$C = \frac{1}{10^4(5 \times 10^3)}\sqrt{\frac{5 \times 10^3}{5 \times 10^2} - 1}$$
$$= 0.2 \times 10^{-7}\sqrt{10 - 1}$$
$$= 0.060 \text{ microfarads} \qquad \text{ANS.}$$

2.11   PRACTICE PROBLEMS

2–1

The circuit shown is that of a thyratron rectifier and its control network. The operating frequency is 60 cps; $L = 10$ henrys; $R = 11,310$ ohms; $e_{ba} = 100$ v.; $e_{co} = e_{od} = 50$ v.

Calculate the magnitude of the voltage e_{og} and the number of degrees it leads or lags e_{ba}.

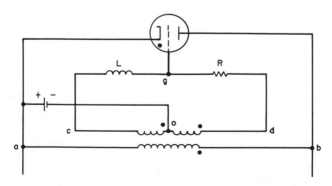

2-2

The transformer shown may be considered ideal. The turns ratios are $N_2/N_1 = 1.5$ and $N_3/N_1 = 2$. The impedances are $Z_2 = 100(1 + j)$ ohms and $Z_3 = 50(1 - j3)$ ohms.

Calculate the magnitude and sign of X_4 which will make the power factor, at the input, equal to unity.

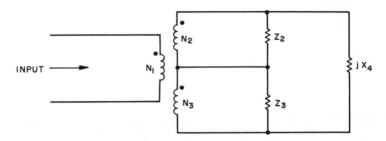

2-3

A 3-coil transformer is used to match two loads to a generator. The first load, a 500-ohm resistor which is to receive 55.6% of the total power, is connected to the first winding of N_1 turns. The second load, equivalent to a 4-ohm resistor, is connected to the second coil of N_2 turns. The generator having an internal resistance of 100 ohms is to be matched when connected to the third coil of N_3 turns.

Calculate the required ratios N_1/N_3 and N_2/N_3, assuming the transformer to be ideal.

2-4

Power at 1000 cps is supplied by a generator having an internal impedance of $100 + j50$ ohms. Maximum power is required in the load consisting of an impedance, $1000 - j100$ ohms. A tuning capacitor is placed in the circuit as shown. If the open-circuit emf of the generator is 75 v., calculate:

(a) the reactance of the required capacitor
(b) the turns ratio N_1/N_2 of the idealized transformer
(c) the power delivered to the load.

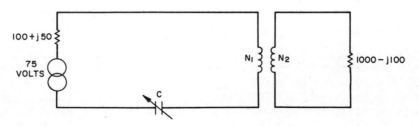

2–5

An autotransformer is connected as shown. For the purposes of this problem, the losses in the transformer and its exciting current may be neglected and the coupling among the various coils may be considered perfect. The turns ratios are $N_2/N_1 = 2$ and $N_3/N_1 = 3$.

Calculate the value and sign of X_x in order that the input to the primary N_1 be at unity power factor.

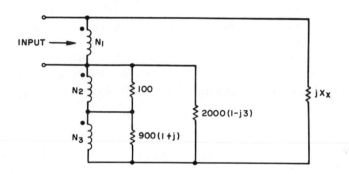

2–6

A 10-kva, 2300/115 v., 60-cycle, single-phase transformer gave the following data on tests:

No-load test (input to the low-voltage side)

Applied voltage	115 v.
Current	0.9 amp
Power	70 watts

Short-circuit test (input to high-voltage side; low side shorted)

Applied voltage	118 v.
Current	4.35 amp
Power	225 watts

(a) Assuming that the core loss varies as the 1.7 power of the flux, find the efficiency of the transformer when supplying 60 amp at unity power factor at 115 v.

(b) Find the corresponding voltage applied to the primary.

2–7

A 100-kva, 11,000/2200-v., 60-cycle, single-phase transformer has an Hysteresis loss of 750 watts, an Eddy-current loss of 225 watts, and a copper loss of 940 watts under the rated conditions of full load. It is desired to export this transformer and to operate it at

45 cps but with the same maximum flux density and the same total loss as at 60 cps.

Calculate the new voltage and kva-rating. Neglect the exciting current.

2–8

When 2200 v. at 60 cps is impressed on a certain transformer at no load, the total iron loss is 200 watts. When the frequency of the impressed voltage is changed to 25 cps and the magnitude of the voltage is made such as to maintain the same maximum flux density as before, the iron loss falls to 75 watts.

Neglect the impedance drop at no load and calculate:

(a) the magnitude of the impressed voltage necessary at 25 cps;

(b) the Eddy-current loss and the Hysteresis loss at 60 cps.

2–9

A transformer consisting of two identical coils is connected in a circuit as shown. Each coil of the transformer has a self-inductance of 10 henrys and the coefficient of coupling between them is 0.90. The power source E has a negligible internal impedance and a terminal voltage of 500 at an angular frequency ω of 1000 rad/sec. The value of C is 1 microfarad.

Calculate the value of the current in the 1000-ohm load resistor.

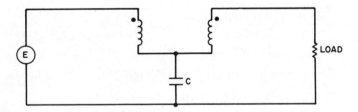

2–10

An audio frequency transformer has two coils. At the frequency of operation, the self-reactances of the primary and secondary coils have reactances of 1000 and 4000 ohms, respectively. The coefficient of coupling, for the purposes of this problem, is unity, and the resistances of the coils may be neglected.

Neglecting the core losses, calculate the input impedance at the terminals of the primary winding when the impedance of the load, connected to the secondary, is $1000(1 - j3)$ ohms.

2–11

The open-circuit emf across the secondary winding of an air-cored transformer is 60 v. when 200 watts at 50 v. and a power factor of

0.6 are applied to the primary. The frequency is 60 cps and the turns ratio a, primary to secondary, is 1:2.

Calculate the self-inductance and leakage inductance of the primary winding and the mutual inductance between the coils.

2–12

A transformer, which for the purposes of this problem may be considered lossless, is required to transmit maximum power from a 3000-ohm generator to a 6-ohm load with half-power points at $f_1 = 200/2\pi$ and $f_2 = 10,000/2\pi$. Both the generator and load impedances are pure resistances.

Calculate the inductances of the primary and secondary windings and the coefficient of coupling in the required transformer.

2–13

The single-phase transformers with equal ratings and turns ratios are operated in parallel to supply a load of 180 kw at a lagging power factor of 0.90. Transformer A has internal drops at full load for resistance and reactance of 1 and 6%, respectively. Transformer B has corresponding drops of 2 and 5%.

Calculate the power delivered by each transformer to the load.

2–14

A radio transmitter operates at a frequency, $f = 10^8/2\pi$ cps. The radiator is a dipole having an effective resistance of 70 ohms at the operating frequency. Power to the radiator is supplied over a 500-ohm line which is matched to the dipole by means of a transformer consisting of two equal coils of 1 microhenry each. This transformer is tuned by means of a single capacitor shunted across the primary winding.

Calculate the size of this tuning capacitor and the coefficient of coupling K necessary in the transformer. Neglect the losses in the reactors and the transmission line.

2–15

A radio-frequency transformer for power transmission purposes consists of two equal coils, each having an inductance of one millihenry. The mutual inductance between the coils can be adjusted from 100 to 150 microhenrys by moving one coil with respect to the other. This transformer is to be used to furnish perfect coupling between a circuit of $1600 - j1000$ ohms and a load of $400 + j500$ ohms at a frequency of 1 Mc, with maximum selectivity.

Calculate the circuit elements required, and show by a diagram how the circuit is connected.

CHAPTER THREE

THREE-PHASE CIRCUITS

SYMBOLS

E	Electromotive force, rms value of a sinusoid, volts
e	Electromotive force, time varying or unknown value, volts
f	Frequency, cycles per second (cps)
I	Current, rms value of a sinusoid, amperes
i	Current, time varying or unknown value, amperes
j	The imaginary operator, $\sqrt{-1}$
kva	Kilovolt-amperes
kw	Kilowatts
P	Power, also wattmeter indication, watts
R	Resistance, ohms
t	Time, seconds
V, v	Voltage drop, volts
va	Volt-amperes
X	Reactance, ohms
Y	Admittance, mhos
Z	Impedance, ohms
η	Efficiency, per unit or per cent
θ	Phase angle of an impedance, angle between voltage and current vectors, radians or degrees
ω	Angular frequency, radians per second

Subscripts

a, b, c	Designating three lines or phases of the 3-phase system
L	Denoting load
l	Line
l-l	Line-to-Line
l-n	Line-to-neutral
n	Denoting the neutral point or neutral line

3.1   GENERATOR VOLTAGES AND CONNECTIONS

Practically all power transmission is carried by three-phase (abbreviated 3-ϕ) systems.

The three generators comprising a three-phase balanced or symmetrical source yield voltages

$$e_1 = \sqrt{2}E \cos \omega t = E \underline{/0} \tag{3-1}$$

$$e_2 = \sqrt{2}E \cos (\omega t + 120) = E \underline{/120} \tag{3-2}$$

$$e_3 = \sqrt{2}E \cos (\omega t - 120) = E \underline{/-120} \tag{3-3}$$

These may be connected in either of two ways designated because of appearance: wye (or star) or delta (or mesh). These two connections with their respective voltage vector diagrams are shown in Fig. 3–1.

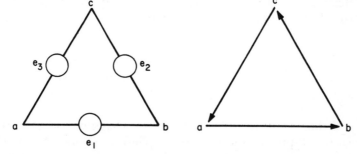

WYE

(a) wye connection and voltage vector diagram

DELTA

(b) delta connection and voltage vector diagram

Figure 3–1 Wye and delta connected three-phase power sources

In the wye connection the junction point designated "n" is the neutral; points a, b, and c are the line connections.

In the wye generator connection loads may be connected either from line to line or from line to neutral yielding either delta or wye connected loads.

The line to line voltages (or more simply the line voltages) of the wye connection are given by

$$e_{ab} = \sqrt{3}E \; \underline{/-30} \qquad\qquad (3\text{--}4)$$

$$e_{bc} = \sqrt{3}E \; \underline{/90} \qquad\qquad (3\text{--}5)$$

$$e_{ca} = \sqrt{3}E \; \underline{/-150} \qquad\qquad (3\text{--}6)$$

These also make up a balanced 3-ϕ set.

3.2   TRANSFORMER CONNECTIONS

Voltage (and current) levels may be readily changed by the use of transformer banks. Further a wye source may be converted to a delta source and vice versa by appropriate connections. Voltage vector diagrams are valuable in determining proper connections.

A 3-ϕ transformer bank may consist either of three single-phase transformers properly interconnected with suitable attention paid to proper phasing or of a single transformer with three sets of coils on a single special core structure.

A special transformer bank is called the open-delta or Vee connection. This is often used in a system to provide limited power capability with the ability to increase the system capacity by closing the delta as required. The open delta can supply 57.7% of the load that could be supplied by the complete delta.

3.2.1   SAMPLE PROBLEM

A balanced load draws 25 kw at a lagging power factor of 0.80 from a 3-phase, 60-cycle line supplied by an open-Vee bank of transformers consisting of two single-phase units. The emf between line wires to the load is 208 v. Specify the minimum output rating of the single-phase units comprising the bank.

SOLUTION

The total kilovolt-amperes supplied to the load is

$$kva = \frac{kw}{power\ factor}$$

$$= \frac{25}{0.8} = 31.25\ kva$$

The line current is

$$I_l = \frac{volt\text{-}amperes}{\sqrt{3}\ volts}$$

$$= \frac{31{,}250}{(1.732)(208)} = 86.6\ amp \qquad \text{ANS.}$$

In the open-Vee bank this current is supplied by each of the transformers. Hence the rating of each transformer is

$$kva\ rating = \frac{VI}{1000}$$

$$= \frac{(208)(86.6)}{1000} = 18\ kva \qquad \text{ANS.}$$

3.3   FOUR WIRE SYSTEM (WYE GENERATOR AND LOAD)

A general wye-connected four-wire system is shown in Fig. 3–2.

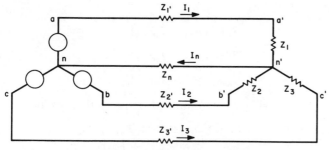

Figure 3–2 Wye-connected system

In this figure Z_1, Z_2, and Z_3 represent the components of the load; Z_1', Z_2', Z_3', and Z_n represent line impedances. Any generator impedance is assumed part of the line impedances. Loop currents are assumed and are to be determined.

The loop equations may be written by inspection.

$$E_{an} = (Z_1 + Z_1' + Z_n)I_1 + \qquad Z_nI_2 \qquad + \qquad Z_nI_3 \qquad (3\text{-}7)$$

$$E_{bn} = \qquad Z_nI_1 \qquad + (Z_2 + Z_2' + Z_n)I_2 + \qquad Z_nI_3 \qquad (3\text{-}8)$$

$$E_{cn} = \qquad Z_nI_1 \qquad + \qquad Z_nI_2 \qquad + (Z_3 + Z_3' + Z_n)I_3 \qquad (3\text{-}9)$$

and also

$$I_n = I_1 + I_2 + I_3 \qquad (3\text{-}10)$$

In the most general case these equations could be solved simultaneously to obtain current values and the other desired quantities.

The equations may be written as

$$I_1(Z_1 + Z_1') + I_nZ_n = E_{an} \qquad (3\text{-}11)$$

$$I_2(Z_2 + Z_2') + I_nZ_n = E_{bn} \qquad (3\text{-}12)$$

$$I_3(Z_3 + Z_3') + I_nZ_n = E_{cn} \qquad (3\text{-}13)$$

Then if the admittances are defined as

$$Y_1 \equiv \frac{1}{Z_1 + Z_1'} \qquad (3\text{-}14)$$

$$Y_2 \equiv \frac{1}{Z_2 + Z_2'} \qquad (3\text{-}15)$$

$$Y_3 \equiv \frac{1}{Z_3 + Z_3'} \qquad (3\text{-}16)$$

one can multiply Eqs. (3-11), (3-12), and (3-13), respectively, by Y_1, Y_2, and Y_3 to obtain

$$I_1 = (E_{an} - I_nZ_n)Y_1 \qquad (3\text{-}17)$$

$$I_2 = (E_{bn} - I_nZ_n)Y_2 \qquad (3\text{-}18)$$

$$I_3 = (E_{cn} - I_nZ_n)Y_3 \qquad (3\text{-}19)$$

But adding Eqs. (3-17), (3-18), and (3-19) together yields

$$I_1 + I_2 + I_3 + I_nZ_n(Y_1 + Y_2 + Y_3) = I_n[1 + Z_n(Y_1 + Y_2 + Y_3)]$$
$$= E_{an}Y_1 + E_{bn}Y_2 + E_{cn}Y_3 \qquad (3\text{-}20)$$

or

$$I_n = \frac{E_{an}Y_1 + E_{bn}Y_2 + E_{cn}Y_3}{1 + Z_n(Y_1 + Y_2 + Y_3)} \qquad (3\text{-}21)$$

The load voltages are

$$V_{a'n'} = I_1 Z_1 \tag{3-22}$$

$$V_{b'n'} = I_2 Z_2 \tag{3-23}$$

$$V_{c'n'} = I_3 Z_3 \tag{3-24}$$

and the total power delivered to the load is

$$P_L = V_{a'n'}I_1 \cos \theta_1 + V_{b'n'}I_2 \cos \theta_2 + V_{c'n'}I_3 \cos \theta_3 \tag{3-25}$$

where the $\cos \theta$'s are the power factors of the individual phase loads.

In the case of balanced load impedance and equal line impedances $Y_1 = Y_2 = Y_3$ and hence it is seen from Eq. (3–21), that $I_n = 0$. (Equal balanced source voltages are assumed.)

Then

$$I_1 = E_{an}Y_1 = \frac{E_{an}}{Z_1 + Z_1'} = \frac{E}{Z} \underline{/0 - \theta} \tag{3-26}$$

$$I_2 = E_{bn}Y_1 = \frac{E_{bn}}{Z_1 + Z_1'} = \frac{E}{Z} \underline{/120 - \theta} \tag{3-27}$$

$$I_3 = E_{cn}Y_1 = \frac{E_{cn}}{Z_1 + Z_1'} = \frac{E}{Z} \underline{/-120 - \theta} \tag{3-28}$$

where θ is the phase angle of $Z = Z_1 + Z_1'$.

If $I_n = 0$ then the line currents are independent of the value of Z_n, hence the neutral connection may be completely removed without disturbing the circuit. If the load is balanced the power becomes

$$\begin{aligned} P_L &= 3V_{a'n'}I_1 \cos \theta_1 \\ &= \sqrt{3}V_{a'b'}I_1 \cos \theta_1 \end{aligned} \tag{3-29}$$

The cases for zero line impedances can be simply deduced from the previous equations.

3.3.1 SAMPLE PROBLEM

A 3-phase, 4-wire power system is shown. Determine the current in each of the lines.

$$E_{an} = 1200\underline{/0}, \ E_{bn} = 1200\underline{/120}, \ E_{cn} = 1200\underline{/-120}$$

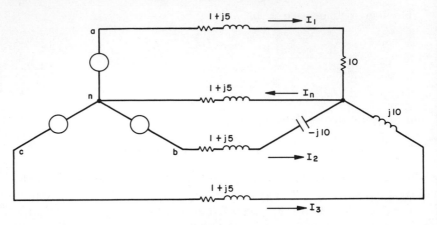

SOLUTION

The currents may be determined using the following relationships.

$$I_n = \frac{E_{an}Y_1 + E_{bn}Y_2 + E_{cn}Y_3}{1 + Z_n(Y_1 + Y_2 + Y_3)}$$

where

$$Y_1 = \frac{1}{10 + 1 + j5} = \frac{1}{11 + j5} = \frac{11 - j5}{121 + 25}$$
$$= 0.0753 - j0.0342 = 0.0827 \ \underline{/-24.5}$$

$$Y_2 = \frac{1}{-j10 + 1 + j5} = \frac{1}{1 - j5} = \frac{1 + j5}{1 + 25}$$
$$= 0.0385 + j0.192 = 0.1965 \ \underline{/78.7}$$

$$Y_3 = \frac{1}{j10 + 1 + j5} = \frac{1}{1 + j15} = \frac{1 - j15}{1 + 225}$$
$$= 0.00443 - j0.0665 = 0.0668 \ \underline{/-86.2}$$

and

$$E_{an} = 1200 \ \underline{/0}, \ E_{bn} = 1200 \ \underline{/120}, \ E_{cn} = 1200 \ \underline{/-120}$$

Thus

$$I_n = \frac{(1200 \ \underline{/0}) \, (0.0827 \ \underline{/-24.5}) + (1200 \ \underline{/120}) \, (0.1965 \ \underline{/78.7})}{1 + (1 + j5) \, (0.0753 - j0.0342 + 0.0385 + j0.192}$$
$$\frac{+ \ (1200 \ \underline{/-120}) \, (0.0668 \ \underline{/-86.2})}{+ \ 0.00443 - j0.0665)}$$

$$= \frac{99.4 \ \underline{/-24.5} + 238 \ \underline{/198.7} + 80.0 \ \underline{/-206.2}}{1 + (1 + j5) \, (0.1182 + j0.0913)}$$

$$= \frac{90.5 - j40.9 - 226 - j76.3 - 71.8 + j35.3}{1 - 0.3383 + j0.6523}$$

$$= \frac{-207.3 - j81.9}{0.6617 + j0.6523} = \frac{223\ \underline{/201.6}}{0.930\ \underline{/44.6}} = 240\ \underline{/157.0}\ \text{amp} \qquad \text{ANS.}$$

$$
\begin{aligned}
I_1 &= (E_{an} - I_n Z_n) Y_1 \\
&= [\,(1200\ \underline{/0} - 240\ \underline{/157.0})\,(5.10\ \underline{/78.7}\,)\,]0.0827\ \underline{/-24.5} \\
&= (1200\ \underline{/0} - 1225\ \underline{/235.7})\,(0.0827\ \underline{/-24.5}) \\
&= (1200 + j0 + 690 + j1010)\,(0.0827\ \underline{/-24.5}) \\
&= (1890 + j1010)\,(0.0827\ \underline{/-24.5}) \\
&= (2150\ \underline{/28.1})\,(0.0827\ \underline{/-24.5}) = 177.5\ \underline{/3.6}\ \text{amp} \qquad \text{ANS.}
\end{aligned}
$$

$$
\begin{aligned}
I_2 &= (E_{bn} - I_n Z_n) Y_2 \\
&= (-600 + j1040 + 690 + j1010)\,(0.1965\ \underline{/78.7}) \\
&= (+90 + j2050)\,(0.1965\ \underline{/78.7}) \\
&= (2055\ \underline{/87.5})\,(0.1965\ \underline{/78.7}) = 405\ \underline{/166.2}\ \text{amp} \qquad \text{ANS.}
\end{aligned}
$$

$$
\begin{aligned}
I_3 &= (E_{cn} - I_n Z_n) Y_3 \\
&= (-600 - j1040 + 690 + j1010)\,(0.0668\ \underline{/-86.2}) \\
&= (+90 - j30)\,(0.0668\ \underline{/-86.2}) \\
&= (95\ \underline{/-18.4})\,(0.0668\ \underline{/-86.2}) = 6.35\ \underline{/-104.6}\ \text{amp} \qquad \text{ANS.}
\end{aligned}
$$

3.4 THREE-WIRE SYSTEM (DELTA SOURCE AND LOAD)

The method of solution of delta systems depends on the circuit. The simplest circuit has no line or source impedances and is shown schematically in Fig. 3–3.

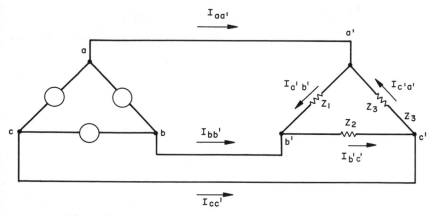

Figure 3-3 Delta-connected system with zero line impedances

The phase voltages are assumed to be

$$E_{ab} = E \underline{/0} \qquad\qquad (3\text{--}30)$$

$$E_{bc} = E \underline{/120} \qquad\qquad (3\text{--}31)$$

$$E_{ca} = E \underline{/-120} \qquad\qquad (3\text{--}32)$$

and the load phase currents are therefore

$$I_{a'b'} = \frac{E_{ab}}{Z_1} = \frac{E}{Z_1} \underline{/-\theta_1} \qquad\qquad (3\text{--}33)$$

$$I_{b'c'} = \frac{E_{bc}}{Z_2} = \frac{E}{Z_2} \underline{/120 - \theta_2} \qquad\qquad (3\text{--}34)$$

$$I_{c'a'} = \frac{E_{ca}}{Z_3} = \frac{E}{Z_3} \underline{/-120 - \theta_3} \qquad\qquad (3\text{--}35)$$

where the θ's are the phase angles of the impedances.

The line currents are the vector sums of the appropriate phase currents.

$$I_{aa'} = I_{a'b'} - I_{c'a'} = \frac{E}{Z_1} \underline{/-\theta_1} - \frac{E}{Z_3} \underline{/-120 - \theta_3} \qquad (3\text{--}36)$$

$$I_{bb'} = I_{b'c'} - I_{a'b'} = \frac{E}{Z_2} \underline{/120 - \theta_2} - \frac{E}{Z_1} \underline{/-\theta_1} \qquad (3\text{--}37)$$

$$I_{cc'} = I_{c'a'} - I_{b'c'} = \frac{E}{Z_3} \underline{/-120 - \theta_3} - \frac{E}{Z_2} \underline{/120 - \theta_2} \quad (3\text{--}38)$$

and the total power consumed by the load is

$$P_L = EI_{a'b'} \cos \theta_1 + EI_{b'c'} \cos \theta_2 + EI_{c'a'} \cos \theta_3 \qquad (3\text{--}39)$$

If the loads are balanced, $Z_1 = Z_2 = Z_3$ and $\theta_1 = \theta_2 = \theta_3$ in which case

$$I_{a'b'} = \frac{E}{Z_1} \underline{/-\theta_1} \qquad\qquad (3\text{--}40)$$

$$I_{b'c'} = \frac{E}{Z_1} \underline{/120 - \theta_1} \qquad\qquad (3\text{--}41)$$

$$I_{c'a'} = \frac{E}{Z_1} \underline{/-120 - \theta_1} \qquad\qquad (3\text{--}42)$$

and

$$I_{aa'} = \sqrt{3}\, \frac{E}{Z_1} \underline{/+30 - \theta_1} \qquad\qquad (3\text{--}43)$$

$$I_{bb'} = \sqrt{3}\,\frac{E}{Z_1}\,\underline{/+150 - \theta_1} \tag{3-44}$$

$$I_{cc'} = \sqrt{3}\,\frac{E}{Z_1}\,\underline{/-90 - \theta_1} \tag{3-45}$$

Finally, the total power delivered to the load is

$$P_L = 3EI_{a'b'}\cos\theta_1$$
$$= \sqrt{3}EI_{aa'}\cos\theta_1 \tag{3-46}$$

The more general case of delta load with line impedances is illustrated in Fig. 3–4.

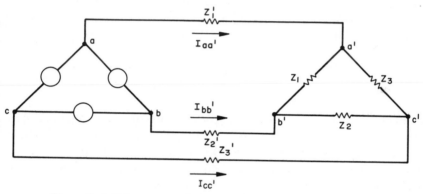

Figure 3–4 Delta-connected system with non-zero line impedances

If the voltages and impedances are known, the most direct method of solution for the line currents is to convert the delta load to a wye, combine the wye elements with the line elements and convert back to a delta. Once the line currents are known the load voltage may be determined by subtracting the line voltage drops from the source voltages. The phase currents are then readily determined.

Figure 3–5 shows the final step in this process; the wye load with no neutral connection.

The wye-delta transformations may be combined with phase current expressions to give the line current directly. Thus

$$I_{aa'} = \frac{E_{ab}Z_c - E_{ca}Z_b}{Z_aZ_b + Z_bZ_c + Z_cZ_a} \tag{3-47}$$

$$I_{bb'} = \frac{E_{bc}Z_a - E_{ab}Z_c}{Z_aZ_b + Z_bZ_c + Z_cZ_a} \tag{3-48}$$

$$I_{cc'} = \frac{E_{ca}Z_b - E_{bc}Z_a}{Z_aZ_b + Z_bZ_c + Z_cZ_a} \tag{3-49}$$

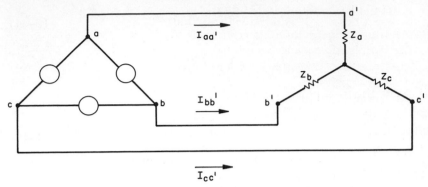

Figure 3-5 Wye-connected load without neutral connection

3.4.1 SAMPLE PROBLEM

Each phase of a wye load has $(10/\sqrt{3})$ $/30°$ ohms. A delta load has 10 ohms of pure resistance as one side, 10 ohms of pure capacitive reactance as a second side, and 10 ohms of pure inductive reactance as the third side. The wye and delta loads are connected in parallel. Calculate the magnitudes of the line currents, the total power consumed, and the power factor of the combination. The power is supplied by a 208/120 v. line.

SOLUTION

The circuit is as shown.

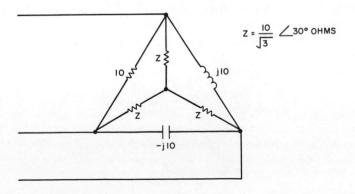

A method of solution is as follows:

(1) convert the delta to its equivalent wye
(2) Parallel the two wye-circuits
(3) Compute each line current, each phase power and each phase volt-ampere product
(4) The total power is the sum of each phase power
(5) Strictly speaking the power factor of an unbalanced system is undefined but it may be taken as the ratio of total power to total volt amperes.

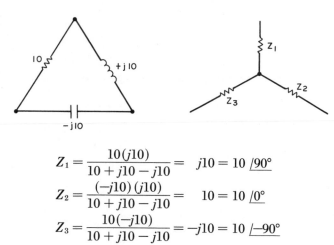

$$Z_1 = \frac{10(j10)}{10 + j10 - j10} = j10 = 10 \ \underline{/90°}$$

$$Z_2 = \frac{(-j10)(j10)}{10 + j10 - j10} = 10 = 10 \ \underline{/0°}$$

$$Z_3 = \frac{10(-j10)}{10 + j10 - j10} = -j10 = 10 \ \underline{/-90°}$$

These put in parallel with $(10/\sqrt{3}) \ \underline{/30°}$ ohms

$$Z_y = \frac{10}{\sqrt{3}} \ \underline{/30°} = 5.0 + j2.88 \text{ ohms}$$

$$Z_y \text{ and } Z_1 \text{ in parallel} = \frac{10 \ \underline{/90} \ (10/\sqrt{3}) \ \underline{/30}}{j10 + 5.0 + j2.88} = \frac{100 \ \underline{/120}}{\sqrt{3}(5.0 + j12.88)}$$
$$= 4.17 \ \underline{/51.2}$$

Call this phase current I_1

$$I_1 = \frac{120}{4.17 \ \underline{/51.2}} = 28.8 \ \underline{/-51.2}$$

$$P_1 = 120(28.8) \cos 51.2° = 2160 \text{ watts}$$
$$va_1 = 120(28.8) = 3450 \text{ va}$$

$$Z_y \text{ and } Z_2 \text{ in parallel} = \frac{10 \ \underline{/0} \ (10/\sqrt{3}) \ \underline{/30}}{10 + 5.0 + j2.88} = \frac{100 \ \underline{/30}}{\sqrt{3}(15 + j2.88)}$$
$$= 3.79 \ \underline{/19.15}$$

Call this phase current I_2

$$I_2 = \frac{120}{3.79\ \underline{/19.15}} = 31.6\ \underline{/-19.15}$$

$$P_2 = 120(31.6)\ \cos 19.15° = 3580 \text{ watts}$$

$$va_2 = 120(31.6) = 3800 \text{ va}$$

$$Z_y \text{ and } Z_3 \text{ in parallel} = \frac{10\ \underline{/-90}\ (10/\sqrt{3})\ \underline{/30}}{-j10 + 5.0 + j2.88} = \frac{100\ \underline{/-60}}{\sqrt{3}(5.0 - j7.12)}$$

$$= 6.62\ \underline{/-5}$$

Call this phase current I_3

$$I_3 = \frac{120}{6.62\ \underline{/-5}} = 18.1\ \underline{/5}$$

$$P_3 = 120(18.1)\ \cos 5° = 2175 \text{ watts}$$

$$va_3 = 120(18.1) = 2180 \text{ va}$$

The total 3-phase power is

$$P = P_1 + P_2 + P_3 = 2160 + 3580 + 2175$$
$$= 7915 \text{ watts} \qquad\qquad \text{ANS.}$$

The power factor:

$$pf = \frac{P_1 + P_2 + P_3}{va_1 + va_2 + va_3}$$

$$= \frac{7915}{3450 + 3800 + 2180} = \frac{7915}{9430} = 0.840 \qquad \text{ANS.}$$

The three line current magnitudes are

$$28.8 \text{ amp, } 31.6 \text{ amp, and } 18.1 \text{ amp} \qquad \text{ANS.}$$

3.5 BALANCED SYSTEM – REDUCTION TO SINGLE PHASE

Often when solving problems involving balanced systems, the solutions are simplified by converting to an equivalent wye system and then solving only one phase as a simple single-phase problem. The voltages and currents in the other two phases are readily determined by adding 120° for one phase and subtracting 120° for the other.

Certain problems are stated in such a way that the algebraic solution of a voltage vector diagram is necessary to determine the required results.

3.5.1   SAMPLE PROBLEM

A 440-v., 3-phase source of power delivers energy to a 500-kw load of 80% power factor over a three-wire line, each conductor of which has 0.05 ohm resistance and negligible reactance. Calculate the voltage at the load. State whether this transmission line is satisfactory for its purpose and give your reasons.

SOLUTION

The calculations will be made on the basis of the single-phase equivalent.

The line-neutral voltage is $440/\sqrt{3} = 255$ v.

The equivalent circuit becomes

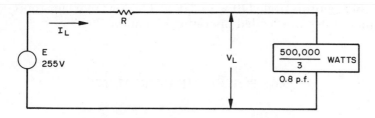

The voltage vector diagram can be drawn as

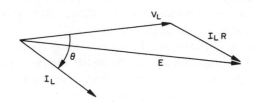

$$\theta = \cos^{-1} 0.8; \quad \sin \theta = 0.6$$

$$E = V_L + I_L R$$

$$I_L = \frac{500,000}{3V_L(0.8)} = \frac{208,000}{V_L}$$

$$(255)^2 = (V_L + I_L R \cos \theta)^2 + (I_L R \sin \theta)^2$$

$$65,000 = \left[V_L + \frac{208,000}{V_L}(0.05)(0.8)\right]^2 + \left[\frac{208,000}{V_L}(0.05)(0.6)\right]^2$$

$$65,000 = \left(V_L + \frac{8320}{V_L}\right)^2 + \left(\frac{6240}{V_L}\right)^2$$

$$= V_L^2 + 2(8320) + \left(\frac{8320}{V_L}\right)^2 + \left(\frac{6240}{V_L}\right)^2$$

$$65{,}000V_L^2 = V_L^4 + 16{,}640V_L^2 + (8320)^2 + (6240)^2$$

Solving for V_L^2,

$$V_L^4 - 4.83 \times 10^4 V_L^2 + 1.08 \times 10^8 = 0$$

$$V_L^2 = 4.55 \times 10^4 \text{ or } V_L^2 = 0.24 \times 10^4$$

$$V_L = 214 \text{ v. or } V_L = 49 \text{ v. equivalent line-to-neutral}$$

Thus the line-line voltage at the load is

$$V_{l-l} = 214\sqrt{3} = 370 \text{ v.}$$

or

$$V_{l-l} = 49\sqrt{3} = 85 \text{ v.} \qquad \text{ANS.}$$

The transmission line would not be satisfactory because of the excessive voltage drop from 440 v. to 370 v. The lower voltage represents an undesirable overloaded operating condition.

3.6   POWER MEASUREMENT

In an n wire system, $n - 1$ wattmeters can be used to indicate total power flow. Thus in the four wire system three wattmeters will measure the total power. Likewise, in the three wire system, two wattmeters will measure the total power.

If the system is unbalanced the total average power is the sum of the wattmeter readings. This is also true for the balanced system and, in addition, in the two wattmeter method, the power factor may also be determined. One wattmeter reading P_1 is

$$P_1 = V_{l-l}I_l \cos(\theta - 30) \qquad (3\text{–}50)$$

The other wattmeter reading P_2 is

$$P_2 = V_{l-l}I_l \cos(\theta + 30) \qquad (3\text{–}51)$$

From these two expressions it can be shown that

$$\tan \theta = \sqrt{3}\,(P_1 - P_2)/(P_1 + P_2) \qquad (3\text{–}52)$$

It may be seen that if the power factor angle exceeds 60°, one of the two wattmeters will indicate negative power which is converted into a positive scale reading by reversing the current coil or potential coil connections. The power is still negative and must be given its own sign when computing total power or power factor angle.

3.6.1   SAMPLE PROBLEM

The voltages applied to the circuit shown are $E_{ab} = 208$, $E_{bc} = -104 - j180$ and $E_{ca} = -104 + j180$. Calculate the indications of each of the wattmeters W_1 and W_2.

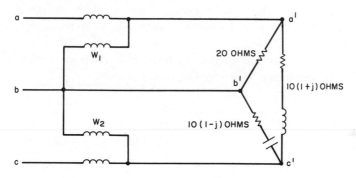

SOLUTION

$E_{ab} = 208 = 208\ \underline{/0}$ $Z_{a'c'} = 10(1 + j) = 14\ \underline{/45}$
$E_{bc} = -104 - j180 = 208\ \underline{/-120}$ $Z_{b'c'} = 10(1 - j) = 14\ \underline{/-45}$
$E_{ca} = -104 + j180 = 208\ \underline{/120}$

Reading of $W_1 = E_{ab}I_{aa'} \cos(\theta_{ab} - \theta_{aa'})$
Reading of $W_2 = E_{cb}I_{cc'} \cos(\theta_{cb} - \theta_{cc'})$

$$I_{aa'} = \frac{E_{ab}}{Z_{a'b'}} + \frac{E_{ac}}{Z_{a'c'}} = \frac{208\ \underline{/0}}{20\ \underline{/0}} + \frac{208\ \underline{/-60}}{14\ \underline{/45}}$$
$$= 10.4\ \underline{/0} + 14.85\ \underline{/-105}$$
$$= +10.4 - 3.81 - j14.2$$
$$= +6.6 - j14.2 = 15.6\ \underline{/-65}$$

Reading of $W_1 = 208(15.6) \cos(0° - 65°) = 1370$ watts   ANS.

$$I_{cc'} = \frac{E_{cb}}{Z_{b'c'}} + \frac{E_{ca}}{Z_{a'c'}} = \frac{208\ \underline{/60}}{14\ \underline{/-45}} + \frac{208\ \underline{/120}}{14\ \underline{/45}}$$
$$= 14.85\ \underline{/105} + 14.85\ \underline{/+75}$$
$$= -3.81 + j14.2 + 3.81 + j14.2$$
$$= +j28.4 = 28.4\ \underline{/+90}$$

Reading of $W_2 = 208(28.4) \cos(60° - 90°) = 5100$ watts   ANS.

3.7 PRACTICE PROBLEMS

3–1

A 3-phase, 3-wire, 2200-v. line supplies power to a 3-phase transformer which in turn supplies three 3-phase balanced loads, as follows:

(1) 200 kva, at 208 v. and a power factor of 0.8, to induction motors driving machine tools

(2) 100 kva, at 120 v. and a power factor of 0.95, to lights

(3) 50 kva, at 208 v. and a power factor of 0.90, to induction motors driving pumps.

Calculate the current in the 3-phase, 2200-v. line, neglecting the exciting currents and losses in the transformer.

3–2

In the circuit shown, the unbalanced 3-phase generator supplies power to an unbalanced 3-phase load. The circuit data are:

$$E_{ga} = E_1 = 120 \underline{/0°} \quad \text{v.} \qquad Z_1 = 10 + j0 \text{ ohms}$$
$$E_{gb} = E_2 = 115 \underline{/120°} \quad \text{v.} \qquad Z_2 = 3 + j4 \text{ ohms}$$
$$E_{gc} = E_3 = 125 \underline{/-120°} \text{ v.} \qquad Z_3 = 5 - j5 \text{ ohms}$$

Calculate the voltages V_{oa}, V_{ob}, V_{oc}.

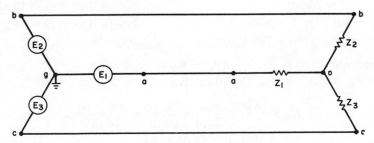

3–3

A 3-phase, wye-connected power system with grounded neutral supplies energy to a 3-phase, wye-connected load shown. The line voltages are:

$$E_{AB} = 2200 \underline{/0°}$$
$$E_{BC} = 2200 \underline{/120°}$$
$$E_{CA} = 2200 \underline{/-120°}.$$

Calculate the potential difference between "O" and ground when the ground connection at "O" is accidentally opened.

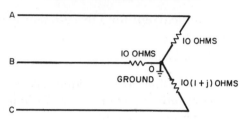

3-4

A 3-wire, 3-phase, 60-cycle transmission line has an impedance, per conductor, of $1 + j10$ ohms. The input to this line is at 13,200 v. between conductors. The power taken by the load is 1000 kw at 100 amp and a lagging power factor.

Calculate:

(a) The efficiency of transmission

(b) The voltage at the load

(c) The power factor of the load.

3-5

A 3-phase, 3-wire transmission line has an impedance per conductor of $60 + j80$ ohms and delivers 1500 kw to a load at 66,000 v. and a power factor of 0.90, lagging.

Calculate the potential difference between line wires at the input end of the line and the power factor at that end.

3-6

A transmission line is 100 miles long and delivers 3-phase 60-cycle power to a load of 24,000 kva at 66,000 v., 0.8 power factor lagging. The series impedance of each line is $0.1901 + j0.740$ ohms/mile; the shunt admittance is $j5.88 \times 10^{-6}$ mhos/mile.

Find the efficiency of the transmission line.

(Note: In the examination when this problem was given the suggestion was made to replace the line by an equivalent pi network.)

3-7

A Y-connected generator rated at 220 v. has 0.2 ohm resistance and 2.0 ohm reactance per phase. The generator is connected by lines each having an impedance of 2.06 $\underline{/29.05°}$ ohms to a Y-Y transformer bank. Each transformer has a total equivalent impedance referred to the high side of 100 $\underline{/60°}$ ohms, and the transformer bank is connected through lines each of which has a resistance of 50 ohms and an inductive reactance of 100 ohms. If the ratio of transformation is 6 and the low voltage side is connected to the generator lines, calculate the actual fault current for a three-phase symmetrical short circuit at the load.

3–8

A 3-phase transmission line 20 miles long has a resistance of 0.6 ohm/mile of conductor and a reactance of 0.27 ohm/mile of conductor, at 60 cps. The line delivers 1000 kw to an inductive load at a power factor of 80%. The potential difference between line wires at the load is 11,000 v.

(a) Calculate the voltage between wires at the input end of the line

(b) Calculate the total rating in kva of a bank of capacitors placed at the input of the line, which will increase the power factor at that point to 90%, lagging.

3–9

A motor load draws 100 kw at a lagging power factor of 0.8 from a 3-phase, 60-cycle, 208/120-v. system. A capacitor bank corrects the power factor of the motor load to 0.9, lagging. In addition, power is supplied to two unity power factor lighting loads, as shown.

Calculate the current in each of the four conductors of this system.

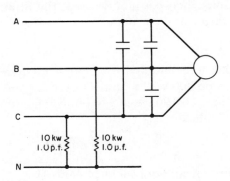
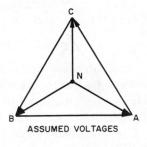

ASSUMED VOLTAGES

3–10

A fully-loaded, 3-phase, 2200-v. circuit supplies 100 kw to a load having a power factor of 70.7%, lagging. The circuit used costs $5000 installed. Additional circuit capacity is required in order to accommodate a greater load at the same power factor. A 3-phase, 150-kva, 2200-v. bank of capacitors is available at $1000.

If this bank were bridged across the line at the load, how many additional kilowatts could the line supply without overloading? Is this method of increasing the transmission capacity of this line economical? Submit calculations substantiating your conclusions.

CHAPTER FOUR

D-C MACHINES

SYMBOLS

B	Flux density, lines per square inch in Mixed English System
b	Number of armature parallel paths
E	Induced or back electromotive force, volts
F	Force, pounds
HP	Horsepower
I	Current, amperes
K	A constant of propotionality
l	Length, inches
m	Multiplicity of wave-wound armature
N	Speed, revolution per second (rev/sec)
n	Speed, revolutions per minute (rpm)
P	Power, watts
p	Number of poles
R	Resistance, ohms
r	Radius, feet
T	Torque, foot-pounds
V	Voltage drop, volts
v	Velocity, feet per second
Z	Total number of armature conductors
η	Efficiency, per cent or per unit
ϕ	Flux per pole, lines
ω	Angular speed of rotation, radians per second (rad/sec)

Subscripts

A	Referring to the armature
B	Brush
F	Shunt, shunt field
G	Generator, generated or induced

I, in   Input
L   Line
M   Mechanical
m   Referring to voltmeter quantities
o, out   Output
oc   Open-circuit
S   Series, series field
T   Torque or terminal

4.1 BASIC PRINCIPLES

The physical principles underlying the operation of d-c machines are the following:

(a) A conductor perpendicular to and moving in a magnetic field has induced in it a voltage proportional to conductor length *l*, magnetic field flux density *B*, and velocity *v*. Mathematically

$$E = K_1 Blv \qquad (4\text{--}1)$$

$\varepsilon = N\frac{d\phi}{dt} \cdot N\frac{d(BA)}{dt} = NBlv$

(b) A current-carrying conductor in a magnetic field perpendicular to its length has a force exerted upon it proportional to the current *I*, the conductor length *l*, and the magnetic field flux density *B*. Mathematically

$\vec{F} = I\vec{l} \times \vec{B}$

$$F = K_2 BlI \qquad (4\text{--}2)$$

or the force acting through a moment arm of radius *r* becomes a torque of magnitude

$\vec{T} = \vec{r} \times \vec{F}$

$$T = K_2 Bllr \qquad (4\text{--}3)$$

Both these effects are present simultaneously in d-c machines. The operating motor generates a voltage which tends to oppose the line current drawn by the machine. Likewise the operating generator develops a torque which opposes the prime mover. Unless the direction of power flow is known, a d-c machine may be either a generator or a motor.

only load is connected

In terms of machine constants, Eqs. (4–1) and (4–3) may be rewritten as

Don't have to divide by 10^8 if ϕ is given in W

$$E_G = \frac{pZ}{60 \times 10^8 b}\phi n = K_G \phi n \qquad (4\text{--}4)$$

$$T = \frac{pZ}{8.5 \times 10^8 b}\phi I_A = K_T \phi I_A \qquad (4\text{--}5)$$

The parameter b has different values for different armature windings

Wave winding	$b = 2$
Multiplex wave winding	$b = 2m$
Simplex lap winding	$b = p$
Duplex lap winding	$b = 2p$

Motor action may also be considered as the interaction of two magnetic fields with opposite magnetic poles tending to line up. One magnetic field is that of the field flux, the other is that set up by the armature current. The commutator changes armature polarity to keep continuous rotation.

4.1.1 SAMPLE PROBLEM

Each pole of a 4-pole d-c machine covers 16 armature slots, each of which contains 8 conductors arranged in two layers. The armature is a simplex lap winding. The average distance of the conductor from the axis of the armature is 10 in. The effective length of each conductor is 20 in. The average flux density under each pole is 50,000 lines/sq in.

Neglecting the effects of fringing and of armature reaction, calculate the torque, in pound-feet, developed by this armature when the total input to it is 100 amp.

SOLUTION

The expressions for developed torque is

$$T = \frac{pZ\phi I}{8.5b10^8} \text{ ft-lbs.}$$

where $p =$ no. of poles $= 4$
$Z =$ total armature conductors $(4)(16)(8) = 512$
$\phi =$ flux per pole $=$ (flux density) (pole area)
pole area $= \dfrac{2\pi rl}{p} = \dfrac{2\pi(10)(20)}{4} = 100\pi$
$\therefore \phi = 50,000\ (100\pi) = 5\pi \times 10^6$ lines
$I =$ armature current $= 100$ amp
$b =$ no. of parallel paths $= 4$ for simplex lap winding

Thus

$$T = \frac{(4)\,(512)\,(5\pi)\,(10^6)\,(100)}{8.5\,(4)\,(10^8)}$$

$$= \frac{2560\pi}{8.5} = 945 \text{ ft-lbs.} \qquad \text{ANS.}$$

4.2   CONSTRUCTION

Typically d-c machines consist of the following parts:

- An outer frame supporting poles on which are wound coils which set up the magnetic field flux (ϕ). In some small machines the coils are replaced by permanent magnets.
- A cylindrical rotor (armature) which rotates within the field poles. This rotor contains armature windings which terminate on commutator segments.
- Brushes mounted on the frame which bear on the commutator and provide electrical connection to the armature.

In addition the machine may include:

- Additional auxiliary field poles (interpoles) to reduce brush arcing under load.
- Additional compensating or pole face windings to prevent commutator arcing under load.
- Rheostat for adjusting field current and hence field flux.
- Starting controller.

4.3   TYPES

Direct-current motors are either shunt, series, or compound wound, depending upon whether the field winding is connected in shunt with the armature, in series with armature, or consists of dual shunt and series connected windings. Direct-current generators are generally shunt or compound. Series generators are seldom used. A discussion of the various machines and their wiring schematics is given by [Kraus, *Studying* (4), p. 327].

The d-c generator shunt winding may be either self-excited or it may be excited from some source external to the machine. When self-excited, the armature voltage supplies the field current and due account must be taken for variations in armature voltage under changing load conditions.

4.4   POWER AND EFFICIENCY

The unit of mechanical work is the horsepower which may be expressed in the following ways:

$$\begin{aligned}
1 \text{ horsepower (HP)} \quad &= 746 \text{ watts}\\
&= 550 \text{ ft-lbs/sec}\\
&= 33{,}000 \text{ ft-lbs/min}\\
W = \quad &= \frac{T\omega}{550}\\
&= \frac{2\pi TN}{550}\\
&= \frac{2\pi Tn}{33{,}000}
\end{aligned}$$

The efficiency η is defined as

$$\eta = \frac{\text{output power}}{\text{input power}} \qquad (4\text{--}6)$$

Using some of the conversions, Eg. (4–6) may be rewritten for a motor

$$\eta = \frac{(\text{HP output}) \, 746}{V_T I_L} \qquad (4\text{--}7)$$

or for a generator

$$\eta = \frac{V_T I_L}{(\text{HP input}) \, 746} \qquad (4\text{--}8)$$

Motor output is often expressed in terms of shaft torque (foot-pounds) and speed (rpm). So that

$$\eta = 0.142 \, \frac{Tn}{V_T I_L} \qquad (4\text{--}9)$$

4.5   MACHINE ANALYSIS

4.5.1   GENERAL

One form of d-c machine analysis is based on a 100% efficient energy conversion process from electrical to mechanical power or vice versa. This conversion takes place in the ideal armature where the electrical power is represented by the product of generated emf and armature current and the mechanical power is represented by the product of torque and speed. Certain electrical losses which can be readily computed are those associated with current flowing through an equivalent resistance. Other losses not easily computed but which may be measured as a single equivalent loss include other electrical losses due to hysteresis, eddy currents, and other magnetic effects and mechanical losses due to friction and windage effects. The electrical losses may be determined by means of a typical equivalent circuit.

4.5.2   MOTOR

In Fig. 4–1 a long shunt, compound motor is illustrated. All the various windings are shown as equivalent resistances because it is resistance which accounts for steady-state loss. The battery designated V_B in series with the armature, represents one method of accounting for the brush contact effect. This method assumes a constant voltage drop of 2 v. (always opposing the armature current hence consuming power) which is essentially independent of armature current. Another method of handling the brush contact is to ignore it and assume that the equivalent armature resistance includes the brush drop effect. The problem statement should indicate which method is to be used.

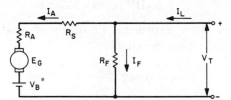

Figure 4–1 An equivalent circuit for a long-shunt compound motor

The electrical power converted to mechanical power is designated P_M and is

$$P_M = E_G I_A \qquad (4\text{--}10)$$

but

$$E_G = V_T - V_B - I_A(R_A + R_S) \qquad (4\text{--}11)$$

and

$$I_A = I_L - \frac{V_T}{R_F} \tag{4-12}$$

therefore

$$P_M = \left[V_T - V_B - \left(I_L - \frac{V_T}{R_F}\right)(R_A + R_S)\right]\left[I_L - \frac{V_T}{R_F}\right] \tag{4-13}$$

$$= V_T I_L - \frac{V_T^2}{R_F} - V_B\left(I_L - \frac{V_T}{R_F}\right) - \left(I_L - \frac{V_T}{R_F}\right)^2(R_A + R_S)$$

power in

To obtain the mechanical output power available at the motor shaft it is necessary to subtract the power required to run the machine at operating speed. This is obtained by repeating the calculation of Eq. (4–13) with the machine running unloaded.

4.5.2.1   SAMPLE PROBLEM

A d-c traction motor is rated at 600 v. and 100 hp at 750 rpm when its efficiency is 0.92. The resistances of the armature and series fields are 0.25 ohm and 0.15 ohm, respectively.

Calculate the voltage required on this motor in order that it may generate the same torque at 850 rpm that it generates at 750 rpm with 600 v. (Neglect the brush drop.)*

SOLUTION

A traction motor is a series motor. The equivalent circuit of Fig. 4–1 may be used by neglecting the shunt field R_F.

Before proceeding to a solution, the impossible nature of the problem will be demonstrated.

If the power output is 100 hp, the input power will be

$$P_{in} = \frac{P_{out}}{\text{efficiency}}$$

$$= \frac{(100)(746)}{0.92} = 81,100 \text{ watts}$$

The electrical power output is 74,600 watts. The total machine losses will be the difference between input and output.

* Author's note: This problem, as were most of the problems in this book, was taken directly from an actual examination. It will be shown that the conditions of the problem are impossible. However, it is still possible to arrive at a solution.

$$P_L = P_{in} - P_{out}$$
$$= 81,100 - 74,600 = 6500 \text{ watts}$$

The line current to the machine will be

$$I_L = \frac{P_{in}}{V_T}$$
$$= \frac{81,100}{600} = 135 \text{ amp}$$

The resistive losses in the machine will be the current squared multiplied by the total winding resistance.

$$P_R = (I_L)^2 (R_S + R_A)$$
$$= (135)^2 (0.15 + 0.25) = 7310 \text{ watts}$$

The impossibility has been shown: On the basis of efficiency, the total machine losses are 6500 watts, while the resistive losses alone have been calculated to be 7310 watts.

If the efficiency were dropped to 0.89, the problem becomes more reasonable. The power output is still 100 hp or

$$P_{out} = (100)(746) = 74,600 \text{ watts}$$

The input power is

$$P_{in} = \frac{P_{out}}{\text{eff}}$$
$$= \frac{74,600}{0.89} = 83,900 \text{ watts}$$

The line current is

$$I_L = \frac{P_{in}}{V_T}$$
$$= \frac{83,900}{600} = 140 \text{ amp}$$

The winding resistance loss is
$$P_R = (I_L)^2 (R_S + R_A)$$
$$= (140)^2 (0.25 + 0.15) = 7810 \text{ watts}$$

The total losses in the machine are

$$P_L = P_{in} - P_{out} = 83,900 - 74,600$$
$$= 9300 \text{ watts}$$

If the losses consist only of friction, windage and winding resistance losses, the friction and windage losses turn out to be

$$P_{FW} = P_L - P_R$$
$$= 9300 - 7810 = 1490 \text{ watts}$$

For a solution, assume that the power output and developed torque includes the friction and windage loss which will be assumed constant over the speed range 750 rpm to 850 rpm.
In general, the following expression is true for this motor

$$V_T = I_L(R_S + R_A) + E_G$$

To determine the new value of terminal voltage, it is necessary to determine first the new value of line current I_L and the new value of armature voltage E_G.

The general expression for developed torque T is

$$T = K_T\phi I_A = K_T\phi I_L$$

If the iron is unsaturated, the flux is directly proportional to the series field current which is the line current. Hence

$$T = K_T K_F I_L^2 \qquad \phi = K_F I_L$$

Thus if the developed torque is the same in both cases, the line current is the same, also.

The expression for armature voltage is

$$E_G = K_G\phi n \qquad \Rightarrow \quad E_G = K_G K_F I_L n$$
$$I_L = E_G / K_G K_F n$$

but since the line current is the same, the flux is the same so that the voltage is directly proportional to speed.

Subscript "1" will denote the values at 750 rpm and subscript "2" will denote values at 850 rpm.

$$I_{L1} = I_{L2}$$

$$E_{G_2} = \frac{850}{750} E_{G_1} \qquad \frac{E_{G_2}}{K_G K_F n_2} = \frac{E_{G_1}}{K_G K_F n_1}$$
$$= 1.133 E_{G_1} \qquad E_{G_2} = \frac{n_2}{n_1} E_{G_1}$$

Using the value of 135 amp for line current

$$E_{G_1} = V_T - I_L(R_A + R_S)$$
$$= 600 - 135(0.40)$$
$$= 546 \text{ v.}$$

Thus

$$V_{T_2} = E_{G_2} + I_L(R_A + R_S)$$
$$= 1.133(546) + 135(0.40)$$
$$= 674 \text{ v.} \qquad\qquad \text{ANS.}$$

4.5.3   GENERATOR

The same analysis may be performed for the generator as for the motor in the previous section. If the generator is self excited, Fig. 4–1 is applicable with the exception that I_A, I_L, and V_B have reversed directions. The power delivered to the mains $V_T I_L$ may be designated P_o while the mechanical power connected to electrical power is P_M.

$$P_M = E_G I_A \tag{4-14}$$

but

$$E_G = V_T + I_A(R_A + R_S) + V_B \tag{4-15}$$

and

$$I_A = I_L + \frac{V_T}{R_F} \tag{4-16}$$

so that

$$
\begin{aligned}
P_M &= \left[V_T + \left(I_L + \frac{V_T}{R_F} \right)(R_A + R_S) + V_B \right]\left[I_L + \frac{V_T}{R_F} \right] \\
&= P_o + \frac{V_T^2}{R_F} + \left(I_L + \frac{V_T}{R_F} \right)^2 (R_A + R_S) + V_B\left(I_L + \frac{V_T}{R_F} \right) \tag{4-17}
\end{aligned}
$$

or simply the sum of output plus electrical losses. The total mechanical driving power may be obtained by adding to Eq. (4–17) the power required to drive the unloaded machine at the operating speed.

4.6   MACHINE TESTING

An alternate form of machine analysis may be performed based on efficiency

$$
\begin{aligned}
\text{Efficiency} &= \frac{\text{output}}{\text{input}} \\
&= \frac{\text{input} - \text{losses}}{\text{input}} \\
&= \frac{\text{output}}{\text{output} + \text{losses}} \tag{4-18}
\end{aligned}
$$

Certain rules concerning machine losses have become accepted. The following information forms part of the American Institute of Electrical Engineers (now Institute of Electrical and Electronics Engineers) and American Standards Association code:

- Copper (I^2R) losses are determined on the basis of the winding d-c resistances at 75° C. Shunt field rheostat loss is not considered part of the machine loss. The brush drop loss is regarded as a constant 2 v. drop.
- Mechanical losses including friction, windage and cooling air circulation are determined by measuring the power to run the machine at the operating speed with the machine unloaded and unexcited. (Curves in [Pender et al, *Handbook* 12], pp. 8–30) indicate that these mechanical losses are approximately proportional to the square of the rotor speed.)
- No-load core loss caused by varying flux density in the iron structures may be determined by measuring the power to run the machine at rated speed and rated excitation and subtracting from this power the mechanical losses and any copper losses. It may be more convenient to make a single measurement of power required to run the machine under no load at rated speed and excitation and then subtract any copper losses to determine combined mechanical losses and core losses.
- Stray-load loss are those additional copper and core losses caused by field distortions and are extremely difficult to determine except by very accurate measurements of loaded machines. By convention it is taken as 1.0% of the machine output.

The term stray power loss is often used to designate the mechanical running losses.

A method of testing machine insulation resistance is given in [Pender et al, *Handbook* (12), pp. 8–33] as specified by the AIEE. A voltage source of around 600 v. in series with a voltmeter is applied between the machine windings and the frame.

If E_L is the applied voltage, E_m is the voltmeter indication and R_m its resistance, the insulation resistance R is given by

$$R = \frac{(E_L - E_m)R_m}{E_m} \qquad (4\text{--}19)$$

The resistance should not be less than 1 megohm (10^6 ohms).

The insulation breakdown strength should be tested by applying a 60 cycle potential whose rms value is 1000 v. plus twice the rated voltage of the machine. This voltage is applied between the windings and frame. The insulation should not breakdown.

4.6.1   SAMPLE PROBLEM

The stator of a 440-v., 50-hp, shunt motor is tested at 75° C. for its insulation resistance between the terminals, connected together, and the grounded frame. When a 50,000-ohm voltmeter is connected in series with a 600-v., d-c source and the insulation resistance, the meter indicates 125 v.

(a) State whether this is a valid test for the insulation resistance

(b) Calculate the insulation resistance

(c) State whether this insulation resistance is adequate for safe operation.

SOLUTION

[Pender et al, *Handbook* (12) pp. 8–33.]

(a) This method is as specified by the AIEE test code and so is a valid test.

(b) The resistance R is calculated from the following relationship

$$R = \frac{(E_l - E_m)}{E_m} R_m$$

where

$$E_L = \text{source voltage} = 600 \text{ v.}$$
$$E_m = \text{meter reading} = 125 \text{ v.}$$
$$R_m = \text{meter resistance} = 50{,}000 \text{ ohms.}$$

Thus

$$R = \frac{(600 - 125)}{125}(50{,}000)$$

$$= \frac{475}{125}(50{,}000) = 190{,}000 \text{ ohms} \qquad \text{ANS.}$$

(c) This is not adequate resistance; as pointed out by Pender and DelMar, the minimum acceptable value is 10^6 ohms.

4.7 SATURATION EFFECTS

At values of flux density well below saturation of the iron, practically all the magnetizing force (ampere-turns) is required to magnetize the air gap between stator and rotor. Since air has constant permeability, the air gap flux or flux density will be directly proportional to field current. As the iron saturates the ampere-turns required to magnetize the iron is no longer insignificant. A typical curve of flux density or total flux as a function of field current for a given pole is shown in Fig. 4–2. By appropriate scale factor this curve can also represent generated voltage for a particular speed.

Then for a particular value of field current the generated voltage will be directly proportional to speed as indicated in Eq. (4–4). This curve is also called the saturation curve.

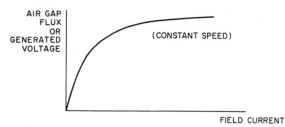

Figure 4–2 *Air-gap flux or generated voltage as a function of field current*

4.7.1   SAMPLE PROBLEM

The saturation curve at 1200 rpm of a certain shunt-wound, d-c generator may be approximated, for the purpose of this problem, by the two lines shown. At what speed must this machine be operated in order to yield an open-circuit voltage of 130 v. when the resistance of the shunt field circuit is 21.67 ohms?

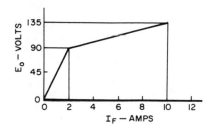

SOLUTION

Neglecting armature resistance drop, the machine when self-excited will supply a field current I_F given by

$$I_F = \frac{E_0}{R_F} = \frac{130}{21.67} = 6.0 \text{ amp}$$

at 1200 rpm, E_o as a function of I_F is from the given curve

$$E_o = 90 + \frac{45}{8}(I_F - 2) \qquad\qquad 2 \le I_F \le 10$$

at 1200 rpm, with $I_F = 6$, E_0 is

$$E_o = 90 + \frac{45}{8}(4) = 112.5 \text{ v.}$$

But with constant field flux,

$$E_o \propto \text{speed}$$

so that

$$\frac{112.5 \text{ volts}}{1200 \text{ rpm}} = \frac{130 \text{ volts}}{n'}$$

Thus

$$n' = \frac{130}{112.5}(1200) = 1385 \text{ rpm} \qquad\qquad \text{ANS.}$$

4.8   MACHINE CHARACTERISTICS

Typical load-speed characteristics for shunt, series and compound motors are shown in Fig. 4–3. The shunt motor is seen to be very nearly a constant speed machine. The speed may be increased by decreasing the field current, hence, care should be taken to prevent overspeed damage in the event that the field circuit opens during operation. The series motor speed decreases with increasing load. It is capable of starting under heavy loads but it may suffer overspeed or runaway damage if it is started without load. The compound motor exhibits compromise characteristics between shunt and series. The curves shown are only relative.

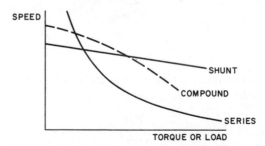

Figure 4–3 Typical d-c motor torque-speed characteristics

Typical voltage-load characteristics for various d-c generators are shown in Fig. 4–4. Only one of many possible compound generator characteristics is shown.

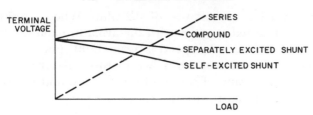

Figure 4–4 Typical d-c generator voltage-load characteristics

For the shunt generator the voltage drop with increasing load is due primarily to armature resistance and armature reaction flux distortion. In the self-excited machine the voltage drop slope is greater because of the cumulative effects of voltage drop and decreasing field current and flux. The compound windings may be connected in such a way that the increased field flux increases the voltage more than the effects of resistance and armature reaction. The series generator may be used to supply a constant current load.

4.9   PRACTICE PROBLEMS

4–1

A shunt-wound interpole motor has a field winding on 4 main poles and an armature with a simplex-wave winding located in 45 slots, each with 8 conductors. When 120 v. are impressed on the shunt field, the flux per pole is 760,000 lines. The armature circuit resistance, including brushes and interpole winding, is 0.08 ohm.

Calculate the speed of this motor when it is driven from 120-v. mains and the armature current is 85 amp.

4–2

A 4-pole, simplex lap-wound, direct-current armature has 48 slots containing 48 coils, each of two turns. The flux per pole, in the field structure for this armature, is 0.5×10^6 lines. The rated current per coil is 10 amp.

Calculate:

(a) The speed for this machine in order that its generated emf be 220 v.

(b) The generated mechanical horsepower when this machine is operated as a motor under the conditions of (a).

4–3

A 220-v., direct current, shunt motor with interpoles drives a constant-torque load at 1200 rpm while drawing 30 amp through the armature which has a resistance of 0.2 ohm. When a resistance of 0.35 ohm is connected in series with the armature and the field current is suitably reduced, the speed is again 1200 rpm.

(a) Calculate the value of the new armature current

(b) Calculate the ratio of the field fluxes, with and without series resistance in the armature circuit.

4-4

A 220-v. shunt motor driving its normal load draws an armature current of 50 amp from 220-v. mains. The armature resistance of this machine, including brushes, is 0.25 ohm and the speed of operation is 1200 rpm.

What armature current will this machine draw from 200-v. mains when driving the same load, with the field adjusted to maintain a speed of 1200 rpm?

4-5

A 220-v., d-c motor has an armature resistance of 0.4 ohm, a shunt field of 175 ohms and a series field of 0.4 ohm. This machine is connected as a short-shunt compound machine to 220-v. mains.

Calculate the line current and the total or gross mechanical horsepower generated in the armature when the armature current is 30 amp. Neglect the brush loss.

4-6

A small traction motor used in street car operation is rated at 50 hp and 760 rpm when its efficiency is 0.89. This motor is constructed with six field poles, and the simplex wave armature has 240 conductors. The resistances of the armature and series field are 0.30 and 0.15 ohm, respectively. The brush and contact resistances are included in the armature resistance. The terminal voltage is 550 v. Calculate

(a) the net output torque at rated load

(b) the stray power loss at rated load

(c) the impressed voltage required to drive the motor at 1000 rpm and deliver the same torque as when the machine is operated with rated voltage and at rated speed

(d) the effective air-gap flux per pole under rated conditions.

4-7

Two shunt field, d-c generators G_1 and G_2 are rated at 100 and 150 kw at 110 v., respectively. Their external load characteristics may be considered as straight lines without serious error. The drop in the external voltage, from no load to full load, is 10 v. in G_1 and 20 v. in G_2.

Calculate the no-load voltages of these generators when they are operated in parallel to supply a 120-v. load of 2000 amp which is divided between them in proportion to their ratings.

4–8

The rated armature current of a 230-v., d-c motor is 75 amp. The maximum allowable momentary armature current for this machine is 225 amp. The resistance of the armature is 0.2 ohm and the brush drop is 2 v.

Determine the resistance of each step of the starter for this motor when the armature current during the starting period is limited to the range from 75 to 225 amp.

CHAPTER FIVE

A-C MACHINES

SYMBOLS

a	Turns ratio
E	Generated voltage, volts
f	Frequency, cycles per second (cps)
h	Pressure head, feet
HP	Horsepower
I	Current, amperes
j	The imaginary operator $\sqrt{-1}$
K, M	Winding constants
kva	Kilovolt amperes
kw	Kilowatts
N	Number of turns
n	Speed, revolutions per minute (rpm)
P	Power, watts
p	Number of poles
Q	Pump discharge, cubic feet per minute
R, r	Resistance, ohms
S	Slip
T	Torque, foot-pounds
V	Terminal or line voltage, volts
W	Liquid density, pounds per cubic feet
X, x	Reactance, ohms
η	Efficiency, per cent or per unit
θ	Power factor angle, degrees or radians
ϕ	Field flux, lines

Subscripts

A	Armature
ar	Armature reaction
c	Core

d	Direct axis, distribution
f	Excitation
g	Generator, air gap
in	Input
L	Line
l	Leakage
m	Motor, mechanical
max	Maximum or peak value
out	Output
p	Pitch
q	Quadrature axis
R	Rotor
r	Resultant, rotor
S	Stator
s	Synchronous
T	Terminal
ϕ	Core excitation

5.1 BASIC PRINCIPLES

Except for small machines up to a few horsepower, a-c motors are designed to operate directly from three-phase lines. A-C generators, again except for small portable power units, supply three-phase power directly.

In the case of a three-phase motor, the electrical power consumed is

$$P_{in} = \sqrt{3} \; V_L I_L \cos \theta \qquad (5\text{-}1)$$

and the output power is

$$P_{out} = \eta_m P_{in}$$
$$= \sqrt{3} \; V_L I_L \; \eta_m \cos \theta \qquad (5\text{-}2)$$

The output power may be expressed either in watts or in horsepower using the conversions listed in Sec. 4.3.

In the case of a three-phase generator the output power is

$$P_{out} = \sqrt{3} \; V_L I_L \cos \theta \qquad (5\text{-}3)$$

The input driving power required is

$$P_{in} = \frac{P_{out}}{\eta_g}$$
$$= \frac{\sqrt{3} \; V_L I_L \cos \theta}{\eta_g} \qquad (5\text{-}4)$$

This also may be expressed in the mechanical units of horsepower or torque-speed.

Alternating-current, three-phase motors are either synchronous motors or induction motors. Three-phase generators or alternators are synchronous motors operated in reverse.

Both types of motors depend for their operation on the interaction of two magnetic fields. One magnetic field is set up by three-phase currents in the stator or armature windings. In the synchronous motor the other magnetic field is set up in the rotor by a d-c source. In the induction motor the second magnetic field is induced by transformer action into the rotor structure.

The three-phase balanced currents flow through windings which are spaced uniformly around the stator structure. The resultant magnetic field rotates about the machine axis at a synchronous speed given by

$$n_s = \frac{120f}{p} \tag{5-5}$$

The minimum number of poles is two so that the maximum synchronous speed of a 60-cps machine is 3600 rpm.

In the case of a three-phase generator, where the rotating d-c field induces voltage in the stator windings, Eq. (5–5) relates rotor speed, number of poles, and frequency of induced voltage.

If the field flux is sinusoidal the rms value of induced voltage is given by

$$E = 4.44 \, fN\phi_{max} \times 10^{-8} \tag{5-6}$$

This voltage is analogous to the induced voltage of d-c machines.

In practice, Eq. (5–6) cannot be used as stated because it assumes concentrated windings. Practical windings are distributed in slots around the stator. Accordingly Eq. (5–6) is modified to include a pitch factor and distribution factor for the windings.

$$E = 4.44 \, fN\phi_{max}K_pK_d \times 10^{-8} \tag{5-7}$$

The pitch factor is

$$K_p = \sin \,(90° \text{ slots spanned by a coil/slots per pole}) \tag{5-8}$$

The distribution factor is

$$K_d = \frac{\sin(m90°/\text{slots per pole})}{m \,\sin(90°/\text{slots per pole})} \tag{5-9}$$

where

m = number of slots per phase per pole = total slots/poles-phases

$$(5\text{--}10)$$

The synchronous machine operates only at synchronous speed. The alternator will generate voltage of rated frequency and the motor will deliver continuous positive torque only when rotating at synchronous speed.

The induction motor delivers continuous positive torque at any speed up to but not including synchronous speed. The induction generator is realizable but is used only rarely when its special characteristics are required.

Synchronous motors are often constructed with auxiliary windings to provide starting torque by induction-motor action. The field is unenergized while the motor is accelerating. When the rotor approaches synchronous speed, the field is energized causing the rotor to synchronize with the rotating armature field.

5.1.1   SAMPLE PROBLEM

A 3-phase, 60-cycle, 6-pole alternator has an air-gap flux which is sinusoidally distributed. The stator has 5 slots per pole per phase and each slot contains 4 conductors arranged in 2 layers. The coil pitch is 12 slots. With normal excitation and rated speed, the voltage induced per conductor is 25 v.

Calculate the open-circuit emf, between line terminals, when this machine is wye-connected and all the conductors per phase are connected in series.

SOLUTION

The expression for generated voltage in a phase winding of an alternator with sinusoidal flux is:

$$E = 4.44 f \phi K_p K_d N \times 10^{-8} \text{ v.}$$

The factor $4.44 f \phi \times 10^{-8}$ would be the voltage induced per coil, which is twice the voltage per conductor, or 50 v.

For a wye-connected machine

$$E_L = \sqrt{3}\, E$$

The factors are

$$K_p = \sin\left[(90°)\,\frac{\text{slots spanned by a coil}}{\text{slots per pole}}\right]$$

$$= \sin\left[(90°)\,\frac{12}{(3)(5)}\right]$$

$$= \sin 72° = 0.952$$

$$K_d = \frac{\sin\left[(\text{slots/phase/pole}[90°])/(\text{slots/pole})\right]}{(\text{slots/phase/pole})\,\sin\left[90/(\text{slots/pole})\right]}$$

$$= \frac{\sin\left[(5)(90)/(3)(5)\right]}{5\,\sin\left[90/(3)(5)\right]} = \frac{\sin 30°}{5\,\sin 6°} = \frac{0.5}{5(0.1042)} = 0.956$$

The total turns per coil N is

N = (5 slots/pole/phase)(6 poles)(4 conductors/slot)(1/2 turn/conductor)
= 60 turns/phase

Thus the line to line voltage is

$$E_L = (1.732)\,(50)\,(0.952)\,(0.956)\,(60)$$

$$= 4730 \text{ v.}$$

ANS.

5.1.2 SAMPLE PROBLEM

A pump, driven by a 440-v., 3-phase induction motor, lifts 1100 cu-ft of water per min against a total head of 100 ft of water. The efficiency of the pump and that of its motor are 0.75 and 0.92, respectively. The power factor of the motor is 0.90.

(a) Calculate the cost of operating this pump for a 24-hour day when power costs $0.03 per kw-hr.

(b) Calculate the line current drawn by the motor.

SOLUTION

(a) Determine pump output, then use efficiencies to determine motor input power in watts, determine energy in watt-hours and finally cost.

assume fresh water, $W = 62.4$ lb/cu ft

$$\text{The overall motor input} = \frac{\text{pump output}}{(\text{motor efficiency})\,(\text{pump efficiency})}$$

If Q is the discharge (cu-ft/min), W the density (lbs/cu ft), and h the head (ft)

$$\text{pump output} = QWh = (1100)(62.4)(100)$$
$$= 6.86 \times 10^6 \text{ ft-lb/min}$$
$$= \frac{(6.86)(10^6)(746)}{33,000}$$
$$= 0.155 \times 10^6 \text{ watts}$$
$$\text{motor input} = \frac{(0.155)(10^6)}{(0.75)(0.92)}$$
$$= 0.225 \times 10^6 \text{ watts}$$
$$\text{Total energy} = (\text{power})(\text{time})$$
$$= (0.225)(10^6)(24)$$
$$= 5.40 \times 10^6 \text{ watt-hours}$$
$$= 5.40 \times 10^3 \text{ kw-hrs}$$
$$\text{Total cost} = (\text{energy})(\text{cost/unit})$$
$$= (5.40)(10^3)(\$0.03) = \$162 \qquad \text{ANS.}$$

(b) The line current may be found from

$$\text{Power} = \sqrt{3} \; E_L I_L \cos \theta$$

Assume voltage given is line-to-line voltage

$$I_L = \frac{\text{Power}}{\sqrt{3} \; E_L \cos \theta}$$
$$= \frac{(0.225) \quad (10^6)}{(1.732) \; (440) \; (0.90)}$$
$$= 328 \text{ amp} \qquad \text{ANS.}$$

5.2   CONSTRUCTION FEATURES

Three-phase machines consist of the following parts:

- An outer frame supporting a slotted iron structure. The armature windings carrying the three-phase currents are imbedded in the stator slots.
- An iron rotor mounted to rotate within the stator. In the synchronous machine the rotor contains field windings which are either imbedded in slots of a smooth-surfaced structure or are wound on salient poles. The windings terminate on slip rings mounted on the shaft. In the induction machine the iron rotor has either a squirrel cage winding structure or a set of three-phase windings terminated on slip rings.
- Carbon brushes mounted on the frame to provide connections to the rotor windings. These are unnecessary on the squirrel cage motor since there is no external connection to the rotor.
- A d-c source of excitation for the synchronous machine field.
- A three-phase variable resistor bank for the wound-rotor induction motor.

In addition the machines may include

- An additional squirrel cage winding on the synchronous machine. This is called a damper or amortisseur which provides starting torque and reduces speed variations due to transient fluctuations in load.
- A starting controller.

5.3 THE SYNCHRONOUS MACHINE SIMPLE EQUIVALENT CIRCUIT

Under steady-state balanced conditions, the smooth rotor synchronous machine may be analyzed as follows:

The total air-gap flux is the result of two magnetmotive forces: the d-c field or excitation, and the armature reaction resulting from the armature current. An equivalent circuit for synchronous machines may be drawn to account for these two flux components and their combined effect on generated or induced voltage. For example, [Fitzgerald et al, *Machinery* (2), Chap. 7] discuss this point and derive a single phase equivalent circuit for the machine shown in Fig. 5–1. Other references have similar derivations.

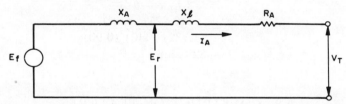

Figure 5–1 A single-phase equivalent circuit for a three-phase synchronous machine

The equivalent circuit of Fig. 5–1 also includes the equivalent armature winding imperfections lumped together in the equivalent resistance R_A and leakage reactance X_l. The voltage E_f is that voltage generated by the field flux alone and is often referred to as the excitation voltage. The voltage E_r represents the voltage generated by the resultant air gap flux. The effects of armature reaction are attributed to the magnetizing reactance X_A. An equation for E_r may be written as

$$E_r = E_f - E_{ar}$$

$$= E_f - jI_A X_A \tag{5-11}$$

which shows that the armature-reaction voltage is proportional to armature current but lags the current by 90°.

The leakage reactance is usually combined with the magnetizing reactance into a single synchronous reactance. Thus

$$X_s = X_A + X_l \tag{5-12}$$

and a loop equation may be written for the equivalent circuit as

$$
\begin{aligned}
V_T &= E_f - I_A R_A - j I_A (X_A + X_l) \\
&= E_f - I_A R_A - j I_A X_s
\end{aligned}
\tag{5-13}
$$

The equivalent circuit as shown is for a generator; for a motor the direction of current is reversed and the signs of the I_A terms are changed accordingly.

The value of synchronous impedance may be obtained from measurements on the machine. [Cf. Siskind, *Machines* (22) Chap. 7]. The measured d-c armature resistance is multiplied by a factor of 1.25 to 1.75 to account for a-c current distribution effects. The open-circuit saturation curve of generated voltage as a function of field current is obtained when the machine is run at rated speed. Again, with the machine run at rated speed, short circuit current as a function of field current is obtained. All quantities are on the basis of the line-to-neutral equivalent. The magnitude of synchronous impedance is the ratio of rated terminal voltage to short-circuit line current at the value of field current that yields rated terminal voltage.

The synchronous machine with a salient pole rotor is analyzed by considering the armature reaction composed of a direct axis component and a quadrature axis component, each component having its own equivalent reactance. Equation (5–13) may be rewritten as

$$V_T = E_f - I_A R_A - j I_d X_d - j I_q X_q \tag{5-14}$$

5.3.1 SAMPLE PROBLEM

A 3-phase, 6600 v., 6000-hp, Y-connected synchronous motor is to be operated under rated conditions with full load and a leading power factor of 0.5. The rotational losses under these conditions are 130 kw and may be taken as constant. The effective resistance and synchronous reactance, per phase, are 0.085 and 2.90 ohm, respectively. What is the current drawn by this machine and the excitation voltage under these conditions?

SOLUTION

The current may be determined knowing the power, power factor, and voltage.

$$P_{in} = \sqrt{3}E_L I_L \cos\theta = P_{out} + P_{losses}$$
$$P_{out} = (6000)(746) = 4.48 \times 10^6 \text{ watts}$$
$$P_{losses} = \text{rotational losses} + \text{copper losses}$$
$$= 130,000 + 3I_L^2(0.085)$$

Thus

$$(1.732)(6600)(0.50)I_L = 4.48 \times 10^6 + 0.130 \times 10^6 + 3I_L^2(0.085)$$

or

$$I_L^2 - 22,400 I_L + 1.81 \times 10^7 = 0$$

Solving

$$I_L = 21,500 \text{ amp, } 900 \text{ amp}$$

The 900-amp value corresponds to normal operation and is the desired result.

Using the single-phase equivalent circuit shown below with its vector diagram, the excitation voltage may be determined

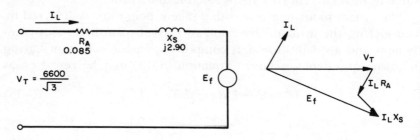

$$V_T - I_L(R_A + jX_s) = E_f$$

The current is at a leading power factor of 0.5 with respect to V_T. Hence

$$\cos\theta = 0.50$$
$$\theta = 60°$$
$$\sin\theta = 0.866$$

and

$$I_L = 900(0.50 + j0.866)$$

Thus

$$E_f = \frac{6600}{\sqrt{3}} - 900(0.50 + j0.866)(0.085 + j2.90)$$
$$= 3810 - 900(-2.47 + j1.52)$$
$$= 6030 - j1370$$
$$= 6190 \text{ v. line-to-neutral}$$

or

$$(\sqrt{3})6190 = 10{,}720 \text{ v. line-to-line} \qquad \text{ANS.}$$

5.4   THE SYNCHRONOUS MOTOR — POWER FACTOR

An important feature of the synchronous motor is the ability to vary the over-all machine power factor. The adjustment is obtained by variation in the d-c field excitation. If the motor is underexcited, the armature current has a lagging power factor relative to the resultant air gap voltage. On the other hand, the condition of overexcitation is obtained when the d-c field excitation is increased beyond that required to run the machine. The excess field excitation causes the machine to operate at leading power factor. Vector diagrams to illustrate this point appear in various references. [cf. Fitzgerald and Kingsley, *Machinery* (2)]

Power factor correction is a valuable characteristic. Synchronous motors are often connected light (unloaded mechanically) across power lines to accomplish this. In this case the synchronous motor is referred to as a synchronous condenser or synchronous capacitor.

The analysis of power factor correction using synchronous capacitors is similar to the analysis with lumped capacitances. Depending on the problem, the machine losses may or may not be significant.

5.4.1   SAMPLE PROBLEM

An industrial plant draws 500 kw at 0.6 pf from a 3-phase system. In order to raise the power factor to 0.866, lagging, and to supply needed additional power, a synchronous motor is added. This motor draws 300 kw, bringing the new total plant load to 800 kw.

Neglecting the losses of the synchronous motor, calculate the exact required kva-rating.

SOLUTION

The kva rating of the machine is determined from the real and reactive power requirements. The reactive requirements may be found by comparing the total requirements before and after the addition of the motor.

Before the motor is added the plant draws 500 kw at 0.6 pf. The reactive load then is

$$\text{Reactive load}_1 = \frac{500}{0.6} \sin \ (\cos^{-1} 0.6)$$

$$= \frac{500}{0.6}(0.8) = 667 \text{ kva}$$

After the motor is added, the plant draws 800 kw at 0.866 pf. The reactive load then is

$$\text{Reactive load}_2 = \frac{800}{0.866} \sin \ (\cos^{-1} 0.866)$$

$$= \frac{800}{0.866}(0.5) = 461 \text{ kva}$$

Thus the motor must supply the leading reactive load of

$$667 - 461 = 206 \text{ kva}$$

The motor load is 300 kw and 206 kva or

$$300 + j206 = 364 \text{ kva} \qquad\qquad \text{ANS.}$$

5.5   THE INDUCTION MOTOR— SIMPLE EQUIVALENT CIRCUIT

Although it is possible to construct and operate a generator which is the reverse of the induction motor, such machines are much less important in a practical sense than the induction motor and will not be considered further.

The operation of the induction motor is based on transformer action. The armature magnetic field induces a voltage in the conductors of the rotor. The continuous rotor electrical circuit allows currents to circulate. These are limited by the rotor equivalent resistance and reactance. The circulating currents, in turn, set up a rotor magnetic field which interacts with the armature magnetic field thereby producing a torque at the shaft.

The armature magnetic field rotates at synchronous speed n_s; the rotor rotates at speed n. The slip is defined by the ratio

$$S = \frac{n_s - n}{n_s} \qquad (5\text{--}15)$$

The slip is seen to have a value of unity at rotor standstill and decreases to zero when the rotor is turning at synchronous speed. The induced frequency in the rotor is $Sn_s/60$ cycles per second.

Equation (5–15) may be solved for rotor speed as

$$n = n_s(1 - S) \qquad (5\text{--}16)$$

An equivalent circuit for the induction motor suitable for simple analyses may be drawn. This circuit is very similar to the transformer equivalent circuit. The significant difference comes about because the rotor-current frequency is a function of rotor speed. The equivalent circuit for one phase (equivalent line-to-neutral) is shown in Fig. 5–2.

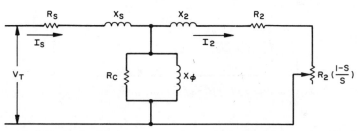

Figure 5–2 A single-phase equivalent circuit for a three-phase induction motor

The similarity to the transformer equivalent circuit should be noted. The rotor resistance and reactance R_2 and X_2 are shown as equivalent impedances transformed through the turns ratio. R_S and X_S represent the equivalent stator resistance and reactance. If a is the equivalent turns ratio stator-to-rotor

$$R_2 = a^2 R_R \qquad (5\text{--}17)$$

$$X_2 = a^2 X_R \qquad (5\text{--}18)$$

The total power delivered across the air gap to the rotor per phase is

$$P_g = I_2^2 \left[R_2 + R_2 \left(\frac{1 - S}{S} \right) \right]$$

$$= I_2^2 \frac{R_2}{S} \qquad (5\text{--}19)$$

The power per phase lost in the rotor is

$$P_r = I_2{}^2 R_2 = SP_g \tag{5-20}$$

while the power per phase available to drive the rotor is

$$P_m = I_2{}^2 R_2\left(\frac{1-S}{S}\right)$$
$$= (1-S)P_g \tag{5-21}$$

To obtain the useful shaft power, Eq. (5–21) must be multiplied by the number of phases and have subtracted from it the various mechanical losses, namely, friction and windage.

A useful simplification which introduces a negligible error in most cases involves moving the core impedance components to the input terminals as shown in Fig. 5–3.

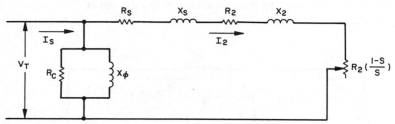

Figure 5–3 An approximate form of the equivalent circuit of Figure 5–2

Using this simplified form

$$I_2 = \frac{V_T}{\sqrt{(R_S + R_2/S)^2 + (X_S + X_2)^2}} \tag{5-22}$$

The mechanical power delivered to the rotor for a three-phase motor becomes

$$P_m = \frac{3V_T{}^2 R_2(1-S)/S}{(R_S + R_2/S)^2 + (X_S + X_2)^2} \tag{5-23}$$

It may be recalled that

$$P_m = \frac{(746)2\pi T n_s(1-S)}{33,000} \tag{5-24}$$

so that an expression for mechanical torque may be written as

$$T = \frac{(7.05)(3)V_T{}^2 R_2/S}{n_s[(R_S + R_2/S)^2 + (X_S + X_2)^2]} \tag{5-25}$$

It may be seen from Eqs. (5–22) and (5–25) that if all other things are equal, the line current is directly proportional to terminal voltage and the torque is directly proportional to the square of the terminal voltage.

In some applications it is necessary to restrict the starting current to reduce the magnitude of power system disturbances. Often a three-phase autotransformer bank is used to lower the starting voltage. However, the starting torque is reduced in the same proportion as the starting current. Equations (5–22) and (5–25) allow the computation of the reduction in starting current and torque.

5.5.1   SAMPLE PROBLEM

A 15-hp, 60-cycle, 4-pole, wound-rotor, 3-phase, 208-v. induction motor draws 13 kw from the line. Its losses are as follows:

Iron Loss	800 watts
Stator Copper Loss	900 watts
Rotor Copper Loss	300 watts
Friction and Windage	150 watts

Calculate the power output and speed of this motor.

SOLUTION

(a) The power output may be found by subtracting the sum of the losses from the input power. Thus

$$P_{out} = P_{in} - \Sigma P_{losses}$$
$$= 13,000 - (800 + 900 + 300 + 150)$$
$$= 13,000 - 2150$$
$$= 10,850 \text{ watts} \qquad \text{ANS.}$$

If the horsepower output is desired it may be found

$$P_{out} = \frac{10,850}{746} = 14.55 \text{ hp} \qquad \text{ALT. ANS.}$$

(b) The motor speed is

$$n = \frac{120f}{p}(1 - S) = \frac{(120)(60)}{4}(1 - S) = 1800(1 - S)$$

but the slip is

$$S = \frac{\text{Power lost in rotor}}{\text{Power delivered across the air gap}}$$

$$= \frac{\text{Rotor copper loss}}{P_{\text{in}} - (\text{stator copper loss} + \text{iron loss})}$$

$$= \frac{300}{13,000 - (900 + 800)} = \frac{300}{11,300} = 0.0265$$

Thus

$$n = 1800(1.00 - 0.0265) = 1800(0.9735) = 1750 \text{ rpm} \qquad \text{ANS.}$$

5.5.2 SAMPLE PROBLEM

A 10-hp, 4-pole, 3-phase, 60-cycle motor draws 21 amp and 7 kw while driving its normal load. Under these conditions its slip is 2%. When running idle, this motor draws 6 amp and 580 watts at normal voltage. With its rotor blocked, this motor draws 15 amp and 500 watts with 50 v. applied.

Calculate the output torque and horsepower, and the efficiency of this motor when driving its normal load.

SOLUTION

The output torque and horsepower may be determined from the output power which in turn may be determined from input and losses. The efficiency may be determined from output and losses.

The output horsepower HP is

$$\text{HP} = \frac{\text{output watts}}{746}$$

$$= \frac{\text{input watts} - \text{losses}}{746}$$

The output torque T is

$$T = \frac{33,000 \text{ HP}}{2\pi n} = \frac{5250 \text{ HP}}{n}$$

The efficiency η is

$$\eta = 100\left(\frac{\text{output}}{\text{input}}\right)$$

The horsepower will be determined first. The input power is given as 7000 watts. The losses include the copper losses, core loss, windage, and friction.

Assume that in the blocked-rotor test, the entire power is consumed by the equivalent winding resistance referred to the stator. Assuming equivalent wye-connected windings, the resistance per phase is

$$R = \frac{P}{3I^2}$$
$$= \frac{500}{3(15)^2} = 0.74 \text{ ohms/phase}$$

The power consumed during the no-load test is assumed to be the full-load core loss and friction and windage loss plus small copper loss. This copper loss P_{NL} is

$$P_{NL} = 3I^2R$$
$$= 3(6)^2(0.740) = 80 \text{ watts}$$

Thus full-load core and friction and windage losses $= 580 - 80 = 500$ watts

The full load copper loss P_{FL} is

$$P_{FL} = 3I^2R$$
$$= 3(21)^2(0.740)$$
$$= 980 \text{ watts}$$

Thus Output watts $=$ Input watts $-$ losses

$$= 7000 - (980 + 500)$$
$$= 7000 - 1480 = 5520 \text{ watts}$$

Thus

$$\text{HP} = \frac{5520}{746} = 7.40 \text{ hp}$$

ANS.

To determine the torque, it is necessary to know the speed n which is

$$n = \frac{120f}{p}(1 - S)$$
$$= \frac{120(60)}{4}(1.0 - 0.02) = 1800(0.98) = 1764 \text{ rpm}$$

Thus

$$T = \frac{5250(7.40)}{1764} = 22 \text{ ft-lb}$$

ANS.

Finally

$$\eta = \frac{(5520)}{7000}100 = 79\%$$

ANS.

5.6 INDUCTION MOTOR CHARACTERISTICS

In induction machines, the torque-speed characteristics may be altered and modified by proper design and selection of the stator and rotor resistances and reactances. In addition it is possible to arrange the rotor reactance to be a function of the frequency of the circulating currents. Hence it is possible to design a wide variety of machine characteristics.

The squirrel-cage rotor structure has an assembly of axial conducting bars imbedded in the rotor iron, around the periphery of the rotor, and connected together by end rings. The size, shape, and material of the bars provides for variety in characteristics. Several typical characteristics are shown in Fig. 5–4. Many more different shapes are possible.

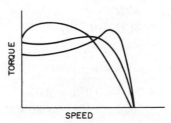

Figure 5–4 Typical squirrel-cage induction motor torque-speed characteristics

The wound-rotor induction motor torque-speed characteristic may be modified during operating by altering the resistance in the rotor current. Typical torque-speed characteristics for different rotor resistances are shown in Fig. 5–5.

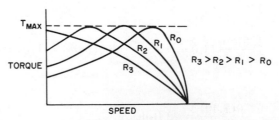

Figure 5–5 Typical wound-rotor induction motor torque-speed characteristics for different values of resistance

The variable rotor resistance allows a load requiring near the maximum machine torque to be started and brought up to speed. Another advantage is that the starting current surge may be limited by the additional rotor resistance.

5.7 PRACTICE PROBLEMS

5–1

A wye-connected, 200-kva, 440-v., 3-phase, 3-wire alternator yields 150 v. between line terminals on open circuit. With the field excitation unchanged, the short circuit current is 300 amp. The ohmic resistance of this machine, between line terminals, is 0.10 ohm and the ratio of effective to ohmic resistance for this machine is 1.25.

Calculate the full-load terminal voltage of this machine when the excitation is adjusted to yield a no-load voltage of 500 v. and the power factor of the load is 0.80, lagging.

5–2

A 3-phase, 1500-kva, 5500-v., Y-connected alternator has an effective resistance and a synchronous reactance of 0.35 and 6.6 ohms per phase, respectively, and delivers full-load current at a lagging power factor of 0.8. What will be the terminal voltage of this machine if its excitation remains unchanged and full-load current is delivered to a load having a leading power factor of 0.8?

5–3

A 3-phase, 230-v., 6-pole, 60-cycle induction motor is loaded by means of a prony brake, the length and dead weight of which are 2 ft and 2 lbs respectively. The power input is measured by two wattmeters P_1 and P_2 according to the two-wattmeter method. With 230 v. impressed on this motor, the total force delivered by the prony brake is 30 lbs, P_1 and P_2 indicate 3.5 and 7.0 kw, respectively, and the slip is 10%.

Calculate:
(a) the horsepower output of the motor
(b) its efficiency
(c) its power factor

5–4

The efficiency and power factor of a 50-hp, 6-pole, 440-v., 60-cycle induction motor are 90% and 92.5%, respectively, at full load. This motor draws 525% of full-load current and develops 175% of full-load torque when started across the line with full voltage. Specify the turns ratio of an autotransformer starter that will permit this motor to be started with a torque equal to 60% of that at full load. What will be the starting current in the line when this starter is used? Neglect the effects of saturation and the losses in the starter.

5–5

A 3-phase, 60-cycle, 220-v., 4-pole, squirrel cage induction motor operates at rated voltage and rated frequency with a line current of 71.4 amp, 4.45% slip, and 88% efficiency. The power input is measured by the two wattmeter method, and the readings are +15,550 watts and +9750 watts. Find:
  (a) shaft speed
  (b) horsepower output
  (c) delivered torque
  (d) power factor
  (e) total losses (watts)

5–6

The losses in a 3-phase, 60-cycle, 4-pole induction motor at full load are:

core	3.0%
friction and windage	2.0%
rotor copper	3.0%
stator copper	5.0%

  (a) Calculate, as accurately as these data permit, the efficiency and speed of this machine at 75% of full load.
  (b) List the assumptions made in your calculations.

5–7

A 440-v., 60-cycle, 4-pole, 3-phase, wound rotor induction motor is directly connected to a pump which delivers 1000 cfm of water against an effective head of 8.7 ft. Under this load, the motor draws 15.62 kw at a power factor of 0.92. When operated without load, the motor draws 803 watts. The stator and rotor resistances, per phase, are 0.202 and 0.022 ohm, respectively. The effective turns ratio between the stator and rotor is 4:1.

Calculate the efficiency of the pump.

√5–8

The data for a 335 hp, 2000-v., three-phase, 6-pole, 50-cycle, Y-connected induction motor are as follows: Ohmic resistance per phase of stator, 0.165 ohm; rotor, 0.0127 ohm; ratio of transfor-

mation, 4:1. No-load test: Line voltage, 2000 v.; line current, 15.3 amp; power, 10,000 watts. The friction and windage of the motor are 2000 watts. Blocked test: Line voltage, 440 v.; line current, 170 amp; power, 40,500 watts. When the slip is 0.015, determine:
 (a) the current in the stator and rotor
 (b) motor output
 (c) speed
 (d) torque developed by rotor and torque at pulley
 (e) power factor
 (f) efficiency

5–9
 A 450-hp, 3-phase, 2200-v., 60-cycle, 6-pole, wound-rotor, induction motor has the following circuit constants per phase, referred to the stator:

rotor resistance	0.15 ohm
rotor leakage reactance	0.75 ohm
stator resistance	0.32 ohm
stator leakage reactance	1.15 ohms
connection of windings	Y-Y

 In addition, the core loss is 2500 watts; the friction and windage losses total 12,000 watts and the magnetizing current is 25 amp.
 Calculate the speed and efficiency of this machine at full load.

5–10
 A 3-phase, 1000-hp, 12-pole, 2200-v., 25-cycle induction motor operates at full load with a slip of 1.75%. The effective resistance and reactance of the stator are 0.195 ohm and 0.59 ohm, respectively, between terminals. The effective resistance and reactance of the rotor are 0.1433 and 0.29 ohm, respectively, between terminals. The transformation ratio from stator to rotor is 22 to 15. Find the voltage required during starting in order that the starting torque be equal to that developed at rated load.

CHAPTER SIX

VACUUM TUBE CIRCUITS

SYMBOLS

A	Gain magnitude
B	Feedback ratio
C	Capacity, farads
ΔC	A change in capacity, farads
E	D-c or a-c non-variable voltage, volts
e	D-c or a-c variable voltage, volts
f	Frequency, cycles per second (cps)
g_m	Mutual conductance, mhos
I	D-c or a-c non-variable current, amp.
i	D-c or a-c variable current, amp
j	The imaginary operator $\sqrt{-1}$
K	A constant, a multiplier denoting multiplication by 1000
L	Inductance, henrys
N	Number of turns
R	Resistance, ohms
r_p	Plate resistance, ohms
Y	Admittance, mhos
Z	Impedance, ohms
ω	Angular frequency, radians/second
μ	Amplification factor
Ω	A symbol denoting ohms

Subscripts

av	Average
b	Average or d-c component in plate circuit

bb	D-c plate supply (voltage)
c	Average or d-c component in control grid circuit
cc	D-c control grid supply (voltage)
d	Diode
f	Feedback
g	Grid, grid terminal, referring to a-c components in grid circuit
H	Referring to frequency higher than midband
I	Referring to midband
i, in	Input, referring to input
k	Cathode, cathode terminal
L	Load; also referring to frequency lower than midband
M	Maximum, peak value
o, out	Output, referring to output
p	Plate, plate terminal, referring to a-c component in plate circuit
p	Primary
piv	Peak inverse voltage
rms	Root mean square, effective
s	Secondary
T	Total

6.1   DIODES

The simplest vacuum tube or electron tube device is the diode or two element tube. This consists of a source of electrons (a directly or indirectly heated cathode) and an electron collector (plate or anode). The ideal diode is a unidirectional switch with zero conduction when the plate is more negative than the cathode and, conversely, with infinite conduction when the plate is more positive than the cathode.

Diodes are used primarily as rectifiers and switch elements.

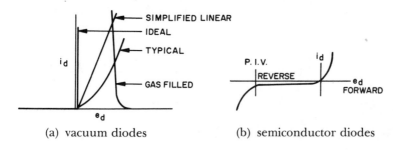

(a) vacuum diodes   (b) semiconductor diodes

Figure 6–1 Various diode characteristics

Figure 6–1 shows several different diode voltage-current characteristics. The gas-filled diode has essentially constant voltage drop once the gas has become ionized.

The current flow to reverse voltage is not shown but for ideal vacuum diodes is zero. Practically, there may be a small current because the insulation resistance is not infinite. The maximum reverse voltage a diode can withstand is limited by insulation breakdown, usually in the form of arc-over. This maximum voltage is called the peak inverse voltage.

Semiconductor diodes are most often fabricated from silicon, germanium, copper oxide, or selenium. In the forward voltage region, the conduction curves are very similar to those of high-vacuum diodes although the voltage drop for a given current may be significantly smaller in a semiconductor diode. In the reverse voltage region, semiconductor diodes always conduct but the conduction current is small for voltages up to the peak inverse voltage. Above this voltage the current increases abruptly with increasing voltage. The peak inverse voltage is defined as the voltage corresponding to a value of reverse current and may be somewhat arbitrarily defined because different manufacturers may use different standards. The abrupt increase in current is called Zener breakdown and occurs at the Zener voltage.

The Langmuir-Childs or three-halves power law for high-vacuum space change limited diode is

$$i_d = K(e_d)^{3/2} \qquad (6\text{--}1)$$

A simple circuit for a half-wave rectifier with resistive load is shown in Fig. 6–2.

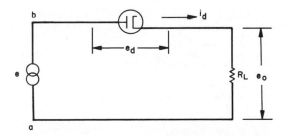

Figure 6–2 Half-wave rectifier with resistive load

When the diode is conducting the loop equation is

$$e = e_d + e_o = e_d + i_d R_L \qquad (6\text{--}2)$$

An exact solution for e_o or i_d may be performed graphically, or a solution may be approximated by assuming that the diode is a linear resistance in the conduction region.

If the diode is assumed ideal and the voltage source e is a sinusoid, Fig. 6–3 shows the input wave and the output voltage developed across R_L.

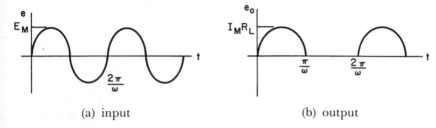

(a) input   (b) output

Figure 6–3 Voltage waveshapes for a half-wave rectifier

The peak current is given by

$$I_M = \frac{E_M}{R_L} \tag{6-3}$$

However, if the diode has a constant resistance r_d

$$I_M = \frac{E_M}{r_d + R_L} \tag{6-4}$$

A d-c ammeter placed in series with R_L will indicate the average of i_d

$$
\begin{aligned}
I_{av} &= \frac{\omega}{2\pi} \int_0^{2\pi/\omega} i_d dt \\
&= \frac{\omega}{2\pi} \int_0^{\pi/\omega} I_M \sin \omega t dt = \frac{I_M}{\pi}
\end{aligned}
\tag{6-5}
$$

A d-c voltmeter across R_L will read a voltage equal to $R_L I_{av}$.

An a-c ammeter in series with R_L will read the rms value of i_d.

$$
\begin{aligned}
I_{rms} &= \left(\frac{\omega}{2\pi} \int_0^{2\pi/\omega} i_d^2 dt \right)^{1/2} \\
&= \left(\frac{\omega}{2\pi} \int_0^{\pi/\omega} I_M^2 \sin {}^2\omega t dt \right)^{1/2} = \frac{I_M}{2}
\end{aligned}
\tag{6-6}
$$

The peak inverse voltage across the diode will be E_M.

Figure 6–4 shows two forms of a full-wave rectifier circuit. One uses a split voltage source most often obtained from a center tapped transformer while the other utilizes a bridge circuit of diodes.

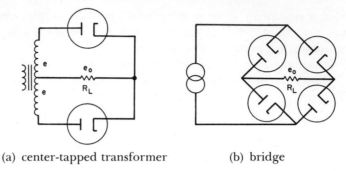

(a) center-tapped transformer   (b) bridge

Figure 6–4 Full-wave single-phase rectifiers with resistive load

In these circuits each diode (or pair of diodes in the bridge) conducts during one half the cycle. The voltage waveforms are as indicated in Fig. 6–5.

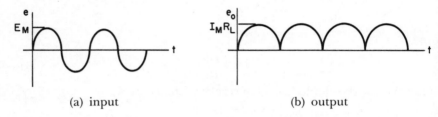

(a) input   (b) output

Figure 6–5 Voltage waveshapes for a full-wave rectifier

The average load current may be found similar to Eq. (6–5) as

$$I_{av} = \frac{2I_M}{\pi} \tag{6–7}$$

and the rms load current is

$$I_{rms} = \frac{I_M}{\sqrt{2}} \tag{6–8}$$

6.1.1 SAMPLE PROBLEM

A half-wave rectifier that can be represented in a circuit as an ideal rectifier in series with a resistance of R_d ohms is connected to a load of 5000 ohms and is subjected to a voltage of 115 sin (377*t*) v. If R_d has a value of 500 ohms, determine the maximum, root-mean-square, and average values of the current that flows in the circuit.

SOLUTION

The maximum load current is

$$I_M = \frac{E_M}{R_d + R_L}$$
$$= \frac{115}{500 + 5000} = \frac{115}{5500}$$
$$= 0.0209 \text{ amp} \qquad \text{ANS.}$$

The rms load current is

$$I_{rms} = \frac{I_M}{2} = \frac{0.0209}{2} = 0.01045 \text{ amp} \qquad \text{ANS.}$$

The average load current is

$$I_{av} = \frac{I_M}{\pi} = \frac{0.0209}{\pi} = 0.00655 \text{ amp} \qquad \text{ANS.}$$

6.2   TRIODES AND PENTODES—AMPLIFIERS

Figure 6–6 shows typical plate current-plate voltage characteristics for triodes, tetrodes, and pentodes along with the symbol for each. The various curves represent different values of control grid voltage. All other grid voltages are held constant. In all curves $e_1 > e_2 > e_3 > e_4$

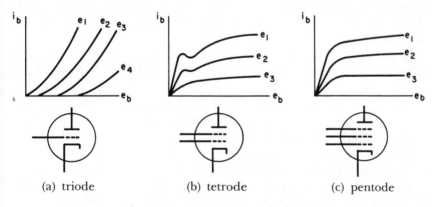

(a) triode   (b) tetrode   (c) pentode

Figure 6–6 Typical triode, tetrode, and pentode characteristics

The triode version of the Langmuir-Childs law may be expressed as

$$i_b = K(e_b + \mu e_c)^{3/2} \qquad (6\text{–}9)$$

This expression is valid only where the grid draws no current and then only to a good approximation.

The tetrode is not generally used except in high power and transmitting circuits.

Although these tubes have non-linear characteristics, under certain conditions they may be considered linear, in which case the a-c small-signal linear equivalent circuit may be used for circuit analysis. The following terms are defined:

amplification factor

$$\mu = -\left.\frac{\partial e_p}{\partial e_g}\right|_{i_p = \text{constant}} \tag{6-10}$$

grid-plate transconductance or mutual conductance

$$g_m = \left.\frac{\partial i_p}{\partial e_g}\right|_{e_p = \text{constant}} \tag{6-11}$$

plate resistance

$$r_p = \left.\frac{\partial e_p}{\partial i_p}\right|_{e_g = \text{constant}} \tag{6-12}$$

The following is true numerically

$$\mu = g_m r_p \tag{6-13}$$

For the purpose of signal analysis only, the actual schematic of the vacuum tube circuit may be redrawn with tubes replaced by their small-signal linear equivalent circuits. All d-c sources used to supply the proper operating potentials are removed leaving only internal impedances.

In the linear equivalent only three elements are significant: the plate (p), the cathode (k), and the control grid (g). The grid draws no current.

Figure 6–7 shows two linear equivalents. Interelectrode capacitances are shown but may often be neglected. Lead resistance and inductance are neglected. Either equivalent circuit may be used.

The grid-to-cathode capacitance C_i represents not only the grid-cathode capacitance but wiring capacitances, and in the case of the tetrode and pentode may include other interelectrode capacitances as well. This statement is also true for C_o, in that it includes the effects of wiring and other capacitances.

A simple amplifier circuit is shown in Fig. 6–8 along with a linear equivalent circuit. The two bypass capacitors are assumed to have negligible reactance hence they do not appear in the equivalent.

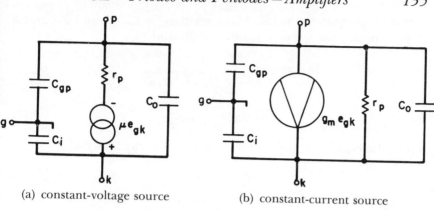

(a) constant-voltage source   (b) constant-current source

Figure 6–7 Vacuum-tube linear equivalent circuits

The heater and its supply is omitted as is customary. Either tube
equivalent circuit could be used yielding the same results. The battery E_{bb} represents the d-c plate supply voltage; grid bias voltage is
developed across the bypassed cathode resistor.

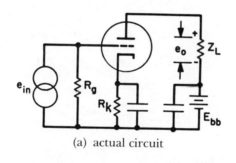

(a) actual circuit

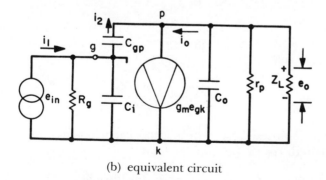

(b) equivalent circuit

Figure 6–8 A simple amplifier circuit and its linear equivalent circuit

Let Z_T represent the parallel combination of C_o, r_p, and Z_L, and Z_i represent the parallel combination of R_g and C_i.

$$Z_T = \frac{1}{j\omega C_o + (1/r_p) + 1/Z_L} \tag{6-14}$$

$$Z_i = \frac{1}{j\omega C_i + 1/R_g} \tag{6-15}$$

From the equivalent the following equations may be written

$$e_o = -i_o Z_T \tag{6-16}$$

$$i_o + i_2 = g_m e_{gk} \tag{6-17}$$

$$e_{in} = e_{gk} = i_1 Z_i - i_2 Z_i \tag{6-18}$$

$$e_o = -i_2\left(\frac{1}{j\omega C_{gp}} + Z_i\right) + i_1 Z_i \tag{6-19}$$

Subtracting Eq. (6–19) from Eq. (6–18) yields

$$e_{gk} - e_o = \frac{i_2}{j\omega C_{gp}} \tag{6-20}$$

Combining Eqs. (6–16), (6–17), and (6–20) yields

$$g_m e_{gk} = i_o + j\omega C_{gp}(e_{gk} + i_o Z_T) \tag{6-21}$$

or

$$i_o = \frac{e_{gk}(g_m - j\omega C_{gp})}{1 + j\omega C_{gp} Z_T} \tag{6-22}$$

Defining the amplifier gain A as

$$A = \frac{e_o}{e_{in}} \tag{6-23}$$

it is apparent that

$$A = \frac{(j\omega C_{gp} - g_m)Z_T}{1 + j\omega C_{gp} Z_T} \tag{6-24}$$

In the often-used case where tube capacitances are neglected, Eq. (6–24) reduces to the familiar form,

$$A = -g_m Z_T = \frac{-g_m r_p Z_L}{r_p + Z_L} = \frac{-\mu Z_L}{r_p + Z_L} \tag{6-25}$$

The input impedance of the tube in this circuit may be found by determining the ratio e_{in}/i_1 which may be obtained from Eqs. (6–18), (6–19), and (6–23) as

$$\frac{e_{in}}{i_1} = Z_{in} = \frac{1}{(1/Z_i) + j\omega C_{gp}(1 - A)} \tag{6–26}$$

This expression shows that the input impedance is not only the direct impedance from grid to cathode but has an added capacitance term

$$\Delta C = C_{gp}(1 - A) \tag{6–27}$$

There are several reasons for using pentodes as amplifiers. The gain is often greater than that obtainable from a triode. In addition, effect of the screen and suppressor grids is to reduce the grid-plate capacitance to a very nearly insignificant quantity.

The output impedance may be found by forming a Thévenin equivalent, or by the often-used analytical method of assuming a generator connected across the output terminals with the input terminals shorted. The ratio of generator voltage to current becomes the output impedance.

Thus for this circuit including Z_L as part of the circuit supplying another load, the output impedance of this amplifier is

$$Z_o = \frac{1}{(1/Z_L) + (1/r_p) + j\omega C_o + j\omega C_{gp}} \tag{6–28}$$

Another circuit is that of the cathode follower shown in Fig. 6–9 with its linear equivalent circuit.

As before let Z_T and Z_i be defined as

$$Z_T = \frac{1}{(1/Z_k) + (1/r_p) + j\omega C_o} \tag{6–29}$$

and

$$Z_i = \frac{1}{(1/R_g) + j\omega C_{gp}} \tag{6–30}$$

The following equations may be written

$$e_o = i_o Z_T \tag{6–31}$$

$$g_m e_{gk} = i_o + i_2 \tag{6–32}$$

$$i_2 = (e_o - e_{in})j\omega C_i \tag{6–33}$$

$$e_{gk} = (e_{in} - e_o) \tag{6–34}$$

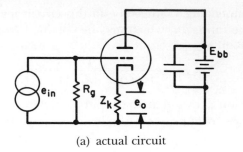

(a) actual circuit

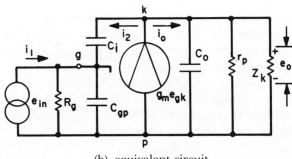

(b) equivalent circuit

Figure 6–9 A cathode-follower and its linear equivalent circuit

These may be manipulated to obtain as an expression for gain

$$A = \frac{(g_m + j\omega C_i)}{(1/Z_T) + j\omega C_i + g_m} \qquad (6\text{–}35)$$

If the interelectrode capacitances are all negligible this reduces to the familiar form

$$A = \frac{\mu Z_k/(r_p + Z_k)}{1 + \mu Z_k/(r_p + Z_k)} = \frac{\mu Z_k}{r_p + (1 + \mu)Z_k} \qquad (6\text{–}36)$$

The input impedance may be found as the ratio e_{in}/i_1 but

$$e_{\text{in}} = (i_1 + i_2)Z_i \qquad (6\text{–}37)$$

and solving Eqs. (6–37), (6–33), and (6–23) simultaneously yields

$$\frac{e_{\text{in}}}{i_1} = Z_{\text{in}} = \frac{1}{(1/Z_i) + j\omega C_i(1 - A)} \qquad (6\text{–}38)$$

This shows an increase in the input capacity but since the gain cannot exceed unity, the increase is not so great as could be obtained in the circuit of Fig. 6–8.

The output impedance may be found by assuming a fictitious generator of voltage e_o connected across Z_k. Analysis shows that in Fig. 6–9b, short-circuiting the input generator e_{in} results in a current i_o supplied by the generator e_o that is

$$i_o = \frac{e_o}{Z_T} + g_m e_o + e_o (j\omega C_i) \qquad (6\text{–}39)$$

from which

$$Z_o = \frac{e_o}{i_o} = \frac{1}{(1/Z_T) + g_m + j\omega C_i} \qquad (6\text{–}40)$$

If several amplifier stages are connected in such a way that the output voltage of one stage supplies the input voltage for the subsequent stage, the overall gain may be found by taking the product of the individual stage gains including the effects of any interstage coupling networks such as transformers or coupling impedances.

The condition of linear operation assumes that no distortion is introduced as a result of circuit non-linearities. One way in which non-linearities may be introduced is by either grid current flow or by plate current cutoff. Grid current flow occurs on positive grid voltage peaks; cutoff on negative grid voltage peaks. Amplifier operation may be classified with respect to grid conduction and cutoff.

Class A_1:   No grid current flow or cutoff

Class A_2:   Grid current flow but no cutoff

Class AB_1: No grid current flow, cutoff for less than one-half cycle of input signal

Class AB_2: Grid current flow, cutoff as in Class AB_1

Class B_1:   No grid current, cutoff for approximately one-half of the cycle of input signal

Class B_2:   Grid current flow, cutoff as in Class B_1

Class C: Grid current flow, cutoff for more than one-half of the cycle of input signal

Class C operation is usually reserved for oscillator and R.F. amplifier circuits where a tuned circuit reduces the effects of discontinuities in plate current.

Class AB and Class B operation is often found in push-pull amplifier circuits. When one tube is cutoff the other is conducting. The load does not see a discontinuity in total plate current.

The Class A_1 circuit is the only one that may be analyzed using the linear equivalent. The Class AB_1 or B_1 may be analyzed under certain conditions using functional relationships between current and various voltages. Generally the other circuits are analyzed graphically using the various tube characteristic curves.

6.2.1 SAMPLE PROBLEM

The operating characteristics of a triode are idealized in the relation

$$i_p = \frac{1}{10^4}\left(\frac{e_p}{5} + e_g\right)^{3/2}$$

where i_p is the plate current in amperes, and e_p and e_g are the plate and grid voltages, respectively, in volts.

Calculate, for the condition when $e_p = 175$ v. and $e_g = -10$ v, the values of the amplification factor μ, the plate resistance r_p and the mutual conductance g_m.

SOLUTION

By definition

$$r_p = \frac{1}{\partial i_p / \partial e_p}$$

But

$$\frac{\partial i_p}{\partial e_p} = \left(\frac{1}{10^4}\right)\left(\frac{3}{2}\right)\left(\frac{e_p}{5} + e_g\right)^{1/2}\left(\frac{1}{5}\right)$$
$$= \frac{3}{10^5}\left(\frac{e_p}{5} + e_g\right)^{1/2}$$

Thus

$$r_p = \frac{1}{3/10^5 (175/5 - 10)^{1/2}} = \frac{1}{3/10^5 (25)^{1/2}} = \frac{10^5}{15} = 6.67 \times 10^3 \text{ ohms}$$
ANS.

By definition

$$g_m = \frac{\partial i_p}{\partial e_g}$$

But

$$\frac{\partial i_p}{\partial e_g} = \left(\frac{1}{10^4}\right)\left(\frac{3}{2}\right)\left(\frac{e_p}{5} + e_g\right)^{1/2} \quad (1)$$

Thus

$$g_m = \left(\frac{3}{2}\right)(10^{-4})\left(\frac{175}{5} - 10\right)^{1/2}$$
$$= \left(\frac{3}{2}\right)(10^{-4})(25)^{1/2} = \frac{15}{2} \times 10^{-4} = 750 \text{ micromhos}$$
ANS.

By definition

$$\mu = \frac{-\partial e_p}{\partial e_g}$$

thus

$$\partial i_p = \left(\frac{1}{10^4}\right)\left(\frac{3}{2}\right)\left(\frac{e_p}{5} + e_g\right)^{1/2}\left(\frac{1}{5}\partial e_p + \partial e_g\right) = 0$$

from which

$$\frac{-\partial e_p}{\partial e_g} = \mu = 5 \qquad\qquad \text{ANS.}$$

As a check

$$\begin{aligned}
\mu &= r_p g_m \\
&= (6.67 \times 10^3)\,(750 \times 10^{-6}) \\
&= 5000 \times 10^{-3} = 5 \qquad\qquad \text{ANS.}
\end{aligned}$$

6.2.2   SAMPLE PROBLEM

Derive the expression for the gain of the circuit shown, from input to output 1 and from input to output 2. Neglect internal capacity reactances.

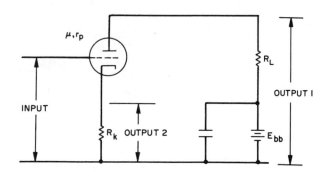

SOLUTION

The gain expression may be derived from the linear equivalent circuit shown.

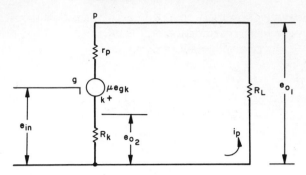

First solve for e_{0_1}

$$e_{0_1} = -i_p R_L$$

But

$$i_p = \frac{\mu e_{gk}}{r_p + R_k + R_L}$$

and

$$e_{gk} = e_{\text{in}} - i_p R_k$$

so that

$$i_p = \frac{\mu(e_{\text{in}} - i_p R_k)}{r_p + R_k + R_L}$$

$$i_p(r_p + R_k + R_L) = \mu e_{\text{in}} - \mu i_p R_k$$

$$i_p = \frac{\mu e_{\text{in}}}{r_p + R_L + (1 + \mu)R_k}$$

or

$$e_{0_1} = \frac{-\mu e_{\text{in}} R_L}{r_p + R_L + (1 + \mu)R_K}$$

The gain may be written as

$$A_1 \equiv \frac{e_{0_1}}{e_{\text{in}}} = \frac{-\mu R_L}{r_p + R_L + (1 + \mu)R_K}$$

Similarly e_{0_2} is

$$e_{0_2} = i_p R_k$$

$$= \frac{\mu e_{\text{in}} R_k}{r_p + R_L + (1 + \mu)R_k}$$

The gain may be written as

$$A_2 \equiv \frac{e_{0_2}}{e_{\text{in}}} = \frac{\mu R_k}{r_p + R_L + (1 + \mu)R_k}$$

Note: It may be observed that the two output voltages are 180°
out of phase where reactances may be neglected. Also if $R_k = R_L$,
the two outputs are of equal magnitude but the gain is less than
unity. This circuit is often used as a driver to provide equal and out-
of-phase voltages for a push-pull amplifier.

6.2.3 SAMPLE PROBLEM

The load $R_L = 1000$ ohms is connected in the circuit of the triode
as shown. The mu-factor of the tube and its plate resistance are 3
and 800 ohms, respectively. The value of R is 4500 ohms. The reactances X_C are negligible and the circuit may be assumed to function
linearly.

Calculate the power delivered to R_L when e is 74.4 v. rms.

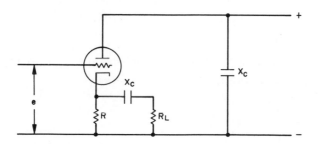

SOLUTION

Ref. [*Data* (17), p. 445]

The problem will be solved using the small-signal equivalent
shown below

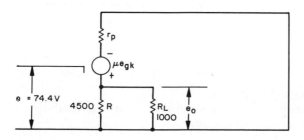

The power in R_L is

$$P_{R_L} = \frac{e_o{}^2}{R_L}$$

The expression for e_o is

$$
\begin{aligned}
e_o &= \frac{e\mu\, R\, R_L/(R + R_L)}{r_p + (1 + \mu)\, R\, R_L/(R + R_L)}\\[4pt]
&= \frac{74.4(3)\ (1000)(4500)/(1000 + 4500)}{800 + (4)\ (1000)(4500)/(1000 + 4500)}\\[4pt]
&= \frac{182{,}800}{800 + 3280} = \frac{182{,}800}{4080} = 44.7 \text{ v. rms}
\end{aligned}
$$

Thus

$$P_{R_L} = \frac{(44.7)^2}{1000} = 2.0 \text{ watts}$$

ANS.

6.2.4 SAMPLE PROBLEM

Assume the operation of the circuit shown to be in Class A_1 and that all capacitors have negligible reactances.
Calculate the signal power in R_L.

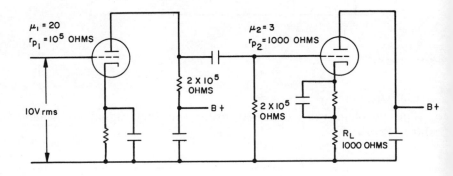

SOLUTION

Ref. [*Data* (17), p. 445]
The result will be determined from an analysis of the small-signal equivalent circuit shown.

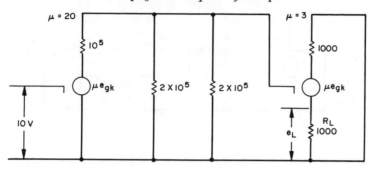

The power developed in R_L is

$$P = \frac{(e_L)^2}{R_L}$$

But e_L is the input voltage amplified by the gains of the two stages

$$e_L = 10A_1A_2$$

Here

$$A_1 = \frac{\mu_1 R_{L_1}}{r_{p_1} + R_{L_1}}$$

$$= \frac{20(10^5)}{10^5 + 10^5} = \frac{20}{2} = 10$$

and

$$A_2 = \frac{\mu_2 R_L}{r_{p_2} + (1 + \mu_2)R_L}$$

$$= \frac{3(1000)}{1000 + (1 + 3)\,1000} = \frac{3}{1 + 4} = \frac{3}{5} = 0.60$$

The power in R_L is

$$P = \frac{[10(10)(0.60)]^2}{1000}$$
$$= 3.60 \text{ watts} \qquad\qquad \text{ANS.}$$

6.3   AMPLIFIER FREQUENCY RESPONSE

The frequency response of an amplifier will depend on the variation of various impedances. Figure 6–10 shows part of a typical amplifier.

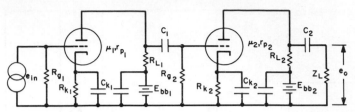

Figure 6–10 A two-stage amplifier circuit using R-C coupling

The linear equivalent is drawn under the following assumptions:

- The bypass capacitors across the cathode resistors and plate batteries provide negligible reactance.
- The grid-to-plate capacitances of both tubes have negligible susceptance.

Figure 6–11 shows the linear equivalent for the circuit of Figure 6–10.

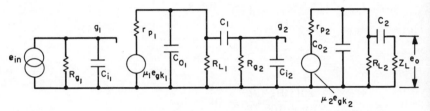

Figure 6–11 The linear equivalent circuit of the amplifier of Figure 6–10

The frequency analysis is generally divided into three regions:

- Mid frequency where the capacitors have no effect.
- High frequencies where the shunt capacitors are significant.
- Low frequencies where the series capacitors are significant.

Not all circuits may be analyzed in this manner. For example, the operating frequency range may be such that the shunt capacity always has significant reactance.

The midband gain of the first stage A_1 is, by inspection

$$A_1 = \frac{e_{g_2}}{e_{in}} = \frac{-\mu_1[R_{L_1}R_{g_2}/(R_{L_1}+R_{g_2})]}{r_{p_1}+(R_{L_1}R_{g_2})/(R_{L_1}+R_{g_2})} = \frac{-g_{m_1}}{1/R_{L_1}+1/R_{g_2}+1/r_{p_1}} \qquad (6\text{--}41)$$

The gain of the second stage A_2 is

$$A_2 = \frac{e_o}{e_{g_2}} = \frac{-\mu_2(R_{L_2}Z_L)/(R_{L_2}+Z_L)}{r_{p_2}+(R_{L_2}Z_L)/(R_{L_2}+Z_L)} = \frac{-g_{m_2}}{1/R_{L_2}+1/Z_L+1/r_{p_2}} \qquad (6\text{--}42)$$

The over-all gain A is

$$A = \frac{e_o}{e_{in}} = A_1 A_2 \qquad (6\text{--}43)$$

The high frequency response of the first stage may be determined from Fig. 6–12.

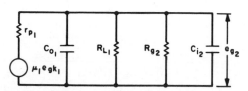

Figure 6–12   The high-frequency equivalent of a portion of the circuit of Figure 6–11

The gain A_H is

$$A_H = \frac{e_{g_2}}{e_{in}} = \frac{e_{g_2}}{e_{gk_1}} = \frac{-\mu_1(1/[j\omega(C_{o_1} + C_{i_2}) + 1/R_{L_1} + 1/R_{g_2}])}{r_{p_1} + (1/[j\omega(C_{o_1} + C_{i_2}) + 1/R_{L_1} + 1/R_{g_2}])}$$

$$= \frac{-g_{m_1}}{j\omega(C_{o_1} + C_{i_2}) + 1/R_{L_1} + 1/R_{g_2} + 1/r_{p_1}} \qquad (6\text{--}44)$$

The high cut-off frequency is defined as that frequency where the gain is 3-db down from midband frequency gain. For this one stage, at the high cut-off frequency, the reactive portion of the denominator equals the real portion so that

$$f_H = \frac{1/R_{L_1} + 1/R_{g_2} + 1/r_{p_1}}{2\pi(C_{o_1} + C_{i_2})} \qquad (6\text{--}45)$$

The high frequency gain of this stage relative to mid-frequency gain becomes very simply

$$\frac{A_H}{A_I} = \frac{1}{1 + jf/f_H} \qquad (6\text{--}46)$$

where f is the actual frequency.

The over-all frequency response may be found by combining the various gain ratios.

The low frequency response of the first stage may be determined from Fig. 6–13.

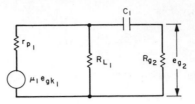

Figure 6–13 The low-frequency equivalent of a portion of the circuit of Figure 6–11

The gain A_L is

$$A_L = \frac{e_{g_2}}{e_{in}} = \frac{e_{g_2}}{e_{gk_1}} = -\left(\frac{\mu R_{L_1}}{r_{p_1} + R_{L_1}}\right) \frac{R_{g_2}}{r_{p_1} R_{L_1}/(r_{p_1} + R_{L_1}) + R_{g_2} + 1/j\omega C_1}$$

$$= \frac{-g_{m_1}}{1/R_{g_2} + 1/r_{p_1} + 1/R_{L_1} + (1/j\omega C_1 R_{g_2})(1/r_{p_1} + 1/R_{L_1})} \qquad (6\text{-}47)$$

The low cut-off frequency is defined as that frequency where the gain is 3-db down from midband frequency gain. At this frequency the reactive portion of the denominator equals the real portion. Thus

$$f_L = \frac{(1/r_{p_1} + 1/R_{L_1})}{2\pi C_1 R_{g_2}(1/R_{g_2} + 1/r_{p_1} + 1/R_{L_1})} \qquad (6\text{-}48)$$

The low frequency gain of this stage relative to mid-frequency gain becomes very simply

$$\frac{A_L}{A_I} = \frac{1}{1 - jf_L/f} \qquad (6\text{-}49)$$

The over-all frequency gain may again be found by combining the various gain ratios.

6.3.1   SAMPLE PROBLEM

For the circuit shown, find the voltage gain E_o/E_i at frequencies of 30, 100, 500, 1000, 5000, and 9000 cycles per second if the value of μ is 35, r_p is 30,000 ohms, R_1 is 50,000 ohms, and R_2 is 100,000 ohms for the following values of C:

   (a) 0.0001 microfarads
   (b) 0.01 microfarads
   (c) 1.0 microfarad

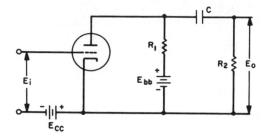

SOLUTION

This problem may be solved using the small-signal equivalent circuit shown below.

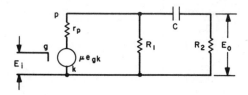

The expression for the gain of this circuit is

$$A = \frac{E_o}{E_i} = \frac{-g_m}{1/R_2 + 1/R_1 + 1/r_p + (1/j\omega CR_2)(1/r_p + 1/R_1)}$$

$$g_m = \frac{\mu}{r_p} = \frac{35}{30,000} = 1.168 \times 10^{-3} \text{ mho}$$

Thus

$$A = -1.168 \times 10^{-3}/\{1/10^5 + 1/5 \times 10^4 + 1/3 \times 10^4 + [1/j2\pi f C(10^5)]$$
$$[1/3 \times 10^4 + 1/5 \times 10^4]$$
$$= 1.68 \times 10^{-3}/[0.633 \times 10^{-4} - j(1.59 \times 10^{-6}/fC)(0.533 \times 10^{-4})]$$
$$= -18.43/[1 - j(1.34 \times 10^{-6})/fC]$$

(a) for $C = 0.0001$ microfarads $= (10^{-4})(10^{-6})$ farads.

$$|A| = \frac{18.43}{|1 - j(1.34 \times 10^4/f)|} \text{ (neglecting phase angle)}$$

at 30 cps $|A| = \dfrac{18.43}{1 - j446} = 0.0413$

100 cps $|A| = \dfrac{18.43}{1 - j134} = 0.137$

500 cps $|A| = \dfrac{18.43}{1 - j26.8} = 0.688$

$$1000 \text{ cps } |A| = \frac{18.43}{1 - j13.4} = 1.38$$

$$5000 \text{ cps } |A| = \frac{18.43}{1 - j2.68} = 6.45$$

$$9000 \text{ cps } |A| = \frac{18.43}{1 - j1.49} = 10.3$$

(b) for $C = 0.01$ microfarads $= (10^{-2})(10^{-6})$ farads

$$|A| = \frac{18.43}{|1 - j(134/f)|}$$

$$\text{at } 30 \text{ cps } |A| = \frac{18.43}{1 - j4.46} = 4.03$$

$$100 \text{ cps } |A| = \frac{18.43}{1 - j1.34} = 11.05$$

$$500 \text{ cps } |A| = \frac{18.43}{1 - j0.268} = 17.8$$

$$1000 \text{ cps } |A| = \frac{18.43}{1 - j0.134} = 18.3$$

$$5000 \text{ cps } |A| = \frac{18.43}{1 - j0.027} = 18.43$$

$$9000 \text{ cps } |A| = \frac{18.43}{1 - j0.015} = 18.43$$

(c) for $C = 1.0$ microfarad $= 10^{-6}$ farads

$$|A| = \frac{18.43}{|1 - j(1.34/f)|}$$

$$\text{at } 30 \text{ cps } |A| = \frac{18.43}{1 - j0.045} = 18.43$$

$$100 \text{ cps } |A| = \frac{18.43}{1 - j0.0134} = 18.43$$

the gain will have the same value for all higher frequencies.

6.4   NON-RESISTIVE LOADS

An amplifier with a reactive load may be handled in a manner similar to that of an amplifier with a purely resistive load by simply taking into account the complex character of the load impedance. In particular resonant loads are often encountered. The frequency response of such an amplifier will often be determined almost exclusively by the variation of the load impedance with frequency. The reactive load will make the gain a complex quantity just as the various circuit capacitances have been shown to make the gain expressions complex.

6.4.1 SAMPLE PROBLEM

An amplifier, operating at a frequency of $10^7/2\pi$ cps, employs a triode having a mu-factor of 50 and a plate resistance of 10^5 ohms. The effective interelectrode capacitances are $C_{gp} = 5 \times 10^{-12}$ farad, $C_{gk} = 10 \times 10^{-12}$ farad, and $C_{pk} = 10 \times 10^{-12}$ farad. The coil used in the tuned circuit has an inductance of 100×10^{-6} henry and a Q-factor, at the operating frequency, of 100. The circuit of this amplifier is as shown (simplified).

Calculate the gain of this amplifier.

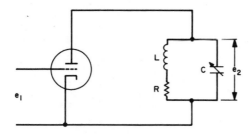

SOLUTION

The gain of this circuit may be computed from

$$A = \frac{(j\omega C_{gp} - g_m)Z_T}{1 + j\omega C_{gp}Z_T}$$

It is assumed that the plate circuit is at resonance at the operating frequency. The angular frequency ω is

$$\omega = 2\pi f$$
$$= 2\pi\left(\frac{10^7}{2\pi}\right) = 10^7 \text{ rad/sec.}$$

The transconductance, g_m, is

$$g_m = \frac{\mu}{r_p}$$
$$= \frac{50}{10^5} = 5 \times 10^{-4} \text{ mho}$$

The total load impedance Z_T is given by

$$Z_T = \frac{1}{j\omega C_o + (1/r_p) + (1/Z_L)}$$

The output capacitance of the tube C_o is included as part of the total capacitance resonating with the plate circuit inductance L. To find Z_L, the load impedance of the resonant circuit, convert the series equivalent for the coil to a parallel equivalent and call the parallel inductance L' and the parallel resistance R'. The impedance of the resonant circuit at reasonance is simply R'. The series $R\text{-}L$ is inverted to obtain its admittance.

$$\begin{aligned} Y_{\text{coil}} &= \frac{1}{R + j\omega L} \\ &= \frac{R - j\omega L}{R^2 + \omega^2 L^2} \end{aligned}$$

Then

$$\begin{aligned} R' &= \frac{R^2 + \omega^2 L^2}{R} \\ &= R\left(1 + \frac{\omega^2 L^2}{R^2}\right) \end{aligned}$$

But in a series $R\text{-}L$ circuit

$$Q = \frac{\omega L}{R}$$

Hence

$$\begin{aligned} R' &= \frac{\omega L}{Q}(1 + Q^2) \\ &= \frac{10^7 (100)(10^{-6})}{100}[1 + (100)^2] \\ &\approx 10^5 \text{ ohms} \end{aligned}$$

to a very good approximation.

Hence

$$\begin{aligned} Z_T &= \frac{1}{(1/r_p) + (1/R')} \\ &= \frac{1}{(1/10^5) + (1/10^5)} = 0.5 \times 10^5 \text{ ohms} \end{aligned}$$

Thus

$$A = \frac{[j(10^7)(5)(10^{-12}) - (5)(10^{-4})]0.5 \times 10^5}{1 + j(10^7)(5)(10^{-12})(0.5)(10^5)}$$
$$= \frac{[j5 \times 10^{-5} - 5 \times 10^{-4}][0.5 \times 10^5]}{1 + j2.5}$$
$$= \frac{-25 + j2.5}{1 + j2.5}$$
$$= \frac{25.1/174.3}{2.69/68.2} = 9.35/106.1 \qquad \text{ANS.}$$

6.5   FEEDBACK

Feedback is added to an amplifier by coupling a portion of the output signal back and combining it with the input signal.

Voltage feedback is obtained by coupling a portion of the output voltage signal into the amplifier.

Current feedback is obtained by allowing part or all of the load current to pass through an impedance which is common to the input circuit. An example of this is the cathode follower.

The analysis of the feedback amplifier linear equivalent circuit is the same as that for the amplifier without feedback except that the various loop equations must be carefully written to include the feedback effects.

A simplified form of feedback is shown in Fig. 6–14.

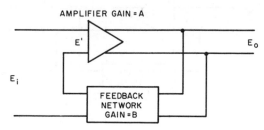

Figure 6–14 An amplifier with feedback

In this circuit

$$E_o = AE' \qquad (6\text{--}50)$$

but

$$E' = E_i - BE_o \qquad (6\text{--}51)$$

so that

$$A_f = \frac{E_o}{E_i} = \frac{A}{1 + AB} \qquad (6\text{--}52)$$

Negative feedback makes the modified gain less than the open-loop gain while positive feedback makes the modified gain greater than the open-loop gain. Since the quantities A and B may be complex, A_f represents a vector or complex quantity.

If there is distortion in the open loop output of an amplifier because of a non-linear input-output transfer characteristic, in the closed loop, the distortion will be altered exactly as the open loop gain is altered; it will be equal to the open loop distortion multiplied by the factor $\frac{1}{1 + AB}$.

6.5.1 SAMPLE PROBLEM

An amplifier has a gain equal to A. The output is then coupled to the input so that there is 100% negative feedback. What is the gain of the modified amplifier?

SOLUTION

The connections are as shown.

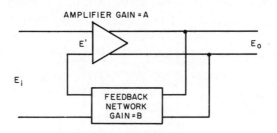

AMPLIFIER GAIN = A

E'   E$_o$

E$_i$

FEEDBACK
NETWORK
GAIN = B

The feedback factor, $B = -1$
The modified gain, A_f is

$$A_f = \frac{E_o}{E_i}$$

But

$$E_o = AE'$$

and
$$E' = E_i - E_o$$

so that
$$E_o = A(E_i - E_o)$$
$$E_o(1 + A) = AE_i$$

or
$$A_f = \frac{E_o}{E_i} = \frac{A}{1 + A} = \frac{1}{1 + (1/A)} \qquad \text{ANS.}$$

6.6   GRAPHICAL ANALYSIS

Vacuum tube amplifier analysis may also be performed graphically using the plate voltage-plate current characteristics.

Figure 6–15 shows a simple triode amplifier.

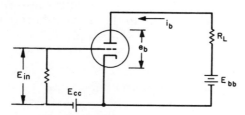

Figure 6–15 A simple triode amplifier

In this circuit
$$e_b = E_{bb} - i_b R_L \qquad (6\text{–}53)$$

This expression may be plotted on the plate characteristics and is called the "load line" as shown in Fig. 6–16.

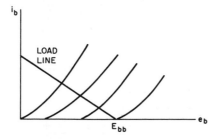

Figure 6–16 Triode plate characteristics showing a load line

The quiescent or zero-input point is determined by the d-c load line, and the value of d-c grid bias which may be obtained from a battery as shown or from a cathode resistor. The output voltage will be developed across R_L and may be obtained from the characteristics. The input signal E_{in} adds to E_{cc} so that the actual grid voltage is the sum of E_{cc} and E_{in}. Corresponding to each grid voltage is an output voltage equal to $E_{bb} - e_b$. By knowing the variation of grid voltage, the output voltage is directly obtainable. Note that the load line to signal frequencies may have a slope different from that at d-c. For example, an amplifier with a transformer in the plate circuit will have a d-c load line determined primarily by the d-c transformer resistance. The a-c load line will be determined primarily by the reflected secondary impedance.

If the input and output signals are sinusoids the peak-to-peak voltages are (input or output).

$$E_{\text{peak-to-peak}} = 2\sqrt{2}\ E_{\text{rms}} \qquad (6\text{--}54)$$

It is important to know in power amplifiers how much power is being dissipated within the tube in the form of heat delivered by the electron beam to the plate. The temperature rise resulting from this power dissipation usually sets a limit to tube operation. The plate dissipation, as this power is called, may be determined from application of the law of conservation of energy. If E_b and I_b represent the average or d-c values of plate-cathode voltage and plate current, respectively, and P_o is the power delivered to load resistors, the dissipation P_p may be expressed as

$$P_p = E_b I_b - P_o \qquad (6\text{--}55)$$

6.7   PUSH-PULL AMPLIFIERS

A simple push-pull amplifier schematic is shown in Fig. 6–17.

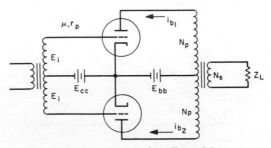

Figure 6–17 A push-pull amplifier

The operating point of each tube is established by the grid bias supply voltage E_{cc} and the plate supply voltage E_{bb}. The input transformer provides equal out-of-phase voltages to each grid. The output transformer primary winding is balanced around the center tap. A linear equivalent circuit is shown in Fig. 6–18.

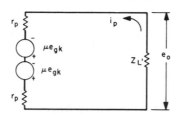

Figure 6–18 A linear equivalent circuit of the push-pull amplifier of Figure 6–17

Each half of the output transformer has N_p turns. The reflected equivalent load impedance from plate to plate is

$$Z_L' = \left(\frac{2N_p}{N_s}\right)^2 Z_L \tag{6–56}$$

The signal plate current is

$$i_p = \frac{2\mu e_{gk}}{2r_p + Z_L'} = \frac{\mu e_{gk}}{r_p + (Z_L'/2)} \tag{6–57}$$

The two generators add because of the reversal of input signals in the input transformer. The output voltage and power are

$$e_o = \frac{\mu e_{gk} Z_L'}{r_p + (Z_L'/2)} \tag{6–58}$$

$$P_o = \frac{\mu^2 e_{gk}^2 Z_L'}{[r_p + (Z_L'/2)]^2} \tag{6–59}$$

The graphical analysis of push-pull amplifiers may be performed on composite characteristic curves derived from individual characteristics using the method of Thompson [Thompson, B. J., Proc. IRE **19**, p. 591, 1933] quoted in a number of textbooks on electronics or by other methods [Millman et al *Electronics* (10), pp. 653–662].

Typical composite characteristics for push-pull triodes are shown in Fig. 6–19.

The individual tube characteristics are shown dotted.

The load line is equivalent to that of a load impedance of $Z_L'/4$. The load line depicted is that of a pure resistance.

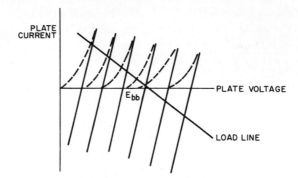

Figure 6–19 Composite push-pull triode plate characteristics

The maximum power output is obtained when $Z'_L/4$ is of such a value that when plotted on the composite characteristics it has a slope equal to the reciprocal of the lines of the composite characteristics. [cf Seely, *Circuits* (21)]

6.7.1 SAMPLE PROBLEM

A push-pull power amplifier employing triodes is to operate into a 500-ohm resistive load. The individual plate-circuit characteristics of the tubes are such that the composite characteristics for the amplifier are straight lines with a slope corresponding to 2000 ohms. The maximum composite current, with zero bias on one tube, is 0.1 amp. Neglecting the effects of distortion and assuming a sinusoidal input voltage to the grids, calculate:

(a) the turns-ratio (total primary to secondary) required in the ideal output transformer for maximum power output without grid current in the tubes

(b) the value of this maximum power.

SOLUTION

(a) Maximum power output is obtained when one-quarter the reflected load resistance equals the equivalent resistance of the lines of the composite characteristics. The reflected resistance R_L' is given by

$$R_L' = \left(\frac{N_p}{N_s}\right)^2 R_L$$

where N_p is the total primary turns. But if $R_L'/4 = 2000$,

$$R_L' = 8000 = \left(\frac{N_p}{N_s}\right)^2 R_L$$

or

$$\frac{N_p}{N_s} = \sqrt{\frac{8000}{R_L}}$$

$$= \sqrt{\frac{8000}{500}} = \sqrt{16} = 4 \qquad \text{ANS.}$$

(b) If the peak current delivered to $R_L'/4$ is 0.1 amp., the rms power is

$$P = (i_{rms})^2 \frac{R_L'}{4}$$

$$= \left(\frac{i_M}{\sqrt{2}}\right)^2 \frac{R_L'}{4}$$

$$= \frac{(i_M)^2 R_L'}{8} = \frac{(0.10)^2(8000)}{8} = 10 \text{ watts} \qquad \text{ANS.}$$

6.8   PRACTICE PROBLEMS

6–1

A full-wave single-phase rectifier consists of two diodes whose internal resistance may be taken as a constant value of 400 ohms. The load resistance is 2500 ohms. The transformer winding is center-tapped with a total voltage of 500 v. and has zero impedance.
Calculate:
(a) the d-c load current
(b) the peak voltage across each diode
(c) the d-c output power

6–2

A selenium half-wave rectifier is rated at 10 amp and a maximum inverse peak voltage of 200 v. This rectifier is used in series with a rheostat to charge batteries from a 120-v., 60-cycle line. The system operates well when five 6-v. batteries are charged in series at 10 amp. When it is attempted to charge ten such batteries in series, the fuse blows before the charging current, as indicated by a d-c ammeter, reaches 10 amp.
State why this happens and give reasons for your answer.

6–3

In the amplifier shown, the tube used is a linear triode having a mu-factor of 8 and a plate resistance of 1800 ohms. The quiescent current of this tube is 0.050 amp. The output transformer is ideal and has a turns ratio N_1/N_2 of 25. The reactance of C at the frequency of the signal is negligible.

Neglecting distortion and its effects, calculate:
(a) the power delivered to the 8-ohm load
(b) the power dissipated in each resistor
(c) the plate dissipation

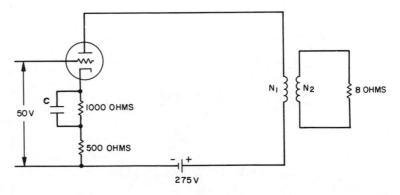

6–4

A resistance-coupled audio amplifier stage uses a tube having a mu of 30 and a r_p of 25,000. The plate-circuit load resistor is 100,000 ohms and the grid-leak resistor of the next following tube is 250,000 ohms. The bias is obtained by means of a cathode resistor of 8000 ohms—but the by-pass condenser is defective (a lead has come loose inside the unit) and it acts as an open circuit. Draw the a-c equivalent circuit and compute the voltage gain of the stage.

6–5

In the circuit shown, the reactances of the capacitors may be neglected, and the vacuum tube may be considered as a linear element with a mutual conductance g_m of 0.001 mho and a plate resistance of one megohm.
(a) explain the purpose of this type of circuit
(b) calculate the value of the voltage V_{ab}.

6–6

A Class A amplifier consists of a pentode coupled by an *R-C* network to a power triode. The voltage gain of the pentode stage is to

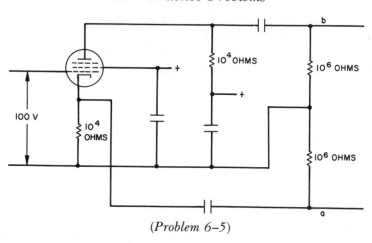

(*Problem 6–5*)

be 100 at mid-frequency, with the upper half-power frequency at 20,000 cps. The μ and g_m of the pentode are 1000 and 0.001 mho, respectively, and its output capacitance is 10 mmf (10^{-11} farad). The input and grid-plate capacitances in the triode are respectively 15 and 10 mmf. All capacitances include the effects of wiring.

Calculate the maximum allowable voltage gain in the triode stage if the upper half-power frequency is to be realized.

6–7

The bypass capacitors C in the circuit shown have negligible reactances. The mutual conductance of the pentode g_m is 1000×10^{-6} mho and its plate resistance r_p is 10^6 ohms. The effective capacitances of C_1, C_2, and C_3 are 10, 5, and 10 micromicrofarads.

Calculate the magnitude of the voltage gain of this amplifier when the angular velocity of the signal is 10^6 rad/sec.

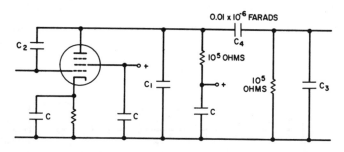

6–8

A simple R-C coupled one stage uncompensated vacuum-tube amplifier has a midband gain of $-200 + j0$. The 3-db frequencies are

50 and 50,000 cps. Negative feedback is introduced with a feedback factor of 1/20 with no other changes.

(a) Find the new magnitude of gain at 50 and 50,000 cps.

(b) Find the new 3-db gain frequencies.

6–9

The amplifier shown is to deliver 1.25 watts to the 2000-ohm load. Both tubes operate in Class A_1. The reactance of all capacitors may be neglected.

Calculate the minimum value of e which will yield the required output.

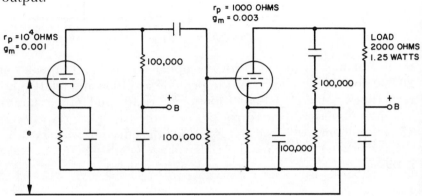

6–10

A pair of triodes, ideal in that their plate characteristics follow the 3/2 power of the effective grid voltage, are used in the ideal push-pull amplifier shown. The excitation on the grids varies the plate current per tube from cut-off to the maximum allowable value of 0.125 amp at zero effective grid voltage.

Calculate the maximum power that this amplifier delivers to its load under the conditions stated, and the optimum turns ratio $2N_1/N_2$ for the output transformer.

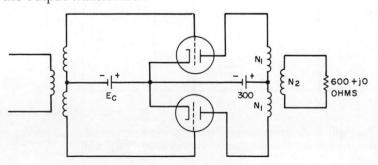

CHAPTER SEVEN

FILTERS

SYMBOLS

A The magnitude of a vector quantity
C Capacitance, farads
E, e Applied emf, volts
f Frequency, cycles per second (cps)
I, i Current, amperes
j The imaginary operator $\sqrt{-1}$
K A constant, also a multiplier indicating multiplication by 10^3
L Inductance, henrys
M A multiplier indicating multiplication by 10^6
m A parameter
n Integer values
P Power, watts
R Resistance, ohms
Z Impedance, ohms
α Attenuation or attenuation constant, nepers
β Phase shift or phase constant, radians
γ Propagation constant (complex)
ϵ The base of the natural logarithms (2.71828 . . .)
ω Angular frequency, radians per second
Ω Ohms

Subscripts

c Cutoff
i Image, also referring to the condition of infinite attenuation in m-derived filters
in   Input
K Referring to the constant-K-filter
L Load
o Output, characteristic
oc Open circuit

163

out   Output
P   Referring to pi network
sc   Short circuit
T   Referring to tee network

7.1   CIRCUITS

Practically all filters may be analyzed either as Tee or Pi networks. It is only for the sake of convenience that one or the other is chosen since Wye or Delta transformations may be used to convert from one to the other. The Tee or Pi is an asymmetrical form which may be an equivalent of a symmetrical network having similar elements in both conductors.

Generally a filter is placed between a power source and a load to separate the frequency band into desired pass (low attenuation) and stop (high attenuation) bands. The filter should be impedance matched to both source and load for maximum power transfer and in addition should be composed of (ideally) zero-loss (reactive) elements to maximize the power transmission efficiency.

Figure 7–1 shows a Tee circuit.

The terminating impedance required at either input or output with the opposite terminal pair properly loaded is called the image impedance and is given by

$$Z_i = \sqrt{Z_{oc}Z_{sc}} \qquad (7\text{--}1)$$

where Z_{oc} and Z_{sc} are the values at the terminal pair at which the image impedance is being evaluated. A symmetrical circuit will have the same image impedance at both terminal pairs.

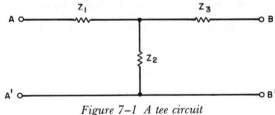

Figure 7–1 A tee circuit

Looking in at terminals A–A'

$$Z_{oc} = Z_1 + Z_2 \qquad (7\text{--}2)$$

$$Z_{sc} = Z_1 + \frac{Z_2 Z_3}{Z_2 + Z_3} \qquad (7\text{--}3)$$

Thus

$$Z_{i_A} = \sqrt{(Z_1 + Z_2)\left(Z_1 + \frac{Z_2 Z_3}{Z_2 + Z_3}\right)} \qquad (7\text{-}4)$$

Similarly

$$Z_{i_B} = \sqrt{(Z_2 + Z_3)\left(Z_3 + \frac{Z_1 Z_2}{Z_1 + Z_2}\right)} \qquad (7\text{-}5)$$

If the network is symmetrical, $Z_1 = Z_3$ and

$$Z_{i_A} = \sqrt{(Z_1 + Z_2)\left(Z_1 + \frac{Z_1 Z_2}{Z_1 + Z_2}\right)} = \sqrt{Z_1^2 + 2Z_1 Z_2} \qquad (7\text{-}6)$$

and

$$Z_{i_B} = \sqrt{(Z_1 + Z_2)\left(Z_1 + \frac{Z_1 Z_2}{Z_1 + Z_2}\right)} = \sqrt{Z_1^2 + 2Z_1 Z_2} \qquad (7\text{-}7)$$

A Pi network is shown in Fig. 7-2.

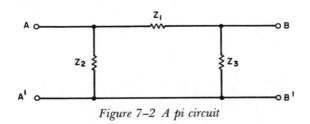

Figure 7-2   A pi circuit

For this network similar equations may be derived, looking into terminals A-A'

$$Z_{oc} = \frac{Z_2(Z_1 + Z_3)}{Z_1 + Z_2 + Z_3} \qquad (7\text{-}8)$$

$$Z_{sc} = \frac{Z_1 Z_2}{Z_1 + Z_2} \qquad (7\text{-}9)$$

so that

$$Z_{i_A} = \sqrt{\left[\frac{Z_1 Z_2}{Z_1 + Z_2}\right]\left[\frac{Z_2(Z_1 + Z_3)}{Z_1 + Z_2 + Z_3}\right]} \qquad (7\text{-}10)$$

and

$$Z_{i_B} = \sqrt{\left[\frac{Z_1 Z_3}{Z_1 + Z_3}\right]\left[\frac{Z_3(Z_1 + Z_2)}{Z_1 + Z_2 + Z_3}\right]} \qquad (7\text{-}11)$$

If the Pi network is symmetrical, $Z_2 = Z_3$, so that

$$Z_{i_A} = \sqrt{\left[\frac{Z_1 Z_2}{Z_1 + Z_2}\right]\left[\frac{Z_2(Z_1 + Z_2)}{Z_1 + 2Z_2}\right]} = \frac{Z_1 Z_2}{\sqrt{Z_1^2 + 2Z_1 Z_2}} \qquad (7\text{--}12)$$

and

$$Z_{i_B} = \sqrt{\left[\frac{Z_1 Z_2}{Z_1 + Z_2}\right]\left[\frac{Z_2(Z_1 + Z_2)}{Z_1 + 2Z_2}\right]} = \frac{Z_1 Z_2}{\sqrt{Z_1^2 + 2Z_1 Z_2}} \qquad (7\text{--}13)$$

Generally the Tee or Pi networks combine together to form a ladder as shown in Fig. 7–3. The significant difference is the end elements: series for the Tee and shunt for the Pi. The ladder is symmetrical as are the basic sections.

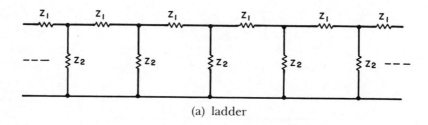

(a) ladder

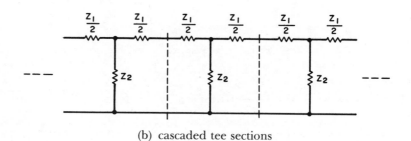

(b) cascaded tee sections

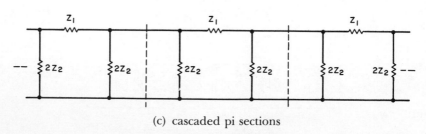

(c) cascaded pi sections

Figure 7–3 Ladder network composed of cascaded sections

The Tee and Pi secions of a ladder may be further bisected into "half sections" of L-sections. Figure 7–4 shows the half sections put together to form a Tee and Pi section.

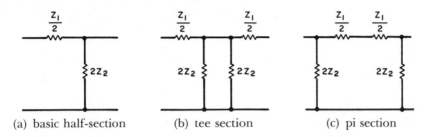

(a) basic half-section   (b) tee section   (c) pi section

Figure 7–4 Tee and pi sections composed of basic half-sections

The charactcristic impedance, often designated Z_0, is a very important quantity. It is the value of terminating impedance that causes the input impedance to equal the terminating impedance. Thus for the Tee and Pi sections shown in Fig. 7–5 the characteristic impedance may be computed.

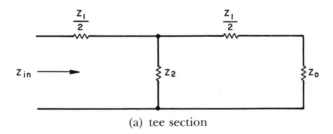

(a) tee section

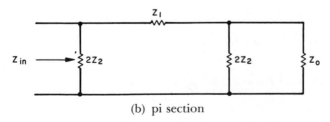

(b) pi section

Figure 7–5 Determination of characteristic impedance

For the Tee

$$Z_o = Z_i = \frac{Z_1}{2} + \frac{[Z_o + (Z_1/2)]Z_2}{Z_o + (Z_1/2) + Z_2}$$

$$Z_o^2 + \frac{Z_o Z_1}{2} + Z_o Z_2 = \frac{Z_1 Z_o}{2} + \frac{Z_1^2}{4} + \frac{Z_1 Z_2}{2} + Z_o Z_2 + \frac{Z_1 Z_2}{2}$$

or

$$Z_o = \sqrt{Z_1 Z_2 \left(1 + \frac{Z_1}{4Z_2}\right)} \qquad (7\text{–}14)$$

and for the Pi

$$Z_o = Z_i = \frac{2Z_2[Z_1 + 2Z_2 Z_o/(2Z_2 + Z_o)]}{2Z_2 + Z_1 + 2Z_2 Z_o/(2Z_2 + Z_o)}$$

$$= \sqrt{\frac{Z_1 Z_2}{1 + Z_1/4Z_2}} \qquad (7\text{–}15)$$

Equations (7–14) and (7–15)* can also be derived from Eqs. (7–6) or (7–7) and (7–10) or (7–11). In general

$$Z_o = Z_i = \sqrt{Z_{oc} Z_{sc}} \qquad (7\text{–}16)$$

Another important property of a filter is the input-output characteristic or more simply the propagation. This may be determined from the so-called propagation constant for which the lower case Greek letter gamma γ is often used as a symbol.

If the filter is terminated in Z_o, the propagation constant is defined as

$$\epsilon^\gamma = \frac{I_1}{I_2} = \frac{V_1}{V_2} \qquad (7\text{–}17)$$

where V_1 and I_1 represent the input voltage and current and V_2 and I_2 represent the output voltage and current.

If several filter sections having propagation constants $\gamma_1, \gamma_2, \gamma_3 \ldots \gamma_n$ are cascaded to form a ladder such that each section effectively sees its own characteristic impedance, an over-all input-output expression may be written as

$$\frac{V_1}{V_n} = \frac{I_1}{I_n} = \epsilon^{\gamma_1}\epsilon^{\gamma_2}\epsilon^{\gamma_3} \ldots \epsilon^{\gamma_n} = \epsilon^{(\gamma_1 + \gamma_2 + \gamma_3 + \ldots + \gamma_n)} \quad (7\text{–}18)$$

*From John D. Ryder, *Networks, Lines, and Fields*, second edition, copyright 1955. Used by permission of Prentice-Hall, Inc., Englewood Cliffs, N.J.

In general the propagation constant will be complex and expressed in the form

$$\gamma = \alpha + j\beta \qquad (7\text{--}19)$$

The units of the attenuation α are nepers where 1 neper $= 8.686$db and the units of the phase shift β are radians. Thus

$$\epsilon^\gamma = \epsilon^{\alpha\,+\,j\beta} = \epsilon^\alpha \epsilon^{j\beta}$$
$$= A \,\underline{/\theta} \qquad (7\text{--}20)$$

This quantity represents a vector quantity where the alpha term represents a magnitude and the beta term represents an angle between the reference axis and the vector.

Figure 7–6 shows a Tee section connected between a generator and a load whose value equals the characteristic impedance Z_o.

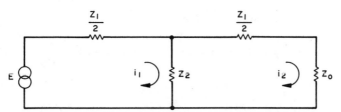

Figure 7–6 *A tee section connected to a generator and load*

The loop equations may be written as

$$E = \left(\frac{Z_1}{2} + Z_2\right)i_1 - Z_2 i_2 \qquad (7\text{--}21)$$

$$0 = -Z_2 i_1 + \left(\frac{Z_1}{2} + Z_o + Z_2\right)i_2 \qquad (7\text{--}22)$$

From Eq. (7–22)

$$\frac{i_1}{i_2} = \frac{Z_1/2 + Z_o + Z_2}{Z_2} = \epsilon^\gamma \qquad (7\text{--}23)$$

or

$$Z_o = Z_2(\epsilon^\gamma - 1) - \frac{Z_1}{2} \qquad (7\text{--}24)$$

If Z_o is eliminated between Eq. (7–24) and (7–14) there results

$$\frac{\epsilon^\gamma + \epsilon^{-\gamma}}{2} = \cosh\gamma = 1 + \frac{Z_1}{2Z_2} \qquad (7\text{--}25)$$

The term cosh γ may be expanded as

$$\cosh(\alpha + j\beta) = \cosh \alpha \cosh j\beta + \sinh \alpha \sinh j\beta$$
$$= \cosh \alpha \cos \beta + j \sinh \alpha \sin \beta \qquad (7\text{--}26)$$

If cosh γ is real, two cases may be defined:

Case I: Pass band $\qquad \alpha = 0, \qquad \beta \neq 0$
Case II: Stop band $\qquad \alpha \neq 0, \qquad \beta = n\pi$

In a pass band

$$\cos \beta = 1 + \frac{Z_1}{2Z_2} \qquad (7\text{--}27)$$

or

$$-1 < \left(1 + \frac{Z_1}{2Z_2}\right) < +1 \qquad (7\text{--}28)$$

while in a stop band with $\cos \beta = \pm 1$

$$\left(1 + \frac{Z_1}{2Z_2}\right) < -1, \beta = \pi \qquad \cosh \alpha = -\left(1 + \frac{Z_1}{2Z_2}\right) \qquad (7\text{--}29)$$

or

$$+1 < \left(1 + \frac{Z_1}{2Z_2}\right), \beta = 0 \qquad \cosh \alpha = \left(1 + \frac{Z_1}{2Z_2}\right) \qquad (7\text{--}30)$$

From Eqs. (7–25) and (7–30) it is possible to define cutoff frequencies where the network changes from pass band to stop band. Using the inequality of Eq. (7–29) at cutoff

$$\frac{Z_1}{4Z_2} = -1 \qquad (7\text{--}31)$$

while using Eq. (7–30)

$$\frac{Z_1}{4Z_2} = 0 \qquad (7\text{--}32)^*$$

The filter elements may be purely reactive or purely resistive in which case cosh γ is real. In the case of complex filter elements the solutions become more elaborate.

The input impedance of a Tee network may be written

$$Z_{\text{in}} = Z_o \left[\frac{Z_o \sinh \gamma + Z_L \cosh \gamma}{Z_L \sinh \gamma + Z_o \cosh \gamma}\right] \qquad (7\text{--}33)$$

The term filter usually refers to networks composed of reactive elements which ideally absorb no power. If the power is not transmitted to the load, it is reflected.

The previous analysis is also valid for networks made up of resistive elements. Such a network is termed an attenuator and all the expressions are equally applicable. If an attenuator is to be designed, the given quantities will generally be the characteristic impedance and propagation. An examination of Eq. (7–25) shows that for real Z_1 and Z_2, cosh $\gamma > 1$ in which case the propagation constant is real, representing attenuation by the network, and is given by Eq. (7–30). The design equations must be reversed to obtain component values. In the case of a symmetrical attenuator Eqs. (7–30) and (7–14) or (7–15) may be solved simultaneously for values of Z_1 and Z_2. In the case of unsymmetrical attenuators the design equations become more involved since there are three unknowns. Design equations and tables may be found in [*Data* (17) pp. 247–262].

7.1.1   SAMPLE PROBLEM

This sample problem is repeated from Chapter 1 to demonstrate an alternate method of solution.

A ladder network is formed of resistors as shown, and the resistances are indicated in ohms.

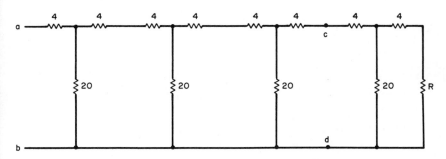

(a) What should be the resistance of load R so that the resistance at points c-d looking toward the right will also be R ohms?

(b) With a resistor of this value at R, what will be the resistance at the network terminals a-b?

(c) If each 4-ohm resistor is replaced by a pure reactor having an inductive reactance of 4 ohms, and each 20-ohm resistor is replaced by a capacitor having a capacitive reactance of 20 ohms, what should be the value of R for a match?

SOLUTION

(a) This may be recognized as a series of identical symmetrical Tee-networks cascaded together. For such a Tee-network

$$Z_o = \sqrt{Z_1 Z_2 \left(1 + \frac{Z_1}{4Z_2}\right)} = R$$

$$\frac{Z_1}{2} = 4 \text{ ohms}, Z_2 = 20 \text{ ohms}$$

$$Z_o = \sqrt{(8)(20)\left(1 + \frac{8}{(4)(20)}\right)} = \sqrt{160(1.10)} = 13.28 \text{ ohms} \quad \text{ANS.}$$

(b) The property of cascaded filter sections of this type is that $R_{ab} = R = 13.28$ ohms.   ANS.

(c) The same expression for characteristic impedance used in part (a) is valid.

$$Z_o = \sqrt{Z_1 Z_2 \left(1 + \frac{Z_1}{4Z_2}\right)} = R$$

$$\frac{Z_1}{2} = j4, Z_2 = -j20$$

$$Z_o = \sqrt{(j8)(-j20)\left(1 + \frac{j8}{(4)(-j20)}\right)}$$

$$= \sqrt{160(0.90)} = 12.0 \text{ ohms} \qquad\qquad \text{ANS.}$$

7.1.2   SAMPLE PROBLEM

(a) Calculate the values of the elements of a Pi-connected attenuator, of pure resistances, which will match a 1,000-ohm circuit and insert therein a 10-db. loss.

(b) Calculate the power rating of each resistor for this attenuator when its output is to be 30 db. above 0.001 watt.

SOLUTION

(a) The circuit is as shown

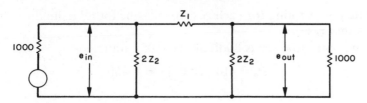

For the symmetrical filter

$$Z_o = \sqrt{\frac{Z_1 Z_2}{1 + Z_1/4Z_2}}$$

and

$$\cosh \gamma = 1 + \frac{Z_1}{2Z_2}$$

But for this circuit

$$\gamma = \alpha = 10 \text{db}$$

$$= \frac{10}{8.68} = 1.152 \text{ nepers}$$

$$\cosh \gamma = 1.741 = 1 + \frac{Z_1}{2Z_2}$$

or

$$\frac{Z_1}{2Z_2} = 0.741$$

and

$$Z_1 = 1.482 \; Z_2$$

This expression may be substituted in the expression for Z_o

$$Z_o = 1000 = \sqrt{\frac{1.482 \; Z_2{}^2}{1 + 1.482/4}} = 1.04 Z_2$$

or

$$Z_2 = \frac{1000}{1.04} = 960 \text{ ohms}$$

The value of the shunt arm is

$$2Z_2 = 2(960) = 1920 \text{ ohms} \qquad \text{ANS.}$$

The value of the series arm is

$$Z_1 = 1.482(960) = 1422 \text{ ohms} \qquad \text{ANS.}$$

(b) The power rating for each resistor may be found from the voltage across that resistor.

If the output power is 30db above 0.001 watt,

$$P_o = (10^3)(0.001) = 1 \text{ watt}$$

But

$$e_{\text{out}} = \sqrt{P_o Z_o} = \sqrt{(1)(1000)} = 31.6 \text{ v.}$$

The power rating of the output resistor is

$$P = \frac{(e_{\text{out}})^2}{R} = \frac{(31.6)^2}{1920} = 0.52 \text{ watts} \qquad \text{ANS.}$$

The power at the input is 10db greater than the output power. Thus

$$P_{\text{in}} = (10)P_o = 10 \text{ watts}$$

and

$$e_{\text{in}} = \sqrt{P_{\text{in}} Z_o} = \sqrt{(10)(1000)} = 100 \text{ v.}$$

The power rating of the input resistor is

$$P = \frac{(e_{\text{in}})^2}{R} = \frac{(100)^2}{1920} = 5.2 \text{ watts} \qquad \text{ANS.}$$

Since e_{out} and e_{in} are in phase, the voltage across the series resistance is the difference between e_{out} and e_{in} and the power becomes

$$P = \frac{(e_{\text{in}} - e_{\text{out}})^2}{R} = \frac{(100 - 31.6)^2}{1422}$$

$$= \frac{(68.4)^2}{1422} = 3.28 \text{ watts} \qquad \text{ANS.}$$

7.2   THE CONSTANT-*K* FILTERS

Zobel in his original paper defined a class of filters in which the following relation was true

$$Z_1 Z_2 = K^2 \qquad (7\text{--}34)$$

In the case of ideal non-dissipative elements Z_1 and Z_2 are reactive and of opposite sign. Filters for which Eq. (7–34) is true are known as constant-*K* filters even though the symbol R or R_K has tended to replace the symbol K.

There are four types of constant-*K* filters: low pass, high pass, band pass, and band reject, which may be either Tee or Pi structures built up from basic half sections.

Figure 7–7 shows schematically the half sections for the four types of constant-*K* filters.

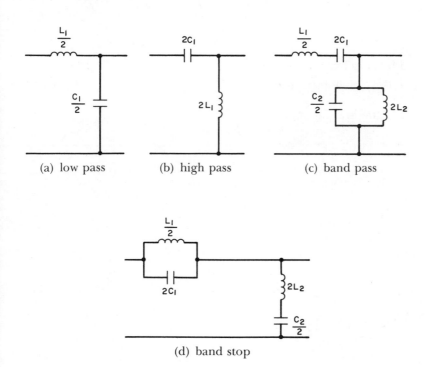

(a) low pass   (b) high pass   (c) band pass

(d) band stop

Figure 7–7 Half-sections for constant-K filters

Design relationships for determination of component values in terms of desired terminating resistance and frequency are given in Terman, *Handbook* (24) and *Data* (17). The latter reference gives further valuable data in the form of expressions and curves for the variation of image impedance, phase shift, and attenuation with frequency. It should be noted that in this reference the series arms are actually $Z_1/2$ while the shunt arms are $2Z_2$. This point should be taken into account when using the design equations.

Some useful information which is missing from various reference works is the determination of image impedance and cutoff frequency in terms of component values.

The image impedances may be obtained from Eqs. (7–14), (7–15), and (7–34) as

$$Z_{o_T} = R_K \sqrt{1 + \frac{Z_1}{4Z_2}} \qquad (7\text{–}35)$$

$$Z_{o_P} = \frac{R_K}{\sqrt{1 + \dfrac{Z_1}{4Z_2}}} \qquad (7\text{–}36)$$

The cutoff frequency may be obtained from Eq. (7–31).

These equations apply very simply to the low-pass and high-pass filters.

For the low-pass filter

$$Z_1 = j\omega L_1 \qquad (7\text{–}37)$$

$$Z_2 = \frac{1}{j\omega C_1} \qquad (7\text{–}38)$$

$$Z_1 Z_2 = \frac{L_1}{C_1} \qquad (7\text{–}39)$$

$$\frac{Z_1}{4Z_2} = -\frac{\omega^2 LC}{4} \qquad (7\text{–}40)$$

and

$$Z_{o_T} = \sqrt{\frac{L_1}{C_1}} \sqrt{1 - \frac{\omega^2 L_1 C_1}{4}} \qquad (7\text{–}41)$$

The cutoff frequency is where

$$\frac{\omega_c^2 LC}{4} = 1 \qquad (7\text{–}42)$$

or

$$\omega_c = \frac{2}{\sqrt{LC}} \qquad (7\text{–}43)$$

For the high-pass filter

$$Z_1 = \frac{1}{j\omega C_1} \qquad (7\text{–}44)$$

$$Z_2 = j\omega L_1 \qquad (7\text{–}45)$$

$$Z_1 Z_2 = \frac{L_1}{C_1} \qquad (7\text{–}46)$$

$$\frac{Z_1}{4Z_2} = -\frac{1}{4\omega^2 L_1 C_1} \qquad (7\text{–}47)$$

and

$$Z_{o_T} = \sqrt{\frac{L_1}{C_1}} \sqrt{1 - \frac{1}{4\omega^2 L_1 C_1}} \qquad (7\text{--}48)$$

The cutoff frequency is

$$\omega_c = \frac{1}{2\sqrt{LC}} \qquad (7\text{--}49)$$

For the band-pass filter

$$Z_1 = \frac{j(\omega^2 L_1 C_1 - 1)}{\omega C_1} \qquad (7\text{--}50)$$

$$Z_2 = \frac{\omega L_2}{j(\omega^2 L_2 C_2 - 1)} \qquad (7\text{--}51)$$

$$Z_1 Z_2 = \frac{L_2}{C_1} \frac{(\omega^2 L_1 C_1 - 1)}{(\omega^2 L_2 C_2 - 1)} \qquad (7\text{--}52)$$

To make this a constant-K filter

$$L_1 C_1 = L_2 C_2 \qquad (7\text{--}53)$$

and

$$Z_1 Z_2 = \frac{L_2}{C_1} = \frac{L_1}{C_2} \qquad (7\text{--}54)$$

$$\frac{Z_1}{4Z_2} = \frac{-(\omega^2 L_1 C_1 - 1)(\omega^2 L_2 C_2 - 1)}{4\omega^2 L_2 C_1} = \frac{-(\omega^2 L_1 C_1 - 1)^2}{4\omega^2 C_1 L_2} \qquad (7\text{--}55)$$

and

$$Z_{o_T} = \sqrt{\frac{L_2}{C_1}} \sqrt{1 - \frac{(\omega^2 L_1 C_1 - 1)^2}{4\omega^2 C_1 L_2}} \qquad (7\text{--}56)$$

The cutoff frequency is where,

$$(\omega_c^2 L_1 C_1 - 1)^2 = 4\omega_c^2 C_1 L_2 \qquad (7\text{--}57)$$

or

$$\omega_c^2 - \frac{2\omega_c}{\sqrt{L_1 C_1}} \sqrt{\frac{L_2}{L_1}} - \frac{1}{L_1 C_1} = 0 \qquad (7\text{--}58)$$

Solving the quadratic equation

$$\omega_c = \frac{1}{\sqrt{L_1 C_1}} \left[\sqrt{\frac{L_2}{L_1}} \pm \sqrt{\frac{L_2}{L_1} + 1} \right] \qquad (7\text{--}59)$$

For the band-stop filter or band-reject filter

$$Z_1 = \frac{\omega L_1}{j(\omega^2 L_1 C_1 - 1)} \tag{7-60}$$

$$Z_2 = \frac{j(\omega^2 L_2 C_2 - 1)}{\omega C_2} \tag{7-61}$$

$$Z_1 Z_2 = \frac{L_1(\omega^2 L_2 C_2 - 1)}{C_2(\omega^2 L_1 C_1 - 1)} = \frac{L_1}{C_2} = \frac{L_2}{C_1} \tag{7-62}$$

if $L_1 C_1 = L_2 C_2$, which is necessary to fulfill constant K requirements. Also

$$\frac{Z_1}{4Z_2} = \frac{-\omega^2 L_1 C_2}{4(\omega^2 L_1 C_1 - 1)(\omega^2 L_2 C_2 - 1)} = \frac{-\omega^2 L_1 C_2}{4(\omega^2 L_1 C_1 - 1)^2} \tag{7-63}$$

so that

$$Z_{o_T} = \sqrt{\frac{L_2}{C_1}} \sqrt{1 - \frac{\omega^2 L_1 C_2}{4(\omega^2 L_1 C_1 - 1)^2}} \tag{7-64}$$

The cutoff frequency is where

$$\omega_c^2 L_1 C_2 = 4(\omega_c^2 L_1 C_1 - 1)^2 \tag{7-65}$$

or

$$\omega_c^2 - \omega_c\left(\frac{1}{2\sqrt{L_1 C_1}}\right)\left(\sqrt{\frac{C_2}{C_1}}\right) - \frac{1}{L_1 C_1} = 0 \tag{7-66}$$

Solving the quadratic equation

$$\omega_c = \frac{1}{\sqrt{L_1 C_1}}\left(\sqrt{\frac{C_2}{16 C_1}} \pm \sqrt{1 + \frac{C_2}{16 C_1}}\right)$$

$$= \frac{1}{\sqrt{L_1 C_1}}\left(\sqrt{\frac{L_1}{16 L_2}} \pm \sqrt{1 + \frac{L_1}{16 L_2}}\right) \tag{7-67}$$

7.2.1 SAMPLE PROBLEM

(a) Design the constant-K T-section of the low pass filter which matches a 500-ohm circuit and has a cut-off at $\omega = 1000$ rps.

(b) Calculate the attenuation of this section, at $\omega = 2000$ rps, in decibels.

SOLUTION

cf. [*Data* (17) pp. 167, 1112]
The filter section is

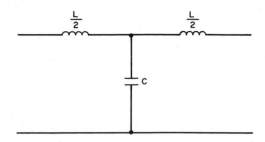

(a) For this filter section

$$C = \frac{2}{\omega_c R}$$

where ω_c is the cutoff radian frequency and R the characteristic resistance.
Substituting

$$C = \frac{2}{(1000)(500)} = 4 \times 10^{-6} \text{ farads} \qquad \text{ANS.}$$

Also

$$\frac{L}{2} = \frac{R}{\omega_c}$$
$$= \frac{500}{1000} = 0.50 \text{ henry} \qquad \text{ANS.}$$

(b) The attenuation α in nepers is given by

$$\alpha = 2 \cosh^{-1} \frac{\omega}{\omega_c}$$
$$= 2 \cosh^{-1} \frac{2000}{1000}$$
$$= 2 \cosh^{-1} 2 = 2(1.318) = 2.636 \text{ nepers}$$

To convert from nepers to decibels, multiply nepers by 8.68. Thus

$$\alpha = 8.68(2.636) = 22.8 \text{ db} \qquad \text{ANS.}$$

7.3 THE *m*-DERIVED FILTERS

In order to obtain a more rapid change in attenuation as a function of frequency in the region of cutoff, Zobel originally proposed and derived the necessary conditions which resulted in the *m*-derived filter. This condition was obtained by putting either a parallel resonant circuit in the series (Z_1) arm or a series resonant circuit in the shunt (Z_2) arm. The resonances are adjusted to fall within the stop band; the closer to the cutoff frequency, the more rapid the change in attenuation. A disadvantage is that the attenuation past the resonant point decreases so that *m*-derived sections are used with constant-*K* sections to maintain the stop band attenuation. However, an advantage of the *m*-derived section is that when properly used as a terminating section, compared to a constant-*K* filter, the image impedance can be made more nearly constant over the pass band.

The variety of *m*-derived half sections is much greater than that of constant-*K* half sections. A number of these sections are illustrated and design equations are given in [Terman, *Handbook* (24)] and [*Data* (17)]. The latter reference is recommended because it is more complete.

The equations for some of the important filter characteristics are of the same form as those for the constant-*K* filters. These characteristics include: propagation constant, image impedance, and cut-off frequency.

7.3.1 SAMPLE PROBLEM

Calculate for the filter section shown, the
(a) matching terminal resistance
(b) cut-off angular velocity, ω_c
(c) angular velocity of infinite attenuation, ω_i

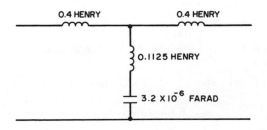

SOLUTION

Cf.: [*Data* (17) p. 167], [Ryder, *Networks* (19) Chap. 4]. This filter section corresponds to a series *m*-derived low-pass filter.

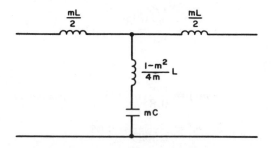

(a) The matching terminal resistance R_K is

$$R_K = \sqrt{\frac{L}{C}}$$

From the figures

$$\frac{mL}{2} = 0.4$$

or

$$L = \frac{0.8}{m}$$

and

$$mC = 3.2 \times 10^{-6}$$

so that

$$C = \frac{3.2 \times 10^{-6}}{m}$$

and

$$R_K = \sqrt{\left(\frac{0.8}{m}\right)\left(\frac{m}{3.2 \times 10^{-6}}\right)} = \sqrt{\frac{1}{4 \times 10^{-6}}} = 500 \text{ ohms} \qquad \text{ANS.}$$

(b) The value of ω_c is given by

$$\omega_c = \frac{2}{\sqrt{LC}}$$

$$L = \frac{0.8}{m}$$

and

$$\frac{1 - m^2}{4m}L = 0.1125$$

or

$$\frac{(1 - m^2)0.8}{4m^2} = 0.1125$$

solving for m

$$(1 - m^2) = \frac{4m^2}{0.8}(0.1125) = 0.5625m^2$$

$$m^2 = \frac{1}{1.5625} = 0.64$$

$$m = 0.80$$

Thus

$$L = \frac{0.8}{0.8} = 1.0 \text{ henry}$$

and

$$C = \frac{3.2 \times 10^{-6}}{0.8} = 4.0 \times 10^{-6} \text{ farad}$$

so that

$$\omega_c = \frac{2}{\sqrt{(1)(4)(10^{-6})}} = 10^3 \text{ rad/sec} \qquad \text{ANS.}$$

(c) The value of ω_i is given by

$$\omega_i = \frac{\omega_c}{\sqrt{1 - m^2}}$$

$$= \frac{10^3}{\sqrt{1 - (0.8)^2}}$$

$$= \frac{10^3}{\sqrt{1 - 0.64}} = \frac{10^3}{\sqrt{0.36}} = 1.667 \times 10^3 \text{ rad/sec} \qquad \text{ANS.}$$

7.4   PRACTICE PROBLEMS

7-1

Design a resistance pad having a loss of 10 db and matching a 200 ohm circuit to one having a resistance of 600 ohms.

7–2

The circuit shown is that of a filter section. Determine the band of frequencies over which the attenuation of signals is zero.

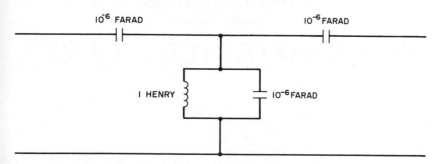

7–3

Calculate the cut-off frequencies and the minimum image resistance in the pass band for the filter section shown.

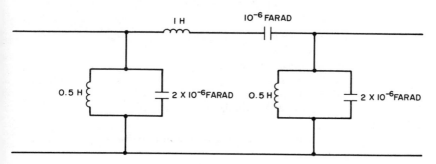

7–4

The network shown is a T-section of an *m*-derived low-pass filter. Determine:
  (a) the cutoff frequency
  (b) the frequency of infinite attenuation
  (c) the attenuation at $\omega = 10,000$ rad/sec.

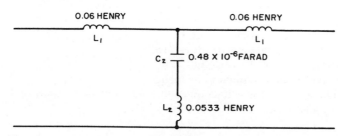

CHAPTER EIGHT

TRANSMISSION LINES

SYMBOLS

B	Susceptance, mhos
b	Normalized susceptance
C	Capacitance, farads
c	The velocity of light (3×10^{10} cm/sec)
E, e	Emf, volts
f	Frequency, cycles per second (cps)
G	Conductance, mhos
g	Normalized conductance
I, i	Current, amperes
j	The imaginary operator $\sqrt{-1}$
K	The magnitude of the reflection coefficient
L	Inductance, henrys
l	Length measured along a transmission line, inches or centimeters
n	Integer values
R	Resistance, ohms
V, v	Emf, volts
v	Velocity of propagation, cm/sec
$VSWR$	Voltage standing wave ratio
Y	Admittance, mhos
y	Normalized admittance
Z	Impedance, ohms
z	Normalized impedance
α	Attenuation or attenuation constant, nepers
β	Phase shift or phase constant, radians
γ	Propagation constant (complex)
ϵ	Base of natural logarithms (2.71828 . . .)
ϵ_r	Relative dielectric constant
λ	Wavelength, centimeters or inches
ϕ	The angle of the reflection coefficient, radians or degrees
ω	Angular frequency, radians per second

Subscripts

c	Cutoff
in	Input
L	Load
max	Maximum
min	Minimum
o	Characteristic
oc	Open circuit
out	Output
s	Stub
sc	Short circuit

8.1   TWO-WIRE TRANSMISSION LINES

A two wire transmission line is considered to have an equivalent series impedance and an equivalent shunt admittance, both of which are usually in units per unit length. The series impedance Z is

$$Z = R + j\omega L \text{ ohms/unit length} \qquad (8\text{-}1)$$

which is the total loop impedance taking into account both conductors.

The shunt admittance Y is

$$Y = G + j\omega C \text{ mhos/unit length} \qquad (8\text{-}2)$$

For analysis, the equivalent circuit of the line is generally shown as an unsymmetrical circuit as in Fig. 8–1. The impedance of both conductors is combined into a single equivalent value.

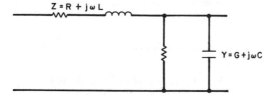

Figure 8–1 Equivalent circuit for a section of transmission line

The propagation constant γ is defined as

$$\gamma = \sqrt{ZY}$$
$$= \sqrt{(R + j\omega L)(G + j\omega C)}$$
$$= \sqrt{(RG - \omega^2 LC) + j(\omega LG + \omega CR)} \qquad (8\text{-}3)$$

The propagation constant is composed of a real part (attenuation) and an imaginary part (phase shift)

$$\gamma = \alpha + j\beta \qquad (8\text{-}4)$$

The units of attenuation are nepers while the units of phase shift are radians.

The characteristic impedance of the line is given by

$$Z_o = \sqrt{\frac{Z}{Y}}$$
$$= \sqrt{\frac{R + j\omega L}{G + j\omega C}} \qquad (8\text{-}5)$$

Figure 8-2 A section of transmission line

In the section of line shown in Fig. 8-2, the input voltage and current are given by

$$V = V_L \cosh \gamma l + I_L Z_o \sinh \gamma l \qquad (8\text{-}6)$$

$$I = I_L \cosh \gamma l + \frac{V_L}{Z_o} \sinh \gamma l \qquad (8\text{-}7)$$

But

$$\frac{V_L}{I_L} = Z_L \qquad (8\text{-}8)$$

Thus Eqs. (8-6) and (8-7) become

$$V = V_L\left(\cosh \gamma l + \frac{Z_o}{Z_L} \sinh \gamma l\right) \qquad (8\text{-}9)$$

$$I = I_L\left(\cosh \gamma l + \frac{Z_L}{Z_o} \sinh \gamma l\right) \qquad (8\text{-}10)$$

The input impedance is the ratio of voltage to current

$$Z_{\text{in}} = \frac{V}{I} = Z_L \frac{(\cosh \gamma l + (Z_o/Z_L) \sinh \gamma l)}{\cosh \gamma l + (Z_L/Z_o) \sinh \gamma l}$$

$$= Z_o\left(\frac{Z_L \cosh \gamma l + Z_o \sinh \gamma l}{Z_o \cosh \gamma l + Z_L \sinh \gamma l}\right)$$

$$= Z_o\left(\frac{Z_L + Z_o \tanh \gamma l}{Z_o + Z_L \tanh \gamma l}\right) \tag{8-11}$$

In Eq. (8–11) the exponential form may be substituted for cosh γl and sinh γl yielding

$$
\begin{aligned}
Z_{in} &= Z_o\left[\frac{Z_L(\epsilon^{\gamma l} + \epsilon^{-\gamma l})/2 + Z_o(\epsilon^{\gamma l} - \epsilon^{-\gamma l})/2}{Z_o(\epsilon^{\gamma l} + \epsilon^{-\gamma l})/2 + Z_L(\epsilon^{\gamma l} - \epsilon^{-\gamma l})/2}\right] \\
&= Z_o\left[\frac{\epsilon^{\gamma l}(Z_L + Z_o) + \epsilon^{-\gamma l}(Z_L - Z_o)}{\epsilon^{\gamma l}(Z_L + Z_o) - \epsilon^{-\gamma l}(Z_L - Z_o)}\right] \\
&= Z_o\left[\frac{1 + K\epsilon^{-2\gamma l}}{1 - K\epsilon^{-2\gamma l}}\right]
\end{aligned}
\tag{8-12}
$$

where K is the voltage reflection coefficient defined as

$$K \equiv \frac{Z_L - Z_o}{Z_L + Z_o} \tag{8-13}$$

Similarly Eqs. (8–9) and (8–10) may be written as

$$
\begin{aligned}
\frac{V}{V_L} &= \frac{1}{Z_L}\left[Z_L\left(\frac{\epsilon^{\gamma l} + \epsilon^{-\gamma l}}{2}\right) + Z_o\left(\frac{\epsilon^{\gamma l} - \epsilon^{-\gamma l}}{2}\right)\right] \\
&= \frac{Z_L + Z_o}{2Z_L}[\epsilon^{\gamma l} + K\epsilon^{-\gamma l}]
\end{aligned}
\tag{8-14}
$$

$$
\begin{aligned}
\frac{I}{I_L} &= \frac{1}{Z_o}\left[Z_o\left(\frac{\epsilon^{\gamma l} + \epsilon^{-\gamma l}}{2}\right) + Z_L\left(\frac{\epsilon^{\gamma l} - \epsilon^{-\gamma l}}{2}\right)\right] \\
&= \frac{Z_L + Z_o}{2Z_o}[\epsilon^{\gamma l} - K\epsilon^{-\gamma l}]
\end{aligned}
\tag{8-15}
$$

The term $\epsilon^{\gamma l}$ refers to the wave travelling from the source to the load while the term $\epsilon^{-\gamma l}$ refers to the wave reflected from the load travelling toward the source.

If V_1 represents the voltage amplitude of the wave travelling toward the load and V_2, the voltage amplitude of the reflected wave, the voltage reflection coefficient is

$$K = \frac{V_2}{V_1} \tag{8-16}$$

and a similar expression may be written for the current.

The combination of the incident wave and the reflected wave results in a stationary standing-wave pattern which may be sampled by a voltage (or current) probe moved along a special section of line.

The voltage standing wave ratio *VSWR* is the ratio of the maximum voltage to the minimum voltage. Thus

$$VSWR = \frac{V_{max}}{V_{min}} = \frac{|V_1| + |V_2|}{|V_1| - |V_2|}$$
$$= \frac{1 + |K|}{1 - |K|} \tag{8-17}$$

The distance along the line separating corresponding points on the standing wave pattern is $\lambda/2$ where λ is given by

$$\lambda = \frac{2\pi}{\beta} \tag{8-18}$$

A maximum of the standing wave pattern is separated from an adjacent minimum by $\lambda/4$.

The velocity of propagation of a wave on a line is

$$v = \frac{\omega}{\beta} \tag{8-19}$$

If a line is terminated in a short circuit ($Z_L = 0$), the reflection coefficient $K = -1$ from which

$$Z_{in} = Z_o \tanh \gamma l \tag{8-20}$$

Equation (8-14) cannot be used to determine V since $V_L = 0$ and the ratio V/V_L is either infinite or indeterminate.

If a line is terminated in an open circuit ($Z_L = \infty$), $K = +1$ from which

$$Z_{in} = Z_o \coth \gamma l \tag{8-21}$$

Equation (8-15) cannot be used to determine I since $I_L = 0$ and the ratio I/I_L is either infinite or indeterminate.

8.1.1 SAMPLE PROBLEM

A certain open-wire line has the following constants per mile of line: $R = 11.9$ ohms; $C = 0.0084$ mfd.; $L = 0.00376$ henry; $G = 10^{-6}$ mhos. What should be the value of the terminating impedance of such a line in order to minimize reflection losses? The angular velocity of the impressed emf is 5000 rad/sec.

SOLUTION

The required value of termination is the characteristic impedance which is

$$Z_o = \sqrt{\frac{Z}{Y}}$$

$$\begin{aligned}
Z = R + j\omega L &= 11.9 + j(5000)(0.00376) \\
&= 11.9 + j18.8 \\
&= 22.2 \ \underline{/57.6} \\
Y = G + j\omega C &= 10^{-6} + j(5000)(0.0084)(10^{-6}) \\
&= 10^{-6}(1 + j42) \\
&= 42 \times 10^{-6} \ \underline{/88.6}
\end{aligned}$$

$$\begin{aligned}
Z_o &= \sqrt{\frac{22.2 \ \underline{/57.6}}{42 \times 10^{-6} \ \underline{/88.6}}} \\
&= \sqrt{0.528 \times 10^6 \ \underline{/-31}} \\
&= 728 \ \underline{/-15.5^\circ} \qquad\qquad\qquad \text{ANS.}
\end{aligned}$$

8.1.2   SAMPLE PROBLEM

A telephone cable has the following coefficients per mile:
Inductance: 1 millihenry
Resistance: 50 ohms
Capacitance: 0.06 microfarads
Conductance: 0

Loading coils are available which will add 35 millihenry and 6 ohms to the line whenever one is inserted.

(a) Determine the permissible spacing of these loading coils so that the cable will transmit all frequencies up to 10 kc without appreciable attenuation.

(b) Determine the improvement of the transmission in decibels to a 5 kc signal provided by the loading.

SOLUTION

(a) The steps in the solution of this problem are as outlined in [Ryder, *Networks* (19) Chap. 5].

The cutoff frequency of the loaded line is given by

$$f_c = \frac{1}{\pi\sqrt{LC}}$$

On a per mile basis, with $f_c = 10$ kc

$$L = \frac{1}{\pi^2 f_c^2 C}$$

$$= \frac{1}{\pi^2 (10^4)^2 (0.06)(10^{-6})}$$

$$= 16.9 \text{ millihenrys/mile}$$

Since the line has 1 millihenry/mile, the loading should add 15.9 millihenries/mile or the spacing is

$$\frac{35 \text{ millihenry/coil}}{15.9 \text{ millihenry/mile}} = 2.2 \text{ miles spacing between coils} \quad \text{ANS.}$$

(b) The attenuation improvement may be found by comparing the attenuations of the propagation constants.

The propagation constant of the unloaded line at 5 kc is (per mile)

$$\gamma_u = \sqrt{ZY}$$
$$= \sqrt{(R + j\omega L)(j\omega C)}$$
$$= \sqrt{(50 + j31.4)(j0.001885)}$$
$$= \sqrt{(59 \,\underline{/32.1})(0.001885 \,\underline{/90})} = 0.333 \,\underline{/61}$$

so that

$$\alpha_u = 0.333 \cos 61° = 0.161 \text{ nepers/mile}$$
$$= 1.40 \text{ db/mile}$$

The attenuation for the loaded cable is given by the approximate formula

$$\alpha_L = \frac{R}{2}\sqrt{\frac{C}{L}}$$

$$R = 50 + \frac{6}{2.2} = 52.73 \text{ ohms/mile}$$

$$C = 0.06 \text{ microfarad/mile}$$

$$L = 16.9 \text{ millihenrys/mile}$$

$$\alpha_L = \frac{52.7}{2}\sqrt{\frac{6 \times 10^{-8}}{16.9 \times 10^{-3}}}$$

$$= 0.0497 \text{ nepers/mile}$$

$$= 0.43 \text{ db/mile}$$

The improvement is the difference of 0.97 db/mile   ANS.
A more exact method for the attenuation to the loaded cable is:

$$\gamma_L = \sqrt{(52.7 + j530)\,(j0.001885)}$$
$$= \sqrt{(530\ \underline{/84.3})\,(0.001885\ \underline{/90})} = 1.0\ \underline{/87.1}$$
$$\alpha_L = 1.0\ \cos 87.1° = 0.0506\ \text{nepers/mile}$$
$$= 0.43\ \text{db/mile}$$

This is the same result as obtained from the approximate formula showing the validity of the approximation.

8.2   THE LOSSLESS TRANSMISSION LINE

Often the line losses are so small as to be neglible. Thus the characteristic impedance and propagation constant expressions with the series resistance and shunt conductance set equal to zero become

$$Z_o = \sqrt{\frac{L}{C}} \tag{8–22}$$

$$\gamma = j\beta = j\omega\sqrt{LC} \tag{8–23}$$

The input impedance given by Eq. (8–11) reduces to

$$Z_{\text{in}} = Z_o\left(\frac{Z_L + jZ_o \tan \beta l}{Z_o + jZ_L \tan \beta l}\right) \tag{8–24}$$

and Eq. (8–12) becomes

$$Z_{\text{in}} = Z_o\left[\frac{1 + K\epsilon^{-j2\beta l}}{1 - K\epsilon^{-j2\beta l}}\right]$$
$$= Z_o\left[\frac{1 + |K|\ \underline{/\phi - 2\beta l}}{1 - |K|\ \underline{/\phi - 2\beta l}}\right] \tag{8–25}$$

The input impedance of a short-circuited and open-circuited line are

$$Z_{sc} = jZ_o \tan \beta l \tag{8–26}$$
$$Z_{oc} = -jZ_o \cot \beta l \tag{8–27}$$

These sections of line may be used to provide the equivalent performance of reactive elements. The variation of Z_{sc} and Z_{oc} as a function of length is shown in Fig. 8–3.

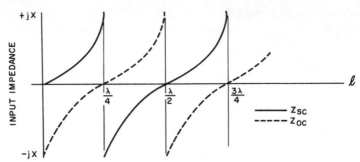

Figure 8–3 The input impedance of a short-circuited and open-circuited lossless transmission line

For lengths between zero and $\lambda/4$, the short-circuited line represents an inductive input reactance while the open-circuited line represents a capacitive input reactance.

A property of a line of one-quarter wavelength is impedance inversion with respect to Z_o.

Equation (8–24) with $\quad l = \dfrac{\lambda}{4}$ or $\beta l = \dfrac{\pi}{2}$

becomes

$$Z_{in} = \frac{Z_o^2}{Z_L} \tag{8–28}$$

or

$$\frac{Z_{in}}{Z_o} = \frac{Z_o}{Z_L} \tag{8–29}$$

Thus the short circuit seen through a quarter wavelength line appears as an open circuit, and vice versa.

It is often convenient to normalize impedance quantities to Z_o or to perform calculations using normalized admittance. The normalized input impedance and admittance for a lossless line are

$$\frac{Z_{in}}{Z_o} = \frac{(Z_L/Z_o) + j\tan\beta l}{1 + j(Z_L/Z_o)\tan\beta l} \tag{8–30}$$

$$\frac{Y_{in}}{Y_o} = \frac{(Y_L/Y_o) + j\tan\beta l}{1 + j(Y_L/Y_o)\tan\beta l} \tag{8–31}$$

For the short-circuited and open-circuited lines

$$\frac{Y_{sc}}{Y_o} = y_{sc} = jb_{sc} = -j\cot\beta l \tag{8–32}$$

$$\frac{Y_{oc}}{Y_o} = y_{oc} = jb_{oc} = j\tan\beta l \tag{8–33}$$

The properties of open-circuited and short-circuited lengths of line are put to good use for impedance matching a line not terminated in its characteristic impedance.

The basic scheme is shown in Fig. 8–4. All quantities are normalized to Y_o.

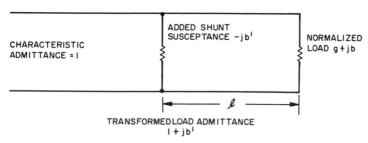

Figure 8–4 Impedance matching with a shunt susceptance

The matching technique is to add in parallel with the line a shunt susceptance equal to—and of opposite sign—the susceptive part of the transformed load at the point where the real portion of the transformed (normalized) load has a value of unity. Between that point and the source the line is matched with unity standing wave ratio.

Mathematically the matching technique is somewhat cumbersome. The admittance at any distance l from the load is

$$y = \frac{g + jb + j \tan \beta l}{1 + j(g + jb) \tan \beta l} = \frac{g + j(b + \tan \beta l)}{(1 - b \tan \beta l) + jg \tan \beta l} \quad (8\text{--}34)$$

By reduction this becomes

$$y = \frac{g(1 + \tan^2 \beta l)}{1 - 2b \tan \beta l + (g^2 + b^2) \tan^2 \beta l} + \frac{j[b + (1 - g^2 - b^2) \tan \beta l - b \tan^2 \beta l]}{1 - 2b \tan \beta l + (b^2 + g^2) \tan^2 \beta l}$$

$$(8\text{--}35)$$

The length of line between the load and the match point is determined by setting the real part equal to unity. The expression for $\tan \beta l$ then is

$$\tan \beta l = \frac{b \pm \sqrt{g[(g - 1)^2 + b^2]}}{(g^2 - g + b^2)} \quad (8\text{--}36)$$

The above value when substituted into the imaginary part of Eq. (8–35) yields the negative of the necessary shunt susceptance to be added. The length of the shunt may be determined from Eq. (8–32) or Eq. (8–33).

The conversion from phase length to physical line length may be obtained from

$$\beta = \frac{2\pi}{\lambda} \text{ rad/wavelength} \qquad (8\text{--}37)$$

and by the fact that in a two-wire or coaxial line propagating the TEM mode which is the normal mode

$$\lambda = \frac{v}{f} \qquad (8\text{--}38)$$

where v is the velocity of propagation.

In free space or air

$$v = c = 3 \times 10^{10} \text{ cm/sec} \qquad (8\text{--}39)$$

In a non-magnetic media having a relative dielectric of ϵ_r

$$v = \frac{c}{\sqrt{\epsilon_r}} \qquad (8\text{--}40)$$

The value of an unknown impedance may be determined from measurements of the voltage standing wave pattern.

The necessary information to solve such a problem include the magnitude of the *VSWR*, the line characteristic impedance, the distance between either a voltage minimum or a voltage maximum, and the load, and the wavelength on the line.

The solution is based on the use of Eq. (8–25)

$$Z_{\text{in}} = Z_o \left[\frac{1 + |K| \underline{/\phi - 2\beta l}}{1 - |K| \underline{/\phi - 2\beta l}} \right]$$

An impedance minimum will occur where $\phi - 2\beta l = (2n + 1)\pi$ radians and an impedance maximum will occur where $\phi - 2\beta l = 2n\pi$ radians. At an impedance minimum there will occur a voltage minumum and at an impedance maximum there will be a voltage maximum.

Thus at voltage minimum

$$Z_{\text{min}} = Z_o \left(\frac{1 - |K|}{1 + |K|} \right) = \frac{Z_o}{VSWR} \qquad (8\text{--}41)$$

and at a voltage maximum

$$Z_{\text{max}} = Z_o \left(\frac{1 + |K|}{1 - |K|} \right) = Z_o(VSWR) \qquad (8\text{--}42)$$

where both Eqs. (8–41) and (8–42) are purely resistive.

The magnitude of the reflection coefficient is easily obtainable from Eq. (8–17) as

$$|K| = \frac{VSWR - 1}{VSWR + 1} \qquad (8\text{–}43)$$

At a distance l from a voltage minimum away from the generator, the impedance is

$$Z = Z_o\left[\frac{1 - |K|\ \underline{/2\beta l}}{1 + |K|\ \underline{/2\beta l}}\right] \qquad (8\text{–}44)$$

while the impedance at a distance l from a voltage maximum is

$$Z = Z_o\left[\frac{1 + |K|\ \underline{/2\beta l}}{1 - |K|\ \underline{/2\beta l}}\right] \qquad (8\text{–}45)$$

The angle has a positive sign since the direction is toward the load instead of toward the generator.

8.3   THE TRANSMISSION LINE CHART

The solution of a number of transmission line problems is greatly simplified by the use of a transmission line chart. Of the several types in use, probably the most popular chart is the one devised by P. H. Smith called the Smith Chart.* The Smith Chart is shown in Fig. 8–5.**

The complete circles represent constant resistance (or conductance) ranging from $R = 0$ at the outside of the chart to $R = \infty$ on the opposite side.

The circular arcs represent constant reactance or susceptance ranging from $X = 0$ at the diameter to $X = \pm \infty$ at the same point where $R = \infty$.

The values of resistance and reactance are normalized to unity so that the point $1.0 + j0.0$ at the center of the chart represents the normalized characteristic impedance of a lossless line.

Circles about the point $1 + j0$ as the center represent constant $VSWR$ and reflection coefficient. The reflection coefficient increases linearly from zero at the chart center $(1 + j0)$ to unity at the outside of the chart where $R = 0$.

---

* Smith, P. H., A transmission line calculator, Electronics, **12** (1), 29 (1939); An improved transmission line calculator, Electronics, **17** (1), 130 (1944).
** Copyright 1949 by Kay Electric Co., Pine Brook, N. J., reprinted with permission.

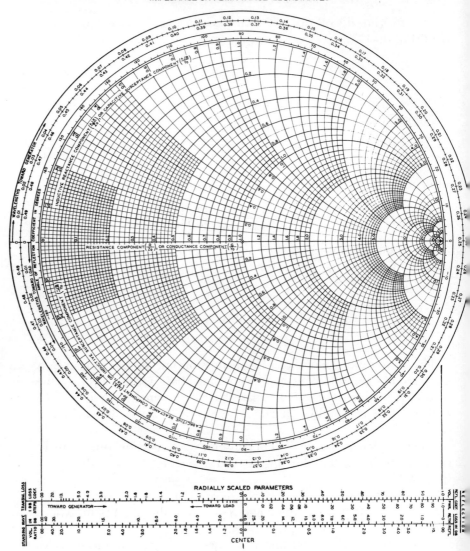

Figure 8–5 The Smith chart (Adapted with permission from Electronics, *vol. 17, no. 1, pp. 130-133, 318-325, Jan. 1944. Copyright 1949 by Kay Electric Co., Pine Brook, N.J.)*

Rotation of a radius vector represents motion along a transmission line. One complete revolution of the chart represents a distance of 0.5 wavelengths.

The angular location of a radius vector also represents the angle of the reflection coefficient.

8.3.1.   GENERAL USAGE OF THE SMITH CHART

Some of the problems whose solutions are simplified by the use of the Smith Chart are:
- determination of an equivalent line impedance at a point, knowing the impedance at another point
- determination of stub locations and lengths for impedance matching
- determination of load impedance from *VSWR* and voltage minimum location
- determination of complex reflection coefficient and *VSWR* from the value of normalized load impedance
- inversion of an impedance to determine an equivalent admittance and vice versa
- effects of line attenuation on impedance and *VSWR*

Complex Normalized Admittance or Impedance Plotting
A normalized complex impedance or admittance may be plotted directly. Using the radially scaled parameters the *VSWR* and reflection coefficient magnitude are determined directly. The angle of reflection coefficient is read at the angle made by a radius vector through the plotted point.

Normalized Admittance or Impedance Inversion
A normalized impedance may be inverted to an admittance (or vice versa) by plotting the value and reading the coordinates of a point at the same radius 180° around the chart.

Line Attenuation
Attenuation in a line not terminated in its characteristic impedance is treated by radial motion on the chart. A *VSWR* or equivalent reflection co-efficient at some point on a lossy line is decreased in magnitude by motion toward the generator and increased by motion toward the load. The scale is identified as Transmission Loss.

Impedance Variation along a Line
The impedance at any point on a lossless line may be determined knowing the impedance at another point and the distance in wavelengths between points. The known point is plotted by its coordinates. All other points on the line lie on the same *VSWR* circle. The value of the impedance at any other point is read as the point on the circle the appropriate number of wave-length in the appropriate direction away from the known point.

Impedance Matching Using Shunt Stubs
The stub matching problem is handled as follows. The normalized load is plotted as an admittance. The distance between the load and the nearest matching stub is the angular rotation in wavelengths toward the generator

between the load point and the intersection of the constant *VSWR* circle of the load with the unity conductance circle. Each subsequent intersection is another stub location. The necessary stub susceptance is the negative of the imaginary part of the transformed load admittance at the stub. The stub length is determined from the number of wavelengths from the appropriate termination (open- or short-circuit) to the necessary value of normalized susceptance required.

Determination of Load Impedance or Admittance From Measurements
A value of load impedance or admittance may be determined from the *VSWR* and voltage minimum location. The distance between the minimum and the load is determined in wavelengths. The impedance at a voltage minimum lies along the zero reactance line between zero resistance and the chart center. From this line the required number of wavelengths toward the load is measured along the load *VSWR* circle. That point is the load impedance. A voltage minimum is generally used as the starting point since its position may be more accurately located on the line that the position of a maximum. The admittance may be determined by inverting the impedance or starting at the other side of the chart.

8.3.2   SAMPLE PROBLEM

A lossless, open-wire transmission line, having a length of 100 cm. and a characteristic resistance of 100 ohms, is terminated in a load having an impedance of 100 $(1 + j)$ ohms when the operating frequency is 10^9 cps. Calculate the length and location, nearest the load, of a short-circuited stub line which will match the load to the line. If this problem is solved by means of a Smith Chart, include a diagram showing how the chart was used to arrive at the answer.

SOLUTION

This problem may be solved either by calculation or by use of the Smith Chart
(a) By calculation:
The normalized load impedance is

$$r + jx = \frac{R + jX}{Z_o} = \frac{100(1 + j)}{100} = 1 + j$$

The normalized load admittance is

$$g - jb = \frac{1}{r - jx} = \frac{1}{(1+j)} \frac{(1-j)}{(1-j)} = 0.50 - j0.50$$

The electrical length to a stub βl may be found from

$$\tan \beta l = \frac{b \pm \sqrt{g[(g-1)^2 + b^2]}}{(g^2 - g + b^2)}$$

$$= \frac{-0.5 \pm \sqrt{0.5[(0.5 - 1.0)^2 + (-0.5)^2]}}{[(0.5)^2 - 0.5 + (-0.5)^2]}$$

$$= \frac{-0.5 \pm \sqrt{0.5[0.25 + 0.25]}}{0}$$

Thus

$$\tan \beta l = \infty$$

So that

$$\beta l = \frac{\pi}{2}$$

or

$$l = \frac{\pi}{2\beta}$$

But

$$\beta = \frac{2\pi}{\lambda} \text{ rad/wavelength}$$

Thus

$$l = \frac{\pi}{2}\left(\frac{\lambda}{2\pi}\right) = \frac{\lambda}{4}$$

In an open-wire line, the velocity of propagation is the same as in free space so that

$$\lambda = \frac{3 \times 10^{10}}{f} \text{ cm}$$

$$= \frac{3 \times 10^{10}}{10^9} = 30 \text{ cm}$$

Thus

$$l = \text{distance from load to stub} = 30/4 = 7.5 \text{ cm} \qquad \text{ANS.}$$

The value of susceptance at the stub location may be found by sub-stituting $\tan \beta l = \infty$ into the following

$$b' = \frac{[b + (1 - g^2 - b^2) \tan \beta l - b \tan^2 \beta l]}{1 - 2b \tan \beta l + (g^2 + b^2) \tan^2 \beta l}$$

which may be rewritten as

$$b' = \frac{(b/\tan^2 \beta l) + [(1 - g^2 - b^2)/\tan \beta l] - b}{(1/\tan^2 \beta l) - (2b/\tan \beta l) + (g^2 + b^2)}$$

substituting

$$\tan \beta l = \infty$$

$$b' = \frac{-b}{g^2 + b^2} = \frac{0.5}{(0.5)^2 + (-0.5)^2} = 1$$

The stub normalized susceptance is equal to -1.

For a short-circuited stub

$$b_{sc} = -\cot \beta l_s = -1$$

or

$$\beta l_s = \frac{\pi}{4} \text{ radians}$$

or

$$l_s = \frac{\pi}{4}\left(\frac{1}{\beta}\right) = \frac{\pi}{4}\left(\frac{\lambda}{2\pi}\right) = \frac{\lambda}{8}$$

$$= \frac{30}{8} = 3.75 \text{ cm} \qquad\qquad \text{ANS.}$$

(b) Solution using Smith Chart:
 (1) Point 1 represents the normalized load impedance, $(1 + j)$
 (2) Point 2 represents point 1 inverted to obtain the normalized load admittance
 (3) Point 3 represents travel along the line toward the generator until the unit conductance circle is intersected. By coincidence, Point 3 is the same as point 1. The distance traversed is $(0.09 + 0.16 = 0.25$ wavelengths). The value of susceptance at point 3 is read off the chart as $+1.0$. This is cancelled by a -1.0 susceptance.
 (4) The length of stub may also be read off the chart. A short circuit (zero-length short-circuited stub) has admittance

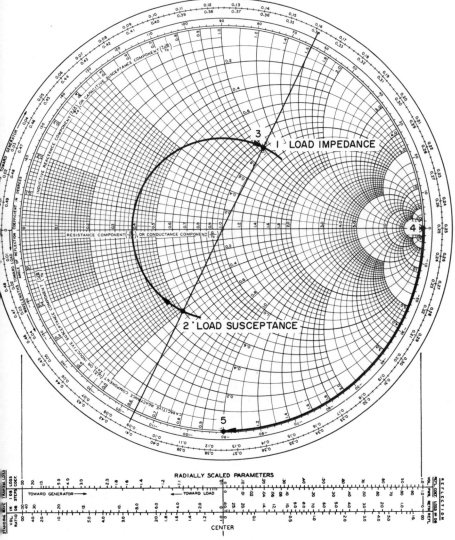

The Smith chart (Adapted with permission from Electronics, *vol. 17, no. 1, pp. 130-133, 318-325, Jan. 1944. Copyright by Kay Electric Co., Pine Brook, N.J.)*

$0 + j\infty$ and is shown as point 4. The chart is traversed clockwise (toward the generator or away from the load in this case the short circuit) until point 5 representing a susceptance of -1.0 is reached. The distance from point 4 to point 5 is read as $0.375 - 0.250$ or 0.125 wavelengths.

(5) The conversion from wavelengths to actual physical length follows directly.

8.4 PRACTICE PROBLEMS

8–1

A 100-mile telephone line has the following parameters per mile of line: $R = 10$ ohms; $L = 0.004$ henry; $C = 0.008 \times 10^{-6}$ farad; and $G = 10^{-6}$ mho.

(a) Calculate the impedance of the termination which will match this line at a frequency, $f = 5000/2\pi$.

(b) If this line included no repeaters, what would be the ratio, at this frequency, of the voltage at the input to that at the termination?

8–2

Each conductor of a 3-phase, 60-cycle transmission line has the following parameters per mile with respect to ground: $R = 0.3$ ohm; $\omega L = 1.2$ ohms; $\omega C = 3 \times 10^{-6}$ mho. The leakage may be neglected.

Calculate the input impedance of a 100-mile length of this conductor, to ground, when the distant end is open-circuited.

8–3

A standing-wave line is used to measure the input impedance of, and RF power flowing into, an antenna. The characteristic impedance of the line is 50 ohms. The voltage standing-wave ratio is 2.0. The first voltage miniumum occurs at a distance 0.4 wave-lengths from the antenna input terminals. The value of the voltage at the first minimum is 120 v. rms.

What is the value of the power delivered to the antenna and what is its input impedance?

8–4

An open-wire, dissipationless transmission line has a characteristic resistance of 200 ohms. When a certain load is connected to this line and power is supplied at 600 Mc, a voltage minimum results at a point 22.5 cm from the load and the voltage standing-wave-ratio is 2.16.

(a) Calculate the impedance of the load.

(b) If a short-circuited stub is used to match the load to the line, calculate the length of the shortest stub and its nearest position to the load.

8–5

When an unknown circuit element is connected as a load to one end of a transmission line having a characteristic resistance of 200 ohms and operated 500 Mc, a voltage minimum of 4 v. results at a point 20 cm from the load. The voltage maximum adjacent to this minimum has a value of 20 v.

Calculate the effective impedance of the load at 500 Mc.

CHAPTER NINE

ADDITIONAL TOPICS

SYMBOLS

A	Cross-sectional area, sq in
a	A constant, also cross-sectional area, sq cm
B	Coefficients of solutions of differential equations; also flux density, lines per square inch
b	A multiplier or coefficient
C	Capacitance, farads
D	The differential operator, d/dt
d	Wire diameter, thousandths of an inch (mils)
E	Electromotive force, volts (d-c or magnitude of a sinusoid)
$e, e(t)$	Variable electromotive force or a function of time, volts
F	Damping factor
$f(t)$	A function of time
I	Current, amperes (d-c or magnitude of a sinusoid)
$i, i(t)$	Variable current or a function of time, amperes
j	The imaginary operator $\sqrt{-1}$
K	Relative dielectric constant
L	Inductance, henrys
l	Length, centimeters
l'	Length, feet
l''	Length, inches
N	Number of capacitor plates; also number of coil turns
Q	Charge, coulombs
$q, q(t)$	Variable charge or a function of time, coulombs
R	Resistance, ohms
r	An exponent of a transient solution; also a radius, inches or centimeters
S	Surface area of one side of one plate of a capacitor, sq cm
s	Spacing between conductors, inches
T	Temperature, °C.
t	Time, seconds
v	Voltage drop, volts

204

α	Attenuation, seconds⁻¹; also temperature coefficient of resistance, ohms/ohm/° C.

α Attenuation, seconds^{-1}; also temperature coefficient of resistance, ohms/ohm/$^\circ$ C.

δ Spacing between capacitor plates, centimeters

ϵ Base of natural logarithms

ϕ Magnetic flux, lines

ρ Resistivity of a material, ohm-cm

θ An angle, radians

Ω Symbol for ohms

ω Angular frequency, rad/sec

τ Time constant, seconds

Subscripts

av Average value or quantity

I Initial, at time $t = 0$

L Load

m Maximum or peak value

o Referring to undamped frequency

oc open circuit

p Peak

rms Root mean square

S Steady-state

T Transient

9.1   TRANSIENTS – THE CLASSICAL SOLUTION

The problems to be dealt with in this section are those for which the solution for a particular variable such as current or voltage cannot be represented by a d-c value or a constant amplitude sinusoid. In these problems it is necessary to consider the storage of energy in a magnetic or electrostatic field and the time that is required to change the amount of energy stored in the fields. The energy stored in a magnetic field is a function of the current in an inductor while the energy in an electrostatic field is a function of the charge or voltage on a capacitor.

The method of solution to be used determines a total solution as the sum of two parts: a complementary function (transient) and a particular solution (steady-state). The complementary function is determined completely by the elements of the system, independent of the driving function or excitation except for amplitude. The particular solution is determined by both the driving function and the system. In any practical passive system, the losses will cause the particular solution eventually to decay to zero.

The majority of engineering problems are solved to determine the steady-state solution. For example, a voltage or current is represented by a constant (d-c) value or a constant amplitude sinusoid. From a mathematically correct standpoint such solutions are special cases of the complete solution discussed above. The special condition is that the system has been operating for a sufficiently long time so that the transient portion of the solution has become insignificant.

The classical solution utilizes Kirchhoff's loop and node equations to sum the transient voltages or currents as defined in Table I of Chapter 1. The resultant differential equations are solved by standard techniques. The methods of solution may be found in [Reddick et al, *Mathematics* (16), Chap. 1]. The CRC tables [*Math Tables* (1) pp. 338–354] list solutions for a number of different differential equations. Various engineering handbooks in the sections on mathematics also provide solutions for many of the ordinarily encountered differential equations.

The method of solution will be demonstrated by a simple problem. Consider the loop shown in Fig. 9–1.

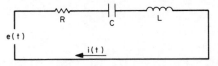

Figure 9–1 A simple loop for transient analysis

Using Kirchhoff's voltage law, one obtains

$$e(t) = v_C + v_L + v_R$$
$$= \frac{1}{C}\int i(t)\,dt + L\frac{di(t)}{dt} + Ri(t) \qquad (9\text{--}1)$$

But by definition

$$i(t) \equiv \frac{dq(t)}{dt} \qquad (9\text{--}2)$$

or

$$q(t) = \int i(t)\,dt + q_I \qquad (9\text{--}3)$$

If q_I is zero, Eqs. (9–2) and (9–3) may be inserted into Eq. (9–1) to obtain

$$e(t) = \frac{1}{C}q(t) + L\frac{d^2q(t)}{dt^2} + R\frac{dq(t)}{dt} \tag{9-4}$$

The operator D is defined as

$$D \equiv \frac{d}{dt} \tag{9-5}$$

Equation (9–4) becomes

$$e(t) = [\frac{1}{C} + LD^2 + RD]q(t) \tag{9-6}$$

The solution of this differential equation consists of the sum of transient and steady-state solutions. The transient solution has terms of the form

$$q_T(t) = b\epsilon^{rt} \tag{9-7}$$

where the values of r are the roots of the polynomial in D of Eq. (9–6) treating the operator as though it were a variable. The values of the coefficient b are determined from the boundary conditions: the charge and current existing at time $t = 0$ or at any other known times.

The fact that Eq. (9–7), or any other function, represents a solution to Eq. (9–6) is readily determined by substitution of the assumed solution into Eq. (9–6) with $e(t)$ set equal to zero. If the operations indicated by the differential equation on the assumed solution yield zero as the result, the assumed solution is an actual solution.

The roots of the polynomial of Eq. (9–6) may be obtained from the solution of the quadratic equation. Thus

$$r = \frac{-R \pm \sqrt{R^2 - 4L/C}}{2L}$$

$$r_1, r_2 = -\frac{R}{2L} \pm \sqrt{\frac{R^2}{4L^2} - \frac{1}{LC}} \tag{9-8}$$

The transient solution, denoted simply as q_T is

$$q_T = b_1\epsilon^{(-R/2L + \sqrt{R^2/4L^2 - 1/LC})t} + b_2\epsilon^{(-R/2L - \sqrt{R^2/4L^2 - 1/LC})t} \tag{9-9}$$

Note the quantity under the radical in Eq. (9–8). Three possible types of transient solution exist which are based on this quantity. These are the overdamped (radical term positive), critically damped (radical term zero), and underdamped (radical term negative).

(a) If the radical term is positive, both exponential expressions have negative exponents. The transient solution is the sum of two decaying exponential terms.

(b) If the radical term is zero, the general solution should be of the form [Reddick et al, *Mathematics* (16)]

$$q_T = b_1 \epsilon^{-(R/2L)t} + b_2 t \epsilon^{-Rt/2L} \tag{9–10}$$

(c) If the radical term is negative, the two exponents are complex so that the transient solution is a dampled sinusoid. This case is probably the most important of the three.

The damped sinusoid solution may be demonstrated as follows. The complex roots may be expressed as

$$r_1, r_2 = -\alpha \pm j\omega \tag{9–11}$$

where

$$\alpha = \frac{R}{2L} \tag{9–12}$$

and

$$\omega = \sqrt{\frac{1}{LC} - \frac{R^2}{4L^2}}$$

$$= \sqrt{\frac{1}{LC} - \alpha^2} \tag{9–13}$$

Often the following definitions are used

$$\omega_0 \equiv \frac{1}{\sqrt{LC}} \tag{9–14}$$

$$F \equiv \frac{\alpha}{\omega_0} \tag{9–15}$$

Using Eqs. (9–14) and (9–15), (9–13) may be written as

$$\omega = \sqrt{\omega_0^2 - \alpha^2}$$

$$= \omega_0 \sqrt{1 - \frac{\alpha^2}{\omega_0^2}}$$

$$= \omega_0 \sqrt{1 - F^2} \tag{9–16}$$

The actual angular frequency ω is expressed in terms of the undamped or natural angular frequency ω_0 and the damping factor F or the attenuation α.

Using the roots as given by Eq. (9–11), the transient solution is expressed as

$$q_T = b_1 \epsilon^{(-\alpha + j\omega)t} + b_2 \epsilon^{(-\alpha - j\omega)t}$$
$$= b_1 \epsilon^{-\alpha t} \epsilon^{j\omega t} + b_2 \epsilon^{-\alpha t} \epsilon^{-j\omega t}$$
$$= \epsilon^{-\alpha t} [b_1 \epsilon^{j\omega t} + b_2 \epsilon^{-j\omega t}] \tag{9-17}$$

But

$$\epsilon^{j\omega t} = \cos \omega t + j \sin \omega t \tag{9-18}$$

and

$$\epsilon^{-j\omega t} = \cos \omega t - j \sin \omega t \tag{9-19}$$

Substituting Eqs. (9–18) and (9–19) into Eq. (9–17), the transient solution becomes

$$q_T = \epsilon^{-\alpha t} [b_1 \cos \omega t + jb_1 \sin \omega t + b_2 \cos \omega t - jb_2 \sin \omega t]$$
$$= \epsilon^{-\alpha t} [(b_1 + b_2) \cos \omega t + j(b_1 - b_2) \sin \omega t]$$
$$= \epsilon^{-\alpha t} [B_1 \cos \omega t + B_2 \sin \omega t]$$
$$= \epsilon^{-\alpha t} \left[\sqrt{B_1{}^2 + B_2{}^2} \cos\left(\omega t - \tan^{-1}\frac{B_2}{B_1}\right) \right] \tag{9-20}$$

Using the definitions of ω_o and F given by Eqs. (9–14) and (9–15) the Eq. (9–6) may be rewritten as

$$e(t) = L\left[D^2 + \frac{R}{L}D + \frac{1}{LC} \right] q(t)$$
$$= L[D^2 + 2F\omega_o D + \omega_o{}^2] q(t) \tag{9-21}$$

The character of the solution may be determined from the value of F the damping factor.

Range of F	Type of Transient Solution
$0 \le F < 1$	Underdamped
$F = 1$	Critically damped
$F > 1$	Overdamped

The steady-state solution will have a form dependent upon the form of the driving function which in this problem is $e(t)$. The form of $e(t)$ will be the form of the steady-state solution. One method for determining the steady-state solution is to assume a solution having the same form as $e(t)$ with undetermined coefficients. This solution is substituted into the differential equation and coefficients equated to make the driving function identical term-by-term to the function resulting from operating upon the assumed solution.

The most-often encountered forms of the driving function are the constant or step function, power series, exponential functions, and sinusoidal functions. In the case of the power series, the steady-state solution may include terms of higher power than that in the driving function.

If the steady-state solution of Eq. (9–6) is written as q_S, the complete solution of this differential equation may be written as

$$q(t) = q_S + q_T \qquad (9\text{--}22)$$

If the driving function $e(t)$ is the sum of several different functions

$$e(t) = e_1(t) + e_2(t) + e_3(t) \qquad (9\text{--}23)$$

there will be a steady-state solution corresponding to each term of the driving function. In this case, Eq. (9–22) may be written as

$$q(t) = q_{1S} + q_{2S} + q_{3S} + q_T \qquad (9\text{--}24)$$

Note that the transient solution depends only on the circuit elements and not on the driving function.

Two useful rules to remember when evaluating constants from boundary conditions are

- The charge on a capacitor cannot change instantaneously.
- The current through an inductor cannot change instantaneously.

Stated simply, whatever these two conditions were before an instantaneous circuit change, they remain immediately after the change.

The exponential function with time as the independent variable is expressed as

$$f(t) = B\epsilon^{rt} \qquad (9\text{--}25)$$

If r is real and positive, $f(t)$ is a function which rapidly increases without bound in magnitude. A negative value results in a function which decreases to zero. The time constant, τ, is

$$\tau = \frac{1}{r} \qquad (9\text{--}26)$$

If r is a negative real, at a time equal to the value of the time constant, $f(t = \tau)$ has a magnitude of ϵ^{-1} or about 36.8% of the magnitude of $f(t = 0)$. Similarly, after a time equal to two time-constants, $f(t = 2\tau)$ has fallen to ϵ^{-2} or about 13.5% of the magnitude of $f(t = 0)$.

There are more advanced mathematical techniques available to facilitate the solution of differential equations and transient problems. The LaPlace transform method is one of these. [Cf. Gardner et al, *Transients (3)*].

The electrical network and its defining differential equation may be used to solve transient problems in mechanical or electro-mechanical systems by use of the method of analogs. In a mechanical system the differential equations may be written, for example, in terms of physical displacement from a reference and the various derivatives thereof; or it may be written in terms of angular rotation and its derivatives, or temperature, or pressure, or any other variables for which differential equations may be written. The variables in the original system are given electrical analogs and the various constants are converted to resistance, inductance, and capacitance as required. An electrical network is then drawn which is an analog of the proto-type system. The solution of the electrical network may then be transformed to yield the solution of the original.

9.1.1   SAMPLE PROBLEM

In the circuit shown, determine the voltage $e(t)$ on the capacitor and the current $i(t)$ if

(a) The ideal switch is thrown to position 1 with the capacitor initially uncharged.

(b) After steady-state conditions are achieved under the conditions of (a), the switch is thrown to position 2 instantaneously.

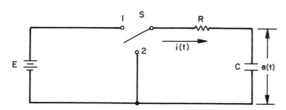

SOLUTION

The desired quantities are determined from a solution of the dif-ferential equation.

(a) When the switch is thrown to position 1, the loop equation is

$$E = v_R + v_C$$
$$= Ri(t) + \frac{1}{C}\int i(t)\,dt$$
$$= R\frac{dq(t)}{dt} + \frac{1}{C}q(t) = \left[RD + \frac{1}{C}\right]q(t)$$

The desired results are determined from

$$e(t) = \frac{q(t)}{C}$$

and

$$i(t) = \frac{d}{dt}q(t)$$

The total solution for $q(t)$ is the sum of a transient q_T and a steady-state q_S, solution.

$$q(t) = q_T + q_S$$

The transient solution is of the form

$$q_T = B_1\epsilon^{rt}$$

From the differential equation, the root of the polynomial in the operator D is obtained from

$$DR + \frac{1}{C} = 0$$

$$r = -\frac{1}{RC}$$

so that

$$q_T = B_1\epsilon^{-t/RC}$$

The steady-state solution is assumed to be

$$q_S = B_2$$

When this is substituted into the differential equation the result is

$$E = \frac{1}{C}B_2$$

so that

$$B_2 = EC$$

The total solution is

$$q(t) = EC + B_1\epsilon^{-t/RC}$$

But from the initial conditions, at $t = 0$, $q(t) = 0$
Thus

$$0 = EC + B_1$$

or

$$B_1 = -EC$$

so that

$$q(t) = EC(1 - \epsilon^{-t/RC})$$

The solution for $e(t)$ is

$$e(t) = \frac{q(t)}{C} = E(1 - \epsilon^{-t/RC}) \qquad \text{ANS.}$$

and $i(t)$ is determined to be

$$i(t) = \frac{d}{dt}q(t)$$

$$= EC\left(-\frac{1}{RC}\right)(-\epsilon^{-t/RC})$$

$$= \frac{E}{R}\epsilon^{-t/RC} \qquad \text{ANS.}$$

These have the general shape as shown

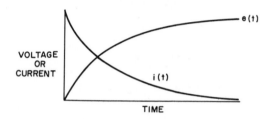

(b) When the switch is thrown to position 2, the loop equation is

$$0 = v_R + v_C$$

The current $i(t)$ flows in the direction opposite to that shown in the circuit diagram.

The differential equation is

$$0 = Ri(t) + \frac{1}{C}\int i(t)\,dt$$

$$= R\frac{d}{dt}q(t) + \frac{1}{C}q(t) = [RD + \frac{1}{C}]q(t)$$

Because there is no driving function, the transient solution is the total solution

$$q(t) = B_3\epsilon^{rt}$$

$$= B_3\epsilon^{-t/RC}$$

and

$$e(t) = \frac{q(t)}{C}$$
$$= \frac{B_3}{C}\epsilon^{-t/RC}$$

At $t = 0^+$, the voltage is the same as at $t = 0^-$ which is the voltage after the transient has diminished to zero, which is

$$e(t = 0^-) = E$$
$$= \frac{B_3}{C}$$

from which

$$B_3 = EC$$

or

$$e(t) = E\epsilon^{-t/RC} \qquad\qquad \text{ANS.}$$

and

$$i(t) = \frac{d}{dt}q(t)$$
$$= \frac{d}{dt}[EC\epsilon^{-t/RC}]$$
$$= \frac{E}{R}\epsilon^{-t/RC} \qquad\qquad \text{ANS.}$$

9.1.2 SAMPLE PROBLEM

Determine the current $i(t)$ in the circuit shown if the ideal switch is closed at $t = 0$ and initially the current in the inductor is zero.

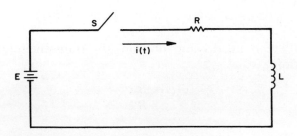

SOLUTION

The current is determined from the solution of the differential equation.

After the switch is closed, the loop equation is

$$E = v_R + v_L$$
$$= Ri(t) + L\frac{d}{dt}i(t)$$
$$= [R + LD]i(t)$$

The current $i(t)$ consists of a transient and a steady-state solution.

$$i(t) = i_T + i_S$$

The transient solution is of the form

$$i_T = B_1\epsilon^{rt}$$

From the differential equation

$$R + LD = 0$$
$$-r = -\frac{R}{L}$$

so that

$$i_T = B_1\epsilon^{-Rt/L}$$

The steady-state solution is of the form

$$i_S = B_2$$

If this solution is substituted into the differential equation, the result is

$$E = B_2R$$

or

$$B_2 = \frac{E}{R}$$

so that

$$i(t) = \frac{E}{R} + B_1\epsilon^{-Rt/L}$$

At time $t = 0^+$, the inductor current is zero. Thus

$$0 = \frac{E}{R} + B_1$$

or

$$B_1 = -\frac{E}{R}$$

Hence

$$i(t) = \frac{E}{R}(1 - \epsilon^{-Rt/L})$$ ANS.

9.2   BASIC ELEMENTS

9.2.1   RESISTOR

The resistance of a conductor of length l and uniform cross-sectional area a and resistivity ρ is

$$R = \frac{\rho l}{a} \tag{9-27}$$

This relationship assumes uniform current density throughout the entire volume of the material.

If the properties of the material are not constant throughout the volume, Eq. (9-27) may be considered to be the resistance of a small volume of the material. The total resistance then becomes the sum total of all the individual elements of the volume remembering that the total resistances of elements in series is the sum of the individual resistances while if the elements are in parallel the total conductance is the sum of the individual conductances.

In electrical work another set of units is used to determine resistance of a circular conductor or to find the size of a conductor of specified resistance. The unit of area is the circular mil. The area in circular mils is not the actual area but is the square of the wire diameter when the diameter is expressed in mils (thousandths of an inch). The length is in feet so that the resistivity has the units of ohms-circular mils per foot. These units may also be abbreviated as mil-foot resistivity or as ohms per mil-foot or as ohms per circular mil-foot. The resistivity at a temperature of 20° C. for the International Annealed Copper Standard (IACS) corresponding to 100% conductivity is [Pender et al., *Handbook* (12), pp. 2–17]:

1.7241   microhm-cm
10.371   ohms (mil, ft)

The resistance of a 10-ft length of 1-mil diameter wire of 100% conductivity copper is

$$R = \frac{10.371 \ (ft)}{d^2}$$
$$= \frac{10.371(10)}{1^2}$$
$$= 103.71 \text{ ohms}$$

The resistance of the same length of 10-mil diameter wire of the same material is

$$R = \frac{10.371(10)}{(10)^2}$$
$$\frac{10.371}{10} = 1.037 \text{ ohms}$$

The resistance of a conductor will change with temperature according to the relationship

$$R_2 = R_1[1 + \alpha(T_2 - T_1)] \qquad\qquad (9\text{--}28)$$

The subscripts refer to the two conditions of temperature and resistance. The value of the temperature coefficient of resistance for 100% conductivity copper at 20° C. is 0.00393 [Pender et al., *Handbook* (12)]. The value of this coefficient is a function of temperature and the composition of the material.

9.2.1.1   SAMPLE PROBLEM

Determine the resistance of a conductor 0.10 m long, with a uniform diameter of 1.0 cm and having a resistivity which varies as a function of length l measured from one end of the conductor according to the formula

$$\rho = 0.003 + 10^{-4}l^2 \text{ ohm-cm}$$

SOLUTION

The resistance of a conductor is given by

$$R = \frac{\rho l}{a}$$

Because the resistivity varies with length, this relationship is modified to become

$$R = \int_{l_1}^{l_2} \frac{\rho dl}{a}$$

Values are substituted and the resistance is determined to be

$$R = \int_0^{10} \frac{(0.003 + 10^{-4}l^2)\ dl}{\pi/4(1)^2}$$

$$= 1.27 \int_0^{10} 0.003 dl + 1.27 \times 10^{-4} \int_0^{10} l^2 dl$$

$$= 1.27[0.003(10)] + 1.27 \times 10^{-4}\left[\frac{(10)^3}{3}\right]$$

$$= 0.0382 + (0.424)(10^{-4})(10^3)$$

$$= 0.0382 + 0.0424$$

$$= 0.0806 \text{ ohms} \qquad \text{ANS.}$$

9.2.1.2 SAMPLE PROBLEM

A motor coil is wound with 150 ft of #18 A.W.G. (diameter: 40.3 mils) 100% conductivity solid copper wire. Determine the d-c resistance of this coil at 55° C. if the coefficient of resistance is 0.00393 ohms/ohm° C.

SOLUTION

Using the value of 10.371 ohms per mil-foot for the resistivity at 20° C., the resistance at 20° C. is

$$R = \frac{10.371\ (ft)}{d^2}$$

$$= \frac{10.371(150)}{(40.3)^2}$$

$$= 0.957 \text{ ohms}$$

At 55 C., the resistance is

$$R_{55} = R_{20}[1 + \alpha(55 - 20)]$$
$$= 0.957[1 + 0.00393(35)]$$
$$= 0.957[1 + 0.1375]$$
$$= 0.957(1.1375) = 1.089 \text{ ohms} \qquad \text{ANS.}$$

9.2.2. CAPACITOR

The capacity is, by definition, the ratio of the charge to the voltage producing that charge.

The capacity of a simple two-plate capacitor is given by [*Measurements*, (15)]

$$C = 0.0885K \, S/\delta \times 10^{-12}$$

(9–29)

This relationship neglects any fringing fields at the edges of the plates.

If the capacitor consists of N similar plates with dielectric between with alternate plates connected together, the capacity is

$$C = 0.0885 \, \frac{K(N-1)S}{\delta} \times 10^{-12}$$

(9–30)

Equation (9–29) may also represent the incremental capacity of a section of a capacitor. The total capacity then becomes the sum total of all incremental capacitances. It should be remembered that the total capacity of parallel capacitors is the sum of the individual capacitances while for capacitors in series, the total capacity equals the reciprocal of the sum of the reciprocals of the individual capacitances.

9.2.2.1 SAMPLE PROBLEM

Determine the capacity of a coaxial capacitor of inner radius r_1 centimeters, outer radius r_2 centimeters, dielectric constant of value K, and length l centimeters.

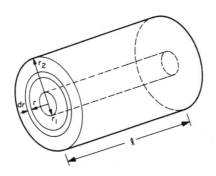

SOLUTION

Consider the total capacity to be the resultant of a number of cylinders connected in series.

$$\frac{1}{C_T} = \Sigma \frac{1}{C}$$

The capacity of each cylinder is

$$C = 0.0885K \frac{2\pi r l}{dr} \times 10^{-12}$$

Then

$$\frac{1}{C} = \frac{dr}{0.556K l r}$$

so that in the limit as $dr \to 0$

$$\frac{1}{C_T} = \int \frac{1}{C}$$

$$= \int_{r_1}^{r_2} \frac{dr}{0.556K l r}$$

$$= \frac{1}{0.556K l r} \Big[ln r \Big]_{r_1}^{r_2} = \frac{1}{0.556K l} ln \frac{r_2}{r_1}$$

The total capacity, then, is

$$C_T = \frac{0.556K l}{ln \ r_2/r_1} \times 10^{-12} \qquad\qquad \text{ANS.}$$

9.2.2.2   SAMPLE PROBLEM

Determine the capacitance of a 1-ft length of a coaxial capacitor if the diameter of the inner conductor is 0.065 in., the inner diameter of the outer conductor is 0.210 in., and the relative dielectric constant of the insulator is 2.1.

SOLUTION

Use the relationship of the previous problem

$$C_T = \frac{0.556K l}{ln \ r_2/r_1} \times 10^{-12}$$

The length must be converted to centimeters; the radii may be left as diameters in inches because the ratio does not change. Hence

$$C_T = \frac{0.556(2.1)(12)(2.54)}{ln\ 0.210/0.065}$$

$$= \frac{35.6}{1.175} = 30.2 \text{ micromicrofarads/ft.} \qquad \text{ANS.}$$

9.2.3   INDUCTOR

The inductance is by definition the ratio of magnetic flux linkages to the current that is responsible for the flux linkages. The flux linkages is the product of the total flux and the number of turns enclosing that flux. In the Mixed-English system of units one henry is the inductance if 10^8 lines result from a current of one ampere. Mathematically the inductance is

$$L = \frac{N\phi}{10^8 I} \qquad (9\text{–}31)$$

The magnetic circuit is discussed in Sec. 2.1.

9.2.3.1   SAMPLE PROBLEM

A coil of 1500 turns is wound on a closed iron core having a cross-sectional area of 1.50 sq. in. The inductance is 10 henrys and may be assumed constant over the range of operation. If the flux density in the iron core is limited to a maximum of 18,000 lines per square inch, what is the maximum current in the coil?

SOLUTION

The formula for inductance may be written as

$$I = \frac{N\phi}{10^8 L}$$

But

$$\phi = BA$$

Hence

$$I_{max} = \frac{NB_{max}A}{10^8 L}$$

$$= \frac{1500(18,000)(1.50)}{10^8(10)}$$

$$= \frac{4.05 \times 10^7}{10^9} = 0.0405 \text{ amp} \qquad \text{ANS.}$$

9.3   FORCE BETWEEN CONDUCTORS

One definition of the ampere is based on the force between two current-carrying conductors. Specifically, if the same current flows in two parallel conductors of infinite length separated by a distance of one meter, the magnitude of the current is one ampere if each conductor experiences a force of 2×10^{-7} newtons per meter of length. This force is the result of the interaction between the current in one conductor and the magnetic field set up by the current in the other conductor. The magnetic field at a point near a conductor is directly proportional to the current in the conductor and inversely proportional to the distance from the center of the conductor. Hence the force between parallel conductors carrying currents I_1 and I_2 may be written

$$\text{Force/unit length} = \frac{B(I_1)(I_2)}{\text{spacing}} \qquad (9\text{--}32)$$

or

$$\text{Force} = \frac{B(I_1)(I_2)(\text{length})}{\text{spacing}} \qquad (9\text{--}33)$$

If the force is to be in pounds, the currents in amperes, the length in feet, and the spacing in inches, the value of B is 5.40×10^{-7}.

This force causes the conductors to repel one another if the two currents flow in the same direction. In the case of a-c sinusoidal currents, if θ is the phase angle between the currents, the repulsive force is given by

$$\text{Force} = \frac{5.40 \times 10^{-7}(I_1)(I_2)(\cos\theta)(\text{length})}{\text{spacing}} \qquad (9\text{--}34)$$

9.3.1   SAMPLE PROBLEM

Two parallel bus bars one foot apart are supported every six feet by insulators. What is the force on each insulator if 50,000 amp d-c flows in the bus bars?

SOLUTION

Assume infinitely long bus bars. The force on each insulator is the force on a 6-ft length of conductor and is given by the following:

$$\text{Force} = \frac{5.40 \times 10^{-7}(I_1)(I_2)(\text{length})}{\text{spacing}}$$
$$= \frac{5.40 \times 10^{-7}(50,000)(50,000)(6)}{12}$$
$$= \frac{8.10 \times 10^3}{12} = 675 \text{ lbs} \qquad \text{ANS.}$$

9.4   ELECTRICAL MEASURING INSTRUMENTS

The three most important electrical measuring instruments are the voltmeter, the ammeter, and the wattmeter. Of the most common basic elements, only one, the electrostatic voltmeter, does not depend for its operation upon the interaction of magnetic fields and current-carrying conductors. Several meter types are listed below:

- Moving coil in a permanent magnetic field. This is also known as the D'Arsonval meter. If the magnetic field strength is uniform, the meter deflection is proportional to the average (over time) current flowing in the coil. Meters having special scales can be made by shaping the magnetic field strength but the deflection is still a function of the average current.
- Rectifier and moving-coil meter. This combination allows the moving coil meter to be used in a-c circuits. The meter deflection is proportional to the average of the rectified current wave.
- Moving iron movements with fixed coils. The moving iron may be a plunger pulled into a coil or may be vanes attracted to or repulsed from the coil. These movements respond to the effective (rms) values of either an alternating or direct current.
- Thermal movements. The alternating or direct current heats a wire which, in turn, either expands allowing the meter to deflect, or changes

the potential of a thermocouple indicated by a d-c instrument. These movements respond to the rms value of the current.

Electrodynamic movement. Current flowing through fixed and moving coils causes an interaction of magnetic fields and a meter deflection which is a function of the rms values of the alternating or direct currents.

These meters are all basically current-measuring devices. The current range may be extended by placing a shunting resistance across the meter. This will cause the total current to divide in proportion to the shunt and meter conductances. These meters may be converted to voltmeters by placing resistors in series with the meter movement. The series resistors or multipliers limit the current which flows at any particular value of applied voltage.

Wattmeters are usually based on the electrodynamic movement. The fixed coil is suitably shunted and connected to carry the load current. The moving coil has the required resistance placed in series and connected to measure the load voltage. The meter response will then be a function of the true load power including the phase angle in the case of a-c circuits.

Figure 9–2 shows two methods of connecting a wattmeter between a power source and a load.

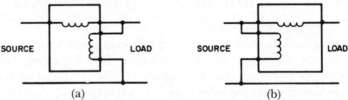

(a)   (b)

(a) voltage coil on load side of current coil; (b) voltage coil on source side of current coil

Figure 9–2 Two methods for connecting a wattmeter

In the method illustrated in Fig. 9–2a, the voltage coil senses the actual load voltage but the current coil senses the combined load and voltage-coil current. In the method illustrated in Fig. 9–2b, the current coil senses the actual load current but the voltage coil senses the voltage of the load plus the voltage drop in the current coil. In either case if exact readings are desired when using an uncompensated wattmeter the readings must be corrected for the error. A compensated wattmeter eliminates this correction by means of an additional coil which automatically subtracts the error from the meter reading. The compensated wattmeter reads correctly when connected as shown in Fig. 9–2a. [Cf. Pender et al *Handbook* (12) pp. 5–30 to 5–32]

All the meter types are characterized by an uncertainty in the indication. This is included in the statement of the meter accuracy. The accuracy of a meter stated as a per cent value gives the maximum error in reading at any position as a per cent of the full-scale deflection.

9.4.1   SAMPLE PROBLEM

A 1-milliampere, 50-ohm, D'Arsonval meter movement requires a damping resistance of 100 ohms. Show how this meter movement may be connected to serve as a properly damped (a) 0–100 v. voltmeter, (b) 0–10 amp ammeter, and determine the value of the resistors required in each case.

SOLUTION

Proper damping requires that the external resistance shunting the meter be 100 ohms.

(a) For a voltmeter, a resistance is put in series with the meter and the damping resistance is put in parallel.

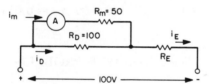

At full-scale deflection of the meter

$$R_E = \frac{100 - v}{i_E}$$

and the meter voltage v is

$$v = i_m R_m = (10^{-3})(50) \text{ v.}$$

However,

$$i_E = i_m + i_D = 10^{-3} + \frac{v}{R_D}$$

$$= 10^{-3} + \frac{50 \times 10^{-3}}{100} = 1.5 \times 10^{-3}$$

Hence,

$$R_E = \frac{100 - 0.050}{1.5 \times 10^{-3}} = \frac{99.95}{1.5 \times 10^{-3}} = 66.67 \times 10^3 \text{ ohms} \qquad \text{ANS.}$$

(b) When the meter is shunted to increase its current range, the circuit is shown.

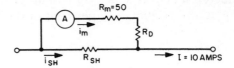

The requirement for proper damping is

$$R_D + R_{SH} = 100 \text{ ohms}$$

For full-scale deflection
$$i_m + i_{SH} = 10 \text{ amps}$$
$$i_{SH} = 10 - 10^{-3} = 9.999 \text{ amps.}$$

But
$$i_{SH}R_{SH} = i_m(R_m + R_D)$$

or
$$(10 - 10^{-3})(100 - R_D) = 10^{-3}(50 + R_D)$$
$$1000 - 10R_D - 0.1 + 10^{-3}R_D = 0.05 + 10^{-3}R_D$$

Hence,
$$R_D = \frac{1000 - 0.15}{10} = 99.985 \text{ ohms} \qquad \text{ANS.}$$

And
$$R_{SH} = 100 - R_D = 100 - 99.985 = 0.015 \text{ ohms} \qquad \text{ANS.}$$

9.4.2   SAMPLE PROBLEM

An iron-vane ammeter with a scale calibrated in rms-values is used to measure the current in the sawtooth wave shown. If the meter indication is 0.5 amp, calculate the peak value of the wave.

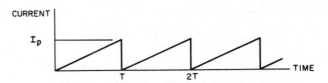

SOLUTION

An iron-vane meter responds to the rms value of the wave so that the indicated 0.5 amp value is the rms value.

Denote the peak value, to be determined, as I_p. The rms value of the wave is

$$I_{rms} = \sqrt{\frac{1}{T}\int_0^T [i(t)]^2 dt}$$

where T is the time of one cycle. For the range $0 \le t \le T$

$$i(t) = \frac{I_p t}{T}$$

so that

$$I_{rms} = \sqrt{\frac{1}{T}\int_0^T \left(\frac{I_p t}{T}\right)^2 dt}$$

$$= \sqrt{\frac{1}{T}\int_0^T \frac{I_p^2 t^2}{T^2} dt}$$

$$= \sqrt{\frac{I_p^2}{T^3}\left[\frac{t^3}{3}\right]_0^T} = \sqrt{\frac{I_p^2}{3}} = \frac{I_p}{\sqrt{3}}$$

or

$$I_p = \sqrt{3}\, I_{rms}$$
$$= \sqrt{3}\,(0.5) = 0.866 \text{ amp} \qquad \text{ANS.}$$

9.5   PRACTICE PROBLEMS

9–1

A time of 10 milliseconds is required for the current to reach 90% of its final (steady state) value in the circuit below.

$E = 10$ v.

$R = 5$ ohms

Switch S_1 was closed at time $t = 0$ with no current flow in the circuit.

(a) What is the time constant in seconds for the circuit?

(b) If $R = 10$ ohms, what is the value of L?

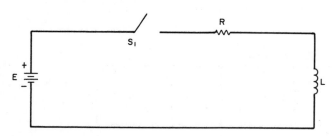

(c) What value of capacitance should be inserted in series with the resistance and inductance of part (b) in order that the frequency of oscillation of resulting current flow be 10^4 cps?

9–2

For the circuit shown develop a functional relationship between current and time at $t = 0$ and $t > 0$. The switch closes at $t = 0$ after having been opened for a long time.

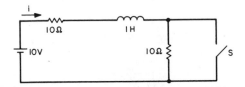

9–3

The ideal switch S is closed until steady-state conditions are established. Then, at an instant of time designated as $t = 0$, the switch is instantaneously opened. Find the value of $i(t)$ at a time 5.1 sec after the switch is opened.

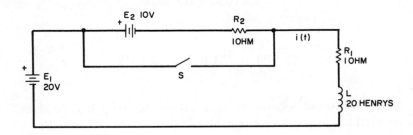

9–4

The ideal switch S is initially open. After steady-state conditions are established, the switch is closed at a given instant of time. Compute the value of the current $i_C(t)$ at 4.5 sec after the switch is closed. Assume E is an ideal battery.

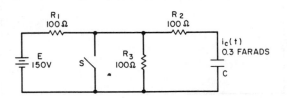

9–5

Determine the current as a function of time $i(t)$ in the following circuit. The ideal switch is closed at $t = 0$. Determine the peak value and the time after switching at which it occurs.

$$e(t) = 10\epsilon^{-5t}$$

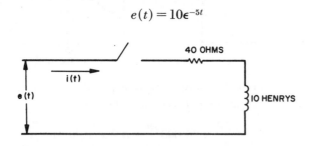

9–6

Certain electric welders have a basic circuit as shown below where S is a switch, operated by an automatic timer, which closes the circuit at any desired point on the 60-cycle, sinusoidal wave of e.

(a) Calculate the magnitude of the transient current resulting when S closes as e is passing through its peak of 100 v.

(b) Calculate the angle at which S should close in order that the transient be zero.

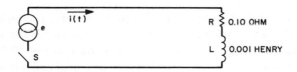

9–7

The circuit shown is that of a simple integrator. For a given repetitive input voltage e_1 the output voltage e_2 is also shown.

Draw the exact waveforms of i and e_1 and calculate the significant values in these waves.

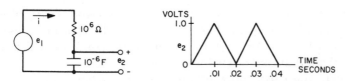

9–8

The voltage e impressed on the circuit shown, varies as indicated. Calculate the value of the steady-state or forced current i.

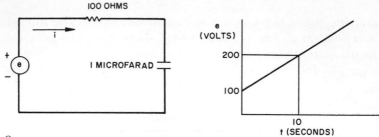

9–9

A torque $T = 5000$ dyne-cm is applied to a certain mechanical system which has a response given by the relation

$$T = 5\frac{d^2\theta}{dt^2} + 20{,}000\frac{d\theta}{dt} + 0.2 \times 10^8\theta$$

where θ is the angular displacement in radians.

(a) Determine the components of the electrical analog consisting of a series circuit driven by a 100-v. source.

(b) Show how the angular velocity of the mechanical system may be determined in the analog circuit by means of a voltage measurement.

(c) Determine whether the mechanical system is over-damped, critically-damped, or under-damped.

9–10

One turn of bar copper is produced by cutting a copper washer along a radius and spreading the ends. The washer is cut from soft-drawn copper having a resistivity at 20° C of 1.724×10^{-6} ohm-cm. The washer is 0.125 in think and has inside and outside diameters of 1 and 9 in, respectively.

Calculate the exact resistance between the ends of the turn, to direct current, taking into account the non-uniform current distribution. Assume the contact at the ends of the turn to be perfect over the entire cross section.

9–11

A capacitor consists of two parallel, plane electrodes each of which has an area of 100 sq cm. The dielectric which separates these electrodes is 0.1 cm thick and has a dielectric constant which varies linearly from 2 at one electrode to 8 at the other.

Calculate the capacitance of this capacitor when fringing is neglected.

9–12

The armature winding of a 4-pole, d-c shunt dynamo has a simplex lap winding arranged in two layers and located in the 58 slots on the armature. Each slot contains 8 conductors. When this machine is operated at 720 rpm with a shunt field current of 10 amp, the open-circuit voltage across the armature is 226 v. The number of turns on each shunt pole is 280.

Calculate the total inductance of the shunt field circuit under these conditions.

9–13

A closed iron-cored reactor has a winding of 250 turns and a cross-sectional area of iron of 4 sq in. This reactor is to be changed by the insertion of an air gap in the core so that its reactance will be 30 ohms at 5 amp and 60 cps. The saturation curve for the iron may be taken as a straight line passing through the point $B = 45,000$ lines/sq in and $NI = 700$ ampere-turns.

Calculate the length of the necessary air gap, neglecting the effects of fringing.

9–14

A given series motor has 2 poles with 95 turns per pole, and with the two coils connected in series. The total resistance of the field coils is 3.02 ohms. With a 60-cycle current of 3.55 amp, the voltage drop across the field coils is 62 v.

Assuming sinusoidal flux and current, find:
(a) the field reactance
(b) the field flux per pole.

9–15

Three straight long circular buses are mounted as shown.
(a) Calculate the magnitudes of the forces per foot of each con-ductor when the currents in conductors A, B, and C are 30,000, 15,000 and 15,000 amps, respectively, and are directed as shown.
(b) Indicate the direction of these forces.

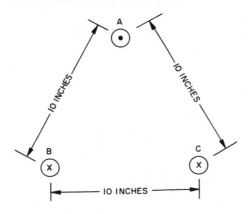

9–16

An ammeter A, a voltmeter V, and wattmeter W, are connected as shown. The wattmeter is uncompensated, and the impedances of its coils may be considered as purely resistive with values of 0.4 and 8000 ohms for the current and voltage coils, respectively. The impedances of the ammeter and voltmeter may also be considered as resistive and their values are 0.1 and 10,000 ohms, respectively.

Calculate the true power delivered to the load when the ammeter, voltmeter, and wattmeter indicate 2.0 amp, 220 v., and 150 watts, respectively.

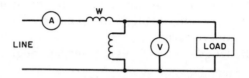

9–17

A 10-ohm resistor carries the output of a perfect half-wave rectifier. The peak value of each half-wave is 10 amp. The voltage across the resistor is measured by three voltmeters as follows:

(a) A conventional d-c voltmeter with D'Arsonval movement and a scale indicating volts

(b) A peak-to-peak voltmeter with a scale indicating rms-volts of the equivalent sine wave

(c) A dynamometer voltmeter with a scale indicating rms-values.

Calculate the voltage indicated by each meter, assuming each meter to be perfect.

9–18

A motor load on one phase of a 208/120-v., 3-phase, 60-cycle system is measured with these three instruments:

INSTRUMENT	FULL SCALE	% ACCURACY
Ammeter	10 amp	0.5
Voltmeter	250 v.	0.5
Wattmeter	2500 watts	0.25

The measurements are as follows:

Amperes	8.7
Volts	210
Watts	135

(a) With what percentages can the power factor be guaranteed?

(b) How much of the error can be assigned to each instrument?
(c) How much error is possible in the phase angle?

9–19

Two types of 100-watt lamps, *A* and *B*, are available. Lamp *A* costs $0.25 each, delivers 18 lumens per watt and has a life of 800 hrs. Lamp *B* costs $0.20 each, delivers 15 lumens per watt and has a life of 1200 hrs.

Calculate; for each type, the cost of the lamps and power for 10^6 lumen-hours of service when the cost of power is $0.04 per kw.-hr.

SOLUTIONS TO PRACTICE PROBLEMS

1–1

The circuit shown consists of pure reactances. This circuit is to yield infinite impedance at $\omega_1 = 1,000$ rad/sec and zero impedance at $\omega_2 = 3,000$ rad./sec. The impedance of the circuit at $\omega_3 = 500$ rad./sec. is $j1,000$ ohms.

Calculate the necessary values of L_1, L_2, and C.

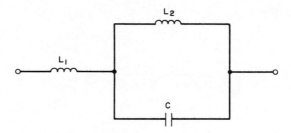

SOLUTION

The overall impedance of this circuit will be written and evaluated at the three stated frequencies.

The overall impedance is

$$Z = j\omega L_1 + \frac{j\omega L_2(1/j\omega C)}{j(\omega L_2 - 1/\omega C)} = j\omega L_1 + \frac{j\omega L_2}{1 - \omega^2 L_2 C}$$

For infinite impedance

$$1 - \omega_1{}^2 L_2 C = 0$$

$$\omega_1{}^2 = \frac{1}{L_2 C} = 10^6$$

or

$$Z = j\left(\omega L_1 + \frac{\omega L_2}{1 - \omega^2/10^6}\right)$$

234

At

$$\omega = \omega_2 = 3 \times 10^3, \ Z = 0$$

$$3 \times 10^3 L_1 + \frac{3 \times 10^3 L_2}{1 - 9 \times 10^6/10^6} = 0$$

or

$$L_1 - \frac{L_2}{8} = 0 \tag{1}$$

At

$$\omega = \omega_3 = 0.5 \times 10^3, \ Z = j1000$$

$$0.5 \times 10^3 L_1 + \frac{0.5 \times 10^3 L_2}{1 - 0.25 \times 10^6/10^6} = 1000$$

or

$$L_1 + \frac{4}{3} L_2 = 2 \tag{2}$$

Solving (1) and (2) simultaneously by substituting in (2) the value of L_1 from (1)

$$\frac{L_2}{8} + \frac{4}{3} L_2 = 2$$

$$3L_2 + 32L_2 = 2(24) = 48$$

so that

$$L_2 = \frac{48}{35} \text{ henry} \qquad\qquad \text{ANS.}$$

and

$$L_1 = \frac{L_2}{8} = \frac{6}{35} \text{ henry} \qquad\qquad \text{ANS.}$$

and

$$C = \frac{1}{10^6 L_2} = \frac{35}{48} \times 10^{-6} \text{ farad} \qquad\qquad \text{ANS.}$$

1-2

The circuit shown is to be adjusted·to unity power factor by the variation of the inductance L. Calculate

(a) the value of R which will result in only one condition of unity power factor as L is varied;

(b) the value of Z at unity power factor under the conditions of (a).

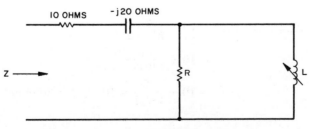

SOLUTION

The solutions will be obtained by expressing the impedance in terms of R and L and setting the imaginary part equal to zero. Thus:

$$Z = 10 - j20 + \frac{j\omega LR}{(R + j\omega L)} \frac{(R - j\omega L)}{(R - j\omega L)}$$

$$= 10 - j20 + \frac{\omega^2 L^2 R + j\omega LR^2}{R^2 + \omega^2 L^2}$$

$$= 10 + \frac{\omega^2 L^2 R}{R^2 + \omega^2 L^2} + j\left(\frac{\omega LR^2}{R^2 + \omega^2 L^2} - 20\right)$$

For unity power factor

$$\frac{\omega LR^2}{R^2 + \omega^2 L^2} - 20 = 0$$

This can be solved for L in terms of R and ω as

$$\omega LR^2 - 20R^2 - 20\omega^2 L^2 = 0$$

or

$$\omega^2 L^2 - \omega L \frac{R^2}{20} + R^2 = 0$$

$$L^2 - \left(\frac{R^2}{20\omega}\right)L + \left(\frac{R^2}{\omega^2}\right) = 0$$

Then

$$L = \frac{1}{2\omega}\left(\frac{R^2}{20} \pm \sqrt{\frac{R^4}{400} - 4R^2}\right)$$

For only one value of L

$$\frac{R^4}{400} - 4R^2 = 0$$

the solutions are $R = 0$ twice, -40, and 40 of which those of zero and -40 are trivial so $R = 40$ and $\omega L = R^2/40 = 40$.

At unity power factor, the value of Z is the real part evaluated as follows:

$$Z|_{\text{unity power factor}} = 10 + \frac{\omega^2 L^2 R}{R^2 + \omega^2 L^2}$$

$$= 10 + \frac{(40)^2(40)}{(40)^2 + (40)^2}$$

$$= 10 + \frac{40}{1 + 1} = 10 + 20 = 30 \text{ ohms} \qquad \text{ANS.}$$

1–3

In the circuit shown, the generator has an internal impedance of 1000(1 + j) ohms and an internal emf of 100 v., both at a frequency of $10^4/2\pi$ cps. This generator is matched to the 500-ohm load by means of L and C.

Calculate the necessary values of L and C which will yield maximum power in the 500-ohm load.

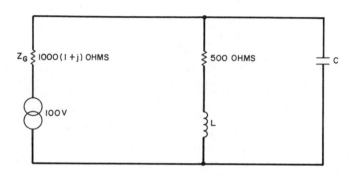

SOLUTION

Maximum power is delivered to the 500-ohm load when the admittance of the load combined with L and C is equal to the complex conjugate of the generator admittance.
The generator admittance is

$$Y_G = \frac{1}{Z_G} = \frac{1}{1000(1+j)}\frac{(1-j)}{(1-j)} = \frac{1-j}{2000}$$

The load admittance is

$$Y_L = \frac{1}{R+j\omega L} + j\omega C$$

$$= \frac{R-j\omega L}{R^2 + \omega^2 L^2} + j\omega C$$

Equate the real parts of Y_L and Y_G

$$\frac{R}{R^2 + \omega^2 L^2} = \frac{1}{2000}$$
$$R^2 + \omega^2 L^2 = 2000R$$
$$\omega^2 L^2 = 2000R - R^2$$
$$= (2000)(500) - (500)^2 = 750{,}000$$

$$L = \frac{1}{\omega}\sqrt{750,000} = \frac{866}{\omega}$$

$$\omega = 2\pi(10^4/2\pi) = 10^4$$

$$L = \frac{866}{10^4} = 0.0866 \text{ henry} \qquad \text{ANS.}$$

The imaginary part of Y_L is equated to the negative of the imaginary part of Y_G.

$$\omega C - \frac{\omega L}{R^2 + \omega^2 L^2} = \frac{1}{2000}$$

$$\omega C = \frac{1}{2000} + \frac{\omega L}{R^2 + \omega^2 L^2}$$

$$= \frac{1}{2000} + \frac{(10^4)(0.0866)}{2000R}$$

$$= \frac{1}{2000} + \frac{866}{10^6} = 0.00050 + 0.000866$$

$$= 1.366 \times 10^{-3}$$

$$C = \frac{1.366 \times 10^{-3}}{\omega} = \frac{1.366 \times 10^{-3}}{10^4} = 0.1366 \times 10^{-6} \text{ farads} \qquad \text{ANS.}$$

1-4

It is required to adjust a series circuit so that it will resonate at 10^6 cps and have a fractional bandwidth at the half-power points of 0.10. A coil of 125 microhenrys and a Q-factor of 20 is to be used in conjunction with a variable capacitor of negligible loss. State how the circuit is to be adjusted to meet the requirements.

SOLUTION

The coil can be represented as a series R-L in series with a tuning capacitor and a bandwidth-adjusting resistor as shown.

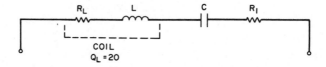

The resonant frequency is

$$f_o = \frac{1}{2\pi\sqrt{LC}} = 10^6$$

Thus

$$C = \frac{1}{4\pi^2 L f_o^2}$$

$$= \frac{1}{4\pi^2 (125) (10^{-6}) (10^6)^2} = 203 \times 10^{-12} \text{ farad}$$

The fractional bandwidth at the half-power points is determined from

$$Q = \frac{f_o}{\Delta f}$$

or

$$\frac{\Delta f}{f_o} = \text{fractional bandwidth} = 0.10 = \frac{1}{Q}$$

or

$$Q = 10 = \frac{\omega_o L}{R_L + R_1}$$

But

$$Q_L = \frac{\omega_o L}{R_L}$$

So that

$$\frac{\omega_o L}{\omega_o L / Q_L + R_1} = 10$$

Substituting for Q_L its value of 20 and solving for R_1 yields

$$\omega_o L = 10 \frac{\omega_o L}{20} + 10 R_1$$

$$R_1 = \frac{\omega_o L}{20}$$

$$= \frac{2\pi (10^6) (125) (10^{-6})}{20} = 39.2 \text{ ohms}$$

The circuit can be adjusted by making C a variable capacitor which is adjusted until the resonant frequency is correct. Then R_1 is adjusted to provide the proper bandwidth.

1-5

The circuit shown represents a direct-current 3-wire system obtained by using a balancer set B_1, B_2 in conjunction with the generator G. For the purposes of this problem, the losses in the balancer set may be neglected, and both armatures may be considered as batteries of equal voltage. Each line wire has a resistance of 0.3 ohms, the generator voltage is 240, and the loads are 4.2 and 6.3 ohms.

Calculate the currents in each line, and in the machines G, B_1, and B_2.

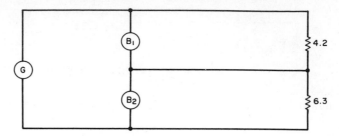

SOLUTION

Redraw figure and write loop equations

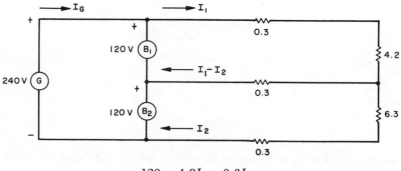

$$120 = 4.8I_1 - 0.3I_2$$
$$120 = -0.3I_1 + 6.9I_2$$

Solving

$$I_1 = \frac{\begin{vmatrix} 120 & -0.3 \\ 120 & 6.9 \end{vmatrix}}{\begin{vmatrix} 4.8 & -0.3 \\ -0.3 & 6.9 \end{vmatrix}} = \frac{828 + 36}{33.12 - 0.09} = \frac{864}{33.03} = 26.16 \text{ amp} \qquad \text{ANS.}$$

$$I_2 = \frac{\begin{vmatrix} 4.8 & 120 \\ -0.3 & 120 \end{vmatrix}}{33.03} = \frac{576 + 36}{33.03} = \frac{612}{33.03} = 18.53 \text{ amp} \qquad \text{ANS.}$$

$$I_1 - I_2 = 26.16 - 18.53 = 7.63 \text{ amp} \qquad \text{ANS.}$$

$$I_G + I_{B_1} = 26.16$$
$$I_{B_1} + I_{B_2} = 7.63$$
$$I_{B_2} + 18.53 = I_G$$

The generator power equals the total load power
$$240I_G = 120I_1 + 120I_2$$
$$I_G = \frac{I_1 + I_2}{2} = \frac{44.69}{2} = 22.35 \text{ amp} \qquad \text{ANS.}$$

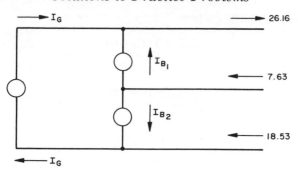

Thus

$$I_{B_1} = 26.16 - I_G = 26.16 - 22.35 = 3.81 \text{ amp} \qquad \text{ANS.}$$
$$I_{B_2} = I_G - 18.53 = 22.35 - 18.53 = 3.82 \text{ amp} \qquad \text{ANS.}$$

1–6

A source of constant current delivers 10 amp to the network shown. Calculate

(a) the value of R which will absorb maximum power from the circuit.

(b) the value of this maximum power.

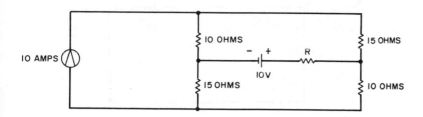

SOLUTION

Remove the branch containing R and the 10-v. battery and make a Thévenin's equivalent circuit of the remainder.

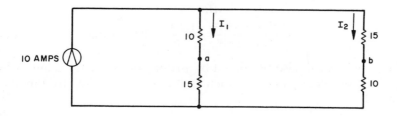

The Thévenin voltage is

$$E_{ab} = 15I_1 - 10I_2$$

But

$$I_1 + I_2 = 10$$

And

$$25I_1 = 25I_2$$

Hence

$$I_1 = I_2 = 5 \text{ amp}$$

or

$$E_{ab} = 15(5) - 10(5) = 5(5)$$
$$= 25 \text{ v.}$$

The Thévenin's impedance is the resistance seen looking back into terminals *a-b*. By inspection this is the parallel combination of two 25-ohm resistances or 12.5 ohms.
The complete circuit is thus reduced to the following

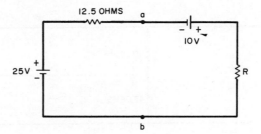

By inspection, the value of R for maximum power is the value of the equivalent circuit resistance:

$$R = 12.5 \text{ ohms} \qquad \text{ANS.}$$

The maximum power in R is

$$P_{max} = \frac{(E/2)^2}{R} = \frac{E^2}{4R}$$
$$= \frac{(25 + 10)^2}{4(12.5)} = \frac{(35)^2}{50} = 24.5 \text{ watts} \qquad \text{ANS.}$$

This problem can also be solved by writing loop equations and solving them simultaneously but such a solution is more involved mathematically.

1–7

Three resistors, each of 1 ohm, are connected in delta. Inside the delta, a 1-ohm resistor is connected from each corner to a common point, thus forming a wye inside the delta. Six batteries, each of a different unknown emf and negligible internal resistance, are inserted into the network, one in each of the six branches. The current in one of the delta resistors is found to be 5 amp. Now an additional resistance of 2 ohms is inserted in the branch which was carrying 5 amp, making a total of 3 ohms in this branch under the new condition. What is the new current in this branch?

SOLUTION

The schematic may be drawn as shown.

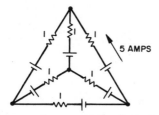
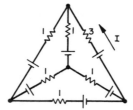

The circuit may be analyzed by writing loop equations. There are 6 branches and 4 nodes; hence the number of loop equations necessary is

$$L = B - N + 1$$
$$= 6 - 4 + 1 = 3$$

The generalized schematic is redrawn with assumed loops.

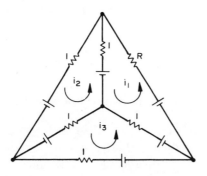

Let the sum of the battery voltages in loop 1 be E_a, in loop 2 E_b and in loop 3 E_c. Loop equations may be written as

$$
\begin{aligned}
E_a &= (R+2)\,i_1 - i_2 - i_3 \\
E_b &= \quad -i_1 \quad +3i_2 - i_3 \\
E_c &= \quad -i_1 \quad\;\; -i_2 + 3i_3
\end{aligned}
$$

These equations are solved for i_1 as

$$
i_1 = \frac{\begin{vmatrix} E_a & -1 & -1 \\ E_b & 3 & -1 \\ E_c & -1 & 3 \end{vmatrix}}{\begin{vmatrix} (R+2) & -1 & -1 \\ -1 & 3 & -1 \\ -1 & -1 & 3 \end{vmatrix}} = \frac{9E_a + E_c + E_b + 3E_c - E_a + 3E_b}{9(R+2) - 1 - 1 - 3 - (R+2) - 3}
$$

$$
= \frac{8E_a + 4E_b + 4E_c}{8(R+2) - 8} = \frac{8E_a + 4E_b + 4E_c}{8R + 8}
$$

When $R = 1$, $i_1 = 5$ amp. Then

$$
\begin{aligned}
8E_a + 4E_b + 4E_c &= 5[8(1) + 8] \\
&= 5(16)
\end{aligned}
$$

When $R = 3$, I is to be determined as

$$
\begin{aligned}
I = i_1' &= \frac{5(16)}{8(3) + 8} \\
&= \frac{80}{24 + 8} \\
&= \frac{80}{32} = 2.5 \text{ amp} \qquad\qquad \text{ANS.}
\end{aligned}
$$

1-8

The open-circuit emf and short-circuit current of an audio oscillator are 50 v. and 0.447 amp, respectively. When a 50-ohm resistance is connected to this oscillator, the terminal potential difference is 17.65 v. What is the absolute value of the internal impedance of this generator?

SOLUTION

The equivalent circuit as shown will be analyzed.

From the data, $E = 50$ v.

$$
\begin{aligned}
|Z_G| &= E/I_{sc} \\
&= 50/0.447 = 112 \text{ ohms}
\end{aligned}
$$

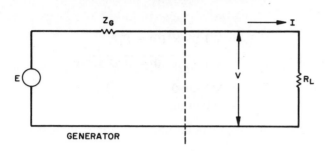

GENERATOR

Let Z_G be represented as

$$R_G \pm jX_G$$

When R_L is a 50-ohm resistor

$$I = \frac{V}{R_L}$$
$$= \frac{17.65}{50} = 0.353 \text{ amp.}$$

But

$$I = \frac{E}{(R_G + R_L) \pm jX_G}$$

and

$$(112)^2 = R_G{}^2 + X_G{}^2$$

or

$$X_G{}^2 = 1.25 \times 10^4 - R_G{}^2$$

Then

$$0.353 = \frac{50}{(50 + R_G) + j\sqrt{1.25 \times 10^4 - R_G{}^2}}$$

Rewriting

$$(50 + R_G)^2 + 1.25 \times 10^4 - R_G{}^2 = \left(\frac{50}{0.353}\right)^2$$
$$2.5 \times 10^3 + 100R_G + R_G{}^2 + 1.25 \times 10^4 - R_G{}^2 = 2.0 \times 10^4$$

from which

$$R_G = \frac{2 \times 10^4 - 1.5 \times 10^4}{100}$$
$$= 50 \text{ ohms}$$

and

$$X_G = \sqrt{1.25 \times 10^4 - R_G{}^2}$$
$$= \sqrt{1.25 \times 10^4 - 0.25 \times 10^4}$$
$$= \sqrt{10,000}$$
$$= 100 \text{ ohms}$$

Thus the generator equivalent internal impedance may be represented as

$$Z_G = 50 \pm j100 \text{ ohms} \qquad\qquad \text{ANS.}$$

The problem does not give enough information to determine the sign of the reactive part of the generator impedance. Only its magnitude can be determined.

1–9

The bridge shown receives power from the generator G at 1,000 cps. This bridge is first balanced with S_1 at 1 and S_2 open. This balance yields $R = 10$ ohms and $C_s = 1,200 \times 10^{-12}$ farad.

The bridge is balanced a second time with S_1 at 2 and S_2 closed. In this case, $R = 100$ ohms and $C_s = 900 \times 10^{-12}$ farad.

Calculate the values of R_x and C_x, considering C_s as lossless.

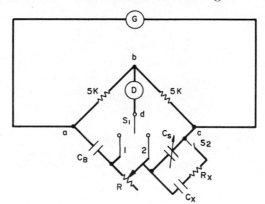

SOLUTION

In a balanced bridge

$$\frac{Z_{ab}}{Z_{bc}} = \frac{Z_{ad}}{Z_{dc}}$$

But since $Z_{ab} = Z_{bc}$ the solution is obtained by solving

$$Z_{ad} = Z_{dc}$$

The first balance indicates that C_B is not lossless but may be represented by a 10-ohm resistance in series with a 1200 $\mu\mu f$ capacitance. Or

$$Z_c = 10 - \frac{j}{2\pi(1000)(1200 \times 10^{-12})} = 10 - j1.33 \times 10^5$$

The second balance yields

$$Z_{ad} = 100 + 10 - j1.33 \times 10^5 = 110 - j1.33 \times 10^5$$
$$Z_{dc} = \frac{(R_x - j/\omega C_x)(-j/\omega C_s)}{R_x - j(1/\omega C_x + 1/\omega C_s)}$$

but

$$\frac{1}{\omega C_s} = \frac{1}{2\pi(1000)(900 \times 10^{-12})} = 1.77 \times 10^5$$

so that

$$Z_{dc} = \frac{-jR_x(1.77 \times 10^5) - 1.77 \times 10^5/\omega C_x}{R_x - j(1/\omega C_x + 1.77 \times 10^5)}$$

Equating Z_{ad} and Z_{dc}

$$110 - j1.33 \times 10^5 = \frac{(-28.2/C_x) - jR_x(1.77 \times 10^5)}{R_x - j(1/\omega C_x + 1.77 \times 10^5)}$$

$$[110 - j1.33 \times 10^5]\left[R_x - j\left(\frac{1}{\omega C_x} + 1.77 \times 10^5\right)\right] = \frac{-28.2}{C_x} - jR_x(1.77 \times 10^5)$$

First equate real parts

$$110R_x - \frac{1.33 \times 10^5}{\omega C_x} - (1.33)(1.77)(10^{10}) = \frac{-28.2}{C_x}$$

$$110R_x + \frac{7}{C_x} = 2.36 \times 10^{10} \tag{1}$$

Next equate imaginary parts

$$-1.33 \times 10^5 R_x - \frac{110}{\omega C_x} - (110)(1.77)(10^5) = -R_x(1.77 \times 10^5)$$

$$4.4 \times 10^4 R_x - \frac{0.0175}{C_x} = 1.95 \times 10^7 \tag{2}$$

Then (1) and (2) can be solved simultaneously as

$$110R_x + \frac{7}{C_x} = 2.36 \times 10^{10}$$

$$\underline{1.76 \times 10^7 R_x - \frac{7}{C_x} = 7.8 \times 10^9}$$

$$1.76 \times 10^7 R_x \qquad = 3.14 \times 10^{10}$$

or

$$R_x = \frac{3.14 \times 10^{10}}{1.76 \times 10^7} = 1.78 \times 10^3 \text{ ohms} \qquad \text{ANS.}$$

Also

$$\frac{7}{C_x} = 2.36 \times 10^{10} - 110R_x$$

or

$$C_x = \frac{7}{2.36 \times 10^{10} - 110(1.78 \times 10^3)}$$
$$\cong 297 \times 10^{12} \text{ farad}$$ ANS.

An alternate method of solution is to match admittances of the two arms.

It should be noted that whenever possible the mathematics should be kept as simple as possible. For example if the expression for Z_{dc} is rationalized before it is equated to Z_{ad}, the resulting expressions obtained by equating real and imaginary parts become much more involved.

1–10

The circuit shown includes a generator with an internal resistance, $R_G = 1000$ ohms; an emf of constant magnitude, $E = 150$ v.; and variable frequency. The coil in the tank circuit has an inductance, $L = 200$ microhenrys, and a Q-factor, $Q = 10$, which may be considered constant. The tuning capacitor is fixed at $C = 10^{-10}$ farad. Calculate

 (a) the frequency of parallel resonance,
 (b) the voltage E_o across the tank at parallel resonance,
 (c) the power delivered to the tank coil at parallel resonance.

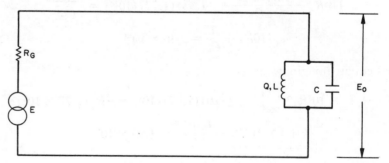

SOLUTION

Let the inductor equivalent circuit be an inductor in parallel with a resistor which provides the losses.

(a) The resonant frequency f_r is

$$f_r = \frac{1}{2\pi\sqrt{LC}}$$

$$= \frac{1}{2\pi\sqrt{200(10^{-6})(10^{-10})}}$$

$$= \frac{1}{2\pi\sqrt{2}(10^{-7})}$$

$$= \frac{10^7}{8.89} = 1.125 \times 10^6 \text{ cps} \qquad \text{ANS.}$$

(b) At parallel resonance, the tank circuit appears purely resistive with a value R_r. The tank voltage may be found by considering R_r and R_G as forming a voltage divider. Thus

$$E_o = E\frac{R_r}{R_G + R_r}$$

But from the definition of Q of a circuit consisting of a coil and a resistor in parallel.

$$Q = \frac{R}{\omega L}$$
$$R_r = \omega_r L Q$$
$$= 2\pi f_r L Q$$
$$= 2\pi(1.125)(10^6)(200)(10^{-6})(10)$$
$$= 14.1 \times 10^3 \text{ ohms}$$

Hence

$$E_o = \frac{14.1 \times 10^3}{10^3 + 14.1 \times 10^3}(150)$$
$$= \frac{14.1 \times 10^3}{15.1 \times 10^3}(150) = 140.1 \text{ volts} \qquad \text{ANS.}$$

(c) The power delivered to the tank at resonance P_r is the power dissipated in the equivalent tank resistance which is

$$P_r = \frac{(E_o)^2}{R_r}$$
$$= \frac{(140.1)^2}{14.1 \times 10^3}$$
$$= \frac{1.97 \times 10^4}{1.41 \times 10^4} = 1.40 \text{ watts} \qquad \text{ANS.}$$

2–1

The circuit shown is that of a thyratron rectifier and its control network. The operating frequency is 60 cps; $L = 10$ henrys; $R = 11{,}310$ ohms; $e_{ba} = 100$ volts; $e_{co} = e_{od} = 50$ volts.

Calculate the magnitude of the voltage e_{og} and the number of degrees it leads or lags e_{ba}.

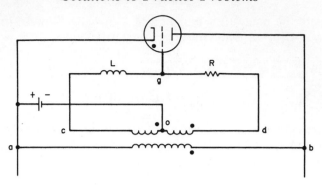

SOLUTION

The voltage, e_{og}, may be found by considering the loop consisting of the transformer secondary winding and L and R.

$$e_{og} = e_{od} + e_{dg}$$
$$= e_{od} + i_{dg}R$$

But

$$i_{dg} = \frac{e_{dc}}{R + j\omega L}$$
$$= \frac{100 \ \underline{/0}}{11{,}310 + j(2\pi)(60)(10)}$$
$$= \frac{100 \ \underline{/0}}{11{,}310 + j3770}$$
$$= \frac{100 \ \underline{/0}}{11{,}950 \ \underline{/18.4}} = 0.00836 \ \underline{/-18.4} \text{ amp}$$

Hence

$$e_{og} = 50 \ \underline{/180} + (0.00836 \ \underline{/-18.4})(11{,}310)$$
$$= 50 \ \underline{/180} + 94.8 \ \underline{/-18.4}$$
$$= -50 + 89.9 - j29.9$$
$$= 39.9 - j29.9 = 50 \ \underline{/-36.9}$$

The magnitude of e_{og} is 50 volts. ANS.

The voltages e_{ba} and e_{dc} are in phase hence the voltage e_{og} lags e_{ba} by 36.9 degrees. ANS.

2–2

The transformer shown may be considered ideal. The turns ratios are $N_2/N_1 = 1.5$ and $N_3/N_1 = 2$. The impedances are $Z_2 = 100(1 + j)$ ohms and $Z_3 = 50(1 - j3)$ ohms.

Calculate the magnitude and sign of X_4 which will make the power factor, at the input, equal to unity.

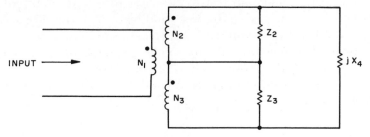

SOLUTION

The three impedances reflect into the primary in parallel. The three reflected impedances are

$$Z_2' = \left(\frac{N_1}{N_2}\right)^2 Z_2$$

$$= \frac{1}{(1.5)^2} 100(1+j) = 44.4(1+j)$$

$$Z_3' = \left(\frac{N_1}{N_3}\right)^2 Z_3$$

$$= \frac{1}{(2)^2} 50(1-j3) = 12.5(1-j3)$$

$$X_4' = \left(\frac{N_1}{N_2+N_3}\right)^2 X_4 = \left(\frac{1}{N_2/N_1+N_3/N_1}\right)^2 X_4$$

$$= \frac{1}{(3.5)^2} X_4 = 0.082 X_4$$

For the three impedances in parallel, add the admittances to obtain the total admittance.

$$Y_T = \frac{1}{44.4(1+j)} + \frac{1}{12.5(1-j3)} + \frac{1}{j0.082 X_4}$$

$$= 0.01127(1-j) + 0.008(1+j3) - j\frac{12.2}{X_4}$$

For unity power factor, the imaginary part of the total admittance is zero.

$$-j0.01127 + j0.024 - j\frac{12.2}{X_4} = 0$$

$$\frac{12.2}{X_4} = 0.01273$$

$$X_4 = \frac{+12.2}{0.01273} = +958 \text{ ohms} \qquad \text{ANS.}$$

2-3

A 3-coil transformer is used to match two loads to a generator. The first load, a 500-ohm resistor which is to receive 55.6% of the total power, is connected to the first winding of N_1 turns. The second load, equivalent to a 4-ohm resistor, is connected to the second coil of N_2 turns. The generator having an internal resistance of 100 ohms is to be matched when connected to the third coil of N_3 turns.

Calculate the required ratios N_1/N_3 and N_2/N_3, assuming the transformer to be ideal.

SOLUTION

The circuit diagram may be drawn as shown.

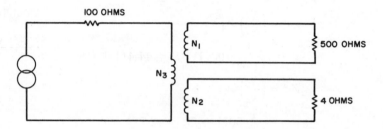

The two loads reflect to the primary by the turns-ratio squared and are in parallel. The total reflected load admittance must equal the generator admittance for impedance match. Thus

$$\frac{1}{100} = \frac{1}{(N_3/N_1)^2 500} + \frac{1}{(N_3/N_2)^2 4}$$

If a primary voltage e is assumed across the reflected admittance, the power in the 500-ohm load may be computed as

$$\frac{e^2}{(N_3/N_1)^2 500} = 0.556\frac{e^2}{100}$$

or

$$\left(\frac{N_3}{N_1}\right)^2 = \frac{100}{0.556(500)} = 0.36$$

$$\frac{N_3}{N_1} = 0.6$$

$$\frac{N_1}{N_3} = 1.667 \qquad \text{ANS.}$$

Substituting this value

$$\frac{1}{100} = \frac{1}{(0.36)500} + \frac{1}{(N_3/N_2)^2 4} = \frac{1}{180} + \frac{1}{(N_3/N_2)^2 4}$$

$$0.01 = 0.00555 + \frac{1}{(N_3/N_2)^2 4}$$

$$\frac{N_3}{N_2} = \sqrt{\frac{1}{4(0.01 - 0.00555)}}$$

$$= \frac{1}{2\sqrt{0.00445}} = \frac{1}{2(0.0667)}$$

or

$$\frac{N_2}{N_3} = 2(0.0667) = 0.1334 \qquad\qquad \text{ANS.}$$

2–4

Power at 1000 cps is supplied by a generator having an internal impedance of $100 + j50$ ohms. Maximum power is required in the load consisting of an impedance, $1000 - j100$ ohms. A tuning capacitor is placed in the circuit as shown. If the open-circuit emf of the generator is 75 v., calculate:

(a) the reactance of the required capacitor
(b) the turns-ratio N_1/N_2 of the idealized transformer
(c) the power delivered to the load.

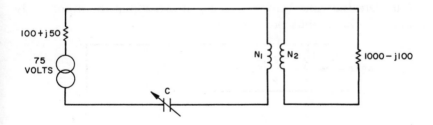

SOLUTION

The capacitor reactance is required to effect a conjugate impedance match between the generator and the reflected load impedance. That is

$$\left(\frac{N_1}{N_2}\right)^2 (1000 - j100) - jX_C = 100 - j50$$

Equating the real parts

$$\left(\frac{N_1}{N_2}\right)^2 1000 = 100$$

thus

$$\frac{N_1}{N_2} = \sqrt{\frac{100}{1000}} = 0.316 \qquad \text{ANS.}$$

Equating the imaginary parts

$$-j\left(\frac{N_1}{N_2}\right)^2 100 - jX_C = -j50$$

$$-j10 - jX_C = -j50$$

thus

$$jX_C = -j40 \text{ ohms} \qquad \text{ANS.}$$

The power delivered to the load is

$$P = I^2 R_L = \left(\frac{E}{R_G + R_L}\right)^2 R_L$$

$$= \left(\frac{75}{100 + 100}\right)^2 100 = \left(\frac{75}{200}\right)^2 100 = 14.1 \text{ watts} \qquad \text{ANS.}$$

2–5

An autotransformer is connected as shown. For the purposes of this problem, the losses in the transformer and its exciting current may be neglected and the coupling among the various coils may be considered perfect. The turns ratios are $N_2/N_1 = 2$ and $N_3/N_1 = 3$.

Calculate the value and sign of X_x in order that the input to the primary N_1 be at unity power factor.

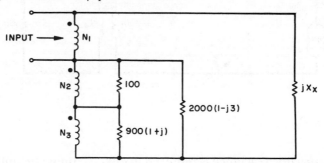

SOLUTION

The various impedances reflect to the input in parallel. For unity power factor the imaginary part of the equivalent impedance or admittance is zero.

There are four impedances reflected to the input:

The 100-ohm reflects as $(N_1/N_2)^2(100) = (\frac{1}{2})^2 100 = 25$ ohms

The $900(1 + j)$-ohm reflects as

$$(N_1/N_3)^2(900)(1 + j) = (\frac{1}{3})^2 900(1 + j) = 100(1 + j)$$

The $2000(1 - j3)$-ohm reflects as

$$\left(\frac{N_1}{N_2 + N_3}\right)^2 2000(1 - j3) = \frac{2000}{(2 + 3)^2}(1 - j3) = \frac{2000}{25}(1 - j3)$$
$$= 80(1 - j3)$$

And jX_x reflects as

$$\left(\frac{N_1}{N_1 + N_2 + N_3}\right)^2 jX_x = \frac{jX_x}{(1 + 2 + 3)^2} = \frac{jX_x}{36}$$

Add the admittances to obtain the total admittance

$$Y_T = \frac{1}{25} + \frac{1}{100(1 + j)} + \frac{1}{80(1 - j3)} + \frac{1}{jX_x/36}$$
$$= 0.040 + 0.005(1 - j) + 0.00125(1 + j3) - j\frac{36}{X_x}$$

The sum of the imaginary parts is

$$-j0.005 + j0.00375 - j\frac{36}{X_x} = 0$$

or

$$jX_x = \frac{-j36}{0.00125} = -j28,800 \text{ ohms} \qquad \text{ANS.}$$

2–6

A 10-kva, 2300/115 v., 60-cycle, single-phase transformer gave the following data on tests:

No-load test (input to the low-voltage side)

Applied voltage	115 v.
Current	0.9 amp
Power	70 watts

Short-circuit test (input to high-voltage side; low side shorted)

Applied voltage	118 v.
Current	4.35 amp
Power	225 watts

(a) Assuming that the core loss varies as the 1.7 power of the flux, find the efficiency of the transformer when supplying 60 amp at unity power factor at 115 v.

(b) Find the corresponding voltage applied to the primary.

SOLUTION

(a) The efficiency may be found as

$$\eta = \frac{\text{output}}{\text{output} + \text{losses}}$$

The output is

$$P_o = EI \cos \theta$$
$$= (115)(60)(1.0) = 6900 \text{ watts}$$

The losses consist of core loss and resistive losses. An equivalent circuit may be drawn as shown.

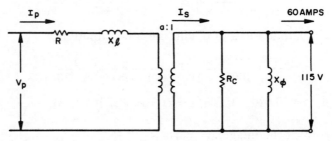

The values for the equivalent circuit are determined from test results. From the short-circuit test

$$R = \frac{P}{I^2} = \frac{225}{(4.35)^2} = 11.9 \text{ ohms}$$

and

$$X_l = \sqrt{Z^2 - R^2} = \sqrt{\left(\frac{V}{I}\right)^2 - R^2}$$

$$= \sqrt{\left(\frac{118}{4.35}\right)^2 - (11.9)^2}$$

$$= \sqrt{737 - 142} = \sqrt{595} = 24.4 \text{ ohms}$$

Because the equivalent circuit has the core voltage and flux-density the same as in the test, no correction in core loss will be necessary. From the open-circuit test, the core components are determined.

$$R_c = \frac{E^2}{P}$$

$$= \frac{(115)^2}{70} = 189 \text{ ohms}$$

$$X_\phi = \frac{E}{I_\phi} = \frac{E}{\sqrt{(I)^2 - (E/R_c)^2}}$$

$$= \frac{115}{\sqrt{(0.9)^2 - (115/189)^2}} = \frac{115}{\sqrt{0.810 - 0.364}}$$

$$= \frac{115}{\sqrt{0.446}} = \frac{115}{0.668} = 173 \text{ ohms}$$

The resistive losses are determined as follows:

$$P_R = (I_p)^2 R$$

$$I_p = \frac{I_s}{a}$$

$$a = \frac{2300}{115} = 20$$

$$I_s = 60 + \frac{115}{189} - j\frac{115}{173} = 60.6 - j0.665$$

$$\approx 60.6$$

$$I_p = \frac{60.6}{20} = 3.03$$

$$P_R = (3.03)^2(11.9)$$

$$= 110 \text{ watts}$$

The core loss is the same as the power of the open-circuit test which is 70 watts. Hence

$$\eta = \frac{(6900)100}{6900 + 110 + 70} = 100\left(\frac{6900}{7080}\right) = 97.5\% \qquad \text{ANS.}$$

(b) From the equivalent circuit the primary voltage is determined as

$$V_p = (115)a + I_p(R + jX_l)$$
$$= 2300 + (3.03)(11.9) + j(3.03)(24.4)$$
$$= 2300 + 36 + j74$$
$$\approx 2336 \text{ v.} \qquad \text{ANS.}$$

2-7

A 100-kva, 11,000/2200-v., 60-cycle, single-phase transformer has an Hysteresis loss of 750 watts, an Eddy-current loss of 225 watts, and a copper loss of 940 watts under the rated conditions of full load. It is desired to export this transformer and to operate it at 45 cps but with the same maximum flux density and the same total loss as at 60 cps.

Calculate the new voltage and kva-rating. Neglect the exciting current.

SOLUTION

Use the expressions for Hysteresis and Eddy-current losses to obtain new values at the new frequency. The new ratings are determined from the values at the new frequency.
The total losses at full load and 60 cps are

$$P_T = P_h + P_e + P_{\text{copper}}$$
$$= 750 + 225 + 940 = 1915 \text{ watts}$$

The expressions for core loss are

$$P_h = K_h f B^n{}_{\text{max}}$$
$$P_e = K_e f^2 B^2{}_{\text{max}}$$

Let the primed values indicate values at the new frequency. The modified core losses are

$$P_h' = \frac{45}{60}(750) = 562 \text{ watts}$$
$$P_e' = \left(\frac{45}{60}\right)^2 (225) = 126.5 \text{ watts}$$

Assume the copper loss to be independent of frequency and flux density. Then.

$$P'_{\text{copper}} = P_T - P'_h - P'_e$$
$$= 1915 - 562 - 126.5 = 1226.5 \text{ watts}$$

If the voltage is sinusoidal

$$E = 4.44 B_{\text{max}} f N A \times 10^{-8}$$

then

$$E'_p = \frac{45}{60}(11{,}000) = 8250 \text{ v.}$$

The rated primary current at 60 cps is

$$I_p = \frac{\text{kva}}{E} = \frac{100{,}000}{11{,}000} = 9.1 \text{ amp}$$

The total equivalent winding resistance referred to the high-voltage winding at 60 cps is

$$R = \frac{P_{\text{copper}}}{I^2{}_p} = \frac{940}{(9.1)^2} = 11.35 \text{ ohms}$$

The primary current at 45 cps is

$$I'_p = \sqrt{\frac{P'_{\text{copper}}}{R}} = \sqrt{\frac{1226.5}{11.35}} = 10.4 \text{ amp}$$

The new kva rating is

$$\text{kva}' = \frac{(8250)(10.4)}{1000} = 86 \text{ kva} \qquad \text{ANS.}$$

The new voltage rating is

$$8250/1650 \qquad \text{ANS.}$$

2-8

When 2200 v. at 60 cps is impressed on a certain transformer at no load, the total iron loss is 200 watts. When the frequency of the impressed voltage is changed to 25 cps and the magnitude of the voltage is made such as to maintain the same maximum flux density as before, the iron loss falls to 75 watts.

Neglect the impedance drop and calculate:
(a) the magnitude of the impressed voltage necessary at 25 cps;
(b) the Eddy-current loss and the Hysteresis loss at 60 cps.

SOLUTION

Assume the applied voltages are rms values of sinusoids
(a) The maximum flux density is given by

$$B_{\text{max}} = \frac{E}{4.44fNA \times 10^{-8}} = K\frac{E}{f}$$

Thus

$$K\frac{E_{60}}{60} = K\frac{E_{25}}{25}$$

or

$$E_{25} = \frac{25}{60}E_{60} = \frac{25}{60}(2200) = 916 \text{ v.} \qquad \text{ANS.}$$

(b) The total core loss is

$$P_c = P_e + P_h$$
$$= K_e f^2 B^2_{\text{max}} + K_h f B^n_{\text{max}}$$

At 60 cps

$$200 \text{ watts} = K_e(60)^2 B^2_{\text{max}} + K_h 60 B^n_{\text{max}}$$

At 25 cps

$$75 \text{ watts} = K_e(25)^2 B^2_{\text{max}} + K_h 25 B^n_{\text{max}}$$

The two equations are solved simultaneously for $K_e(B_{max})^2$

$$200(25) = K_eB^2{}_{max}(60)^2(25) + K_hB^n{}_{max}(60)(25)$$
$$\underline{-75(60) = -K_eB^2{}_{max}(25)^2(60) - K_hB^n{}_{max}(60)(25)}$$
$$200(25) - 75(60) = K_eB^2{}_{max}[(60)^2(25) - (25)^2(60)]$$
$$200 - 180 = K_eB^2{}_{max}[(60)^2 - (25)(60)]$$
$$20 = K_eB^2{}_{max}[(60)^2 - (25)(60)]$$
$$1 = K_eB^2{}_{max}[(60)(3) - (25)(3)]$$
$$K_eB^2{}_{max} = \frac{1}{180 - 75} = \frac{1}{105}$$

Thus at 60 cps

$$P_e = K_eB^2{}_{max}f^2$$
$$= \frac{1}{105}(60)^2 = 34.3 \text{ watts} \qquad \text{ANS.}$$

and

$$P_h = P_c - P_e = 200 - 34.3 = 165.7 \text{ watts} \qquad \text{ANS.}$$

2–9

A transformer consisting of two identical coils is connected in a circuit as shown. Each coil of the transformer has a self-inductance of 10 henrys and the coefficient of coupling between them is 0.90. The power source E has a negligible internal impedance and a terminal voltage of 500 at an angular frequency ω of 1000 rad/sec. The value of C is 1 microfarad.

Calculate the value of the current in the 1000-ohm load resistor.

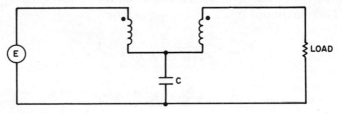

SOLUTION

Analyze the circuit using loop equations.

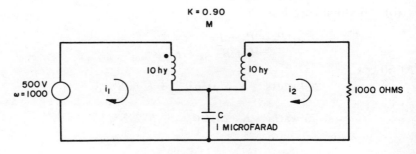

The loop equations may be written as

$$500 = i_1\left(j\omega L_1 - \frac{j}{\omega C}\right) + i_2\left(+\frac{j}{\omega C} - j\omega M\right)$$

$$0 = i_1\left(+\frac{j}{\omega C} - j\omega M\right) + i_2\left(1000 + j\omega L_2 - \frac{j}{\omega C}\right)$$

The value of the mutual inductance is found from

$$K \equiv \frac{M}{\sqrt{L_1 L_2}}$$

$$M = K\sqrt{L_1 L_2} = 0.9\sqrt{(10)(10)} = 9 \text{ henrys}$$

Thus the loop equations become

$$500 = ji_1\left[10(10)^3 - \frac{1}{10^3(10^{-6})}\right] + ji_2\left[\frac{1}{10^3(10^{-6})} - 9 \times 10^3\right]$$

$$0 = ji_1\left[\frac{1}{10^3(10^{-6})} - 9 \times 10^3\right] + i_2\left[10^3 + j10 \times 10^3 - \frac{j}{10^3(10^{-6})}\right]$$

$$500 = ji_1[10^4 - 10^3] + ji_2[10^3 - 9 \times 10^3] = $$
$$ji_1[9 \times 10^3] - ji_2[8 \times 10^3]$$

$$0 = ji_1[10^3 - 9 \times 10^3] + i_2[10^3 + j(10^4 - 10^3)] = $$
$$-ji_1[8 \times 10^3] + i_2[10^3 + j9 \times 10^3]$$

From which

$$i_2 = \frac{\begin{vmatrix} j9 \times 10^3 & 500 \\ -j8 \times 10^3 & 0 \end{vmatrix}}{\begin{vmatrix} j9 \times 10^3 & -j8 \times 10^3 \\ -j8 \times 10^3 & 10^3 + j9 \times 10^3 \end{vmatrix}} = \frac{j4 \times 10^6}{j9(10^6 + j9 \times 10^6) + 64 \times 10^6}$$

$$= \frac{j4}{j9 - 81 + 64} = \frac{j4}{j9 - 17} = \frac{4\ \underline{/90}}{19.35\ \underline{/152}} = 0.207\ \underline{/-62}$$

$$|i_2| = 0.207 \text{ amp} \hspace{4cm} \text{ANS.}$$

2–10

An audio frequency transformer has two coils. At the frequency of operation, the self-reactances of the primary and secondary coils have reactances of 1000 and 4000 ohms, respectively. The coefficient of coupling, for the purposes of this problem, is unity, and the resistances of the coils may be neglected.

Neglecting the core losses, calculate the input impedance at the terminals of the primary winding when the impedance of the load, connected to the secondary, is $1000(1 - j3)$ ohms.

SOLUTION

An equivalent circuit is shown below with assumed currents. Assume a primary voltage e causes the primary current i. The ratio of e/i is the input impedance.

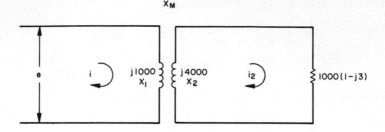

The coefficient of coupling is

$$K = \frac{X_M}{\sqrt{X_1 X_2}}$$

or

$$X_M = K\sqrt{X_1 X_2} = 1\sqrt{(10^3)(4)(10^3)} = 2 \times 10^3$$

The loop equations are

$$e = i(j1000) - i_2(j2000)$$
$$o = -i(j2000) + i_2(1000 - j3000 + j4000)$$

Solving for the input current

$$i = \frac{\begin{vmatrix} e & -j2000 \\ o & 1000 + j1000 \end{vmatrix}}{\begin{vmatrix} j1000 & -j2000 \\ -j2000 & 1000 + j1000 \end{vmatrix}} = \frac{e(10^3)(1+j)}{j10^6(1+j) + 4 \times 10^6}$$

$$= \frac{e}{j10^3 + (4 \times 10^3)/(1+j)}$$

Thus

$$\frac{e}{i} = Z_{\text{in}} = j10^3 + \frac{4 \times 10^3}{1+j} = 10^3(j + 2 - j2)$$
$$= 10^3(2-j) \text{ ohms} \qquad \text{ANS.}$$

2-11

The open-circuit emf across the secondary winding of an air-cored transformer is 60 v. when 200 watts at 50 v. and a power factor of 0.6 are applied to the primary. The frequency is 60 cps and the turns ratio a, primary to secondary, is 1:2.

Calculate the self-inductance and leakage inductance of the primary winding and the mutual inductance between the coils.

SOLUTION

The desired values may be obtained from an analysis of a transformer equivalent circuit shown below.

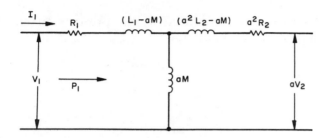

The turns ratio a is 0.5

$$V_2 = 60 \text{ v.}$$
$$V_1 = 50 \text{ v.}$$
$$P_1 = 200 \text{ watts @ } 0.6 \text{ power factor}$$
$$f = 60 \text{ cps, } \omega = 2\pi f = 377 \text{ rad/sec}$$

The power factor is the ratio of power to volt-amperes or

$$\frac{P_1}{V_1 I_1} = 0.60$$

or

$$I_1 = \frac{P_1}{0.6 V_1}$$
$$= \frac{200}{0.6(50)} = 6.67 \text{ amp}$$

The total impedance is

$$\frac{V_1}{I_1} = R_1 + j\omega L_1$$

or

$$\omega L_1 = \sqrt{\left(\frac{V_1}{I_1}\right)^2 - (R_1)^2} = \sqrt{\left(\frac{V_1}{I_1}\right)^2 - \left(\frac{P_1}{I_1^2}\right)^2}$$
$$= \sqrt{\left(\frac{50}{6.67}\right)^2 - \left[\frac{200}{(6.67)^2}\right]^2}$$
$$= \sqrt{56.25 - 20.25} = \sqrt{36} = 6 \text{ ohms}$$

so that

$$L_1 = \frac{\omega L_1}{\omega} = \frac{6}{2\pi(60)}$$

$$= \frac{6}{377} = 0.0159 \text{ henry} \qquad \text{ANS.}$$

The secondary voltage is induced by the primary current flowing through the mutual reactance. Or

$$|aV_2| = I_1(a\omega M)$$

Then

$$M = \frac{aV_2}{a\omega I_1} = \frac{V_2}{\omega I_1}$$

$$= \frac{60}{377(6.67)} = 0.0239 \text{ henry} \qquad \text{ANS.}$$

The leakage inductance is $L_1 - aM$

$$= 0.0159 - 0.5(0.0239)$$
$$= 0.0159 - 0.0119$$
$$= 0.0040 \text{ henry} \qquad \text{ANS.}$$

2–12

A transformer, which for the purposes of this problem may be considered lossless, is required to transmit maximum power from a 3000-ohm generator to a 6-ohm load with half-power points at $f_1 = 200/2\pi$ and $f_2 = 10,000/2\pi$. Both the generator and load impedances are pure resistances.

Calculate the inductances of the primary and secondary windings and the coefficient of coupling in the required transformer.

SOLUTION

The various quantities may be determined by an analysis of an equivalent circuit shown below. The transformer is shown lossless.

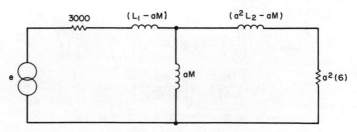

The actual primary and secondary inductances are L_1 and L_2. The turns ratio a is

$$a = \frac{N_1}{N_2} = \sqrt{\frac{L_1}{L_2}}$$

For maximum power transfer the reflected load resistance equals the generator resistance.

$$a^2(6) = 3000$$

Thus

$$a^2 = \frac{3000}{6} = 500$$

$$a = 22.4$$

The coefficient of coupling K is

$$K = \frac{aM}{\sqrt{L_1 a^2 L_2}} = \frac{M}{\sqrt{L_1 L_2}}$$

$$= \frac{aM}{L_1}$$

In determining frequency response, the series reactances are negligible and the shunt reactance is infinite at mid-band. Thus the load is matched to the generator for maximum power transfer. In this case the load and generator are both 3000 ohms. At low frequencies, the shunt reactance causes the power delivered to the load to drop as the reactance becomes smaller. Loop equations may be written as shown.

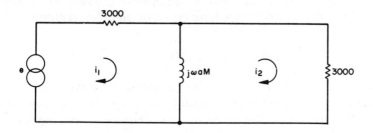

$$e = (3000 + j\omega aM)i_1 - j\omega aM i_2$$
$$0 = -j\omega aM i_1 + (3000 + j\omega aM)i_2$$

These equations may be solved for i_2

$$i_2 = \frac{\begin{vmatrix} 3000 + j\omega aM & e \\ -j\omega aM & 0 \\ (3000 + j\omega aM) & -j\omega aM \\ -j\omega aM & (3000 + j\omega aM) \end{vmatrix}}{}$$

$$= \frac{je\omega aM}{(3000 + j\omega aM)^2 + (\omega aM)^2} = \frac{je\omega aM}{(3000)^2 + j6000\omega aM}$$

The magnitude of this current is equal to 0.707 times the midband current at the lower 3-db frequency. The midband current I_o is

$$I_o = \frac{e}{6000}$$

Thus at the lower 3-db frequency

$$\frac{e\omega aM}{|(3000)^2 + j6000\omega aM|} = \frac{0.707e}{6000}$$

$$\frac{\omega aM}{|1500 + j\omega aM|} = 0.707$$

or

$$\frac{(\omega aM)^2}{(1500)^2 + (\omega aM)^2} = \frac{1}{2}$$
$$2(\omega aM)^2 = (1500)^2 + (\omega aM)^2$$
$$(\omega aM)^2 = (1500)^2$$
$$\omega aM = 1500$$

Hence

$$aM = \frac{1500}{\omega}$$

$$= \frac{1500}{2\pi(200/2\pi)} = 7.50 \text{ henrys}$$

At higher frequencies, the series reactance becomes appreciable and causes the current and hence the power delivered to the load to drop. Thus the simple series loop equation may be written

$$i_1 = \frac{e}{6000 + j\omega(L_1 - aM) + j\omega(a^2L_2 - aM)}$$

At the upper 3-db frequency the magnitude of this current is equal to 0.707 times the midband current. Thus the reactive part of the denominator equals the resistive part. Hence at the upper 3-db frequency

$$\omega[L_1 - aM + a^2L_2 - aM] = 6000$$

But

$$a^2 = \frac{L_1}{L_2}$$

Thus

$$2L_1 - 2aM = \frac{6000}{\omega}$$

$$L_1 - aM = \frac{3000}{\omega}$$

$$= \frac{3000}{2\pi(10,000/2\pi)} = 0.30$$

or

$$L_1 = 0.30 + aM$$
$$= 0.30 + 7.50$$
$$= 7.80 \text{ henrys} \qquad \text{ANS.}$$

and

$$L_2 = \frac{L_1}{a^2}$$

$$= \frac{7.80}{(22.4)^2} = \frac{7.80}{500} = 0.0156 \text{ henry ANS.}$$

$$K = \frac{aM}{L_1} = \frac{7.50}{7.80} = 0.962 \qquad \text{ANS.}$$

2–13

Two single-phase transformers with equal ratings and turns ratios are operated in parallel to supply a load of 180 kw at a lagging power factor of 0.90. Transformer *A* has internal drops at full load for resistance and reactance of 1 and 6%, respectively. Transformer *B* has corresponding drops of 2 and 5%.

Calculate the power delivered by each transformer to the load.

SOLUTION

The problem can be solved by means of a transformer equivalent circuit. Neglecting core components and referring all quantities to the secondary side, a simple equivalent may be drawn as shown.

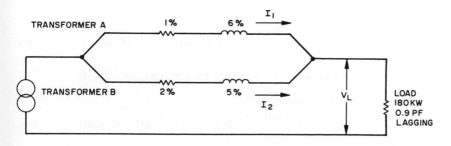

The per cent impedances may be considered actual impedance values and it is permissible to equate the voltage drops in the two transformers as

$$I_1(1 + j6) = I_2(2 + j5)$$

or

$$I_1(6.1\underline{/80.55}) = I_2(5.4\underline{/68.2})$$

or

$$I_2 = I_1(1.135\underline{/12.35})$$

But

$$(I_1 + I_2)V_L(0.9) = 180 \text{ kw}$$

$$I_1 + 1.135\underline{/12.35}I_1 = \frac{180,000}{0.90V_L}$$

$$= I_1(1.00 + 1.11 + j0.242)$$

$$= I_1(2.11 + j0.242) = I_1(2.13\underline{/6.6})$$

The total current responsible for the load power is $2.13\underline{/6.6}\ I_1$. Vectorially

$$I_1 = \frac{1}{2.13\underline{/6.6}}I_T = 0.470\underline{/-6.6}I_T$$

and

$$I_2 = 1.135\underline{/12.35}I_1 = 0.532\underline{/5.75}I_T$$

The total current I_T is the sum of I_1 and I_2, and has a power factor which is 0.9 lagging. Hence the total current lags the load voltage by an angle $(\cos^{-1} 0.9)$ or 25.9 degrees. Thus

$$I_1 = 0.470|I_T|\underline{/-25.9° - 6.6°} = 0.470|I_T|\underline{/-32.5°}$$
$$I_2 = 0.532|I_T|\underline{/-25.9° + 5.75°} = 0.532|I_T|\underline{/-20.15°}$$

But

$$|I_T| = \frac{180,000}{0.9V_L} = \frac{200,000}{V_L}$$

Hence the power delivered by transformer A, denoted P_A, is

$$P_A = I_1V_L\cos(32.5°)$$
$$= (0.470)\left(\frac{200,000}{V_L}\right)V_L(0.843) = 79,600 \text{ watts} \qquad \text{ANS.}$$

and the power delivered by transformer B, denoted P_B, is

$$P_B = I_2V_L\cos(20.15°)$$
$$= (0.532)\left(\frac{200,000}{V_L}\right)V_L(0.939) = 100,400 \text{ watts} \qquad \text{ANS.}$$

2–14

A radio transmitter operates at a frequency, $f = 10^8/2\pi$ cps. The radiator is a dipole having an effective resistance of 70 ohms at the operating frequency. Power to the radiator is supplied over a 500-ohm line which is matched to the dipole by means of a transformer consisting of two equal coils of 1 microhenry each. This transformer is tuned by means of a single capacitor shunted across the primary winding.

Calculate the size of this tuning capacitor and the coefficient of coupling K necessary in the transformer. Neglect the losses in the reactors and the transmission line.

SOLUTION

Draw an equivalent circuit as shown; write loop equations and solve for the input admittance to the transformer. The real part of the input admittance equals the reciprocal of the line resistance which is assumed matched. The imaginary part of this admittance must be cancelled by the tuning capacitor.

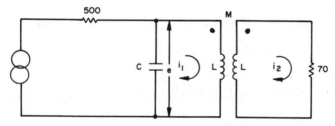

By definition the coefficient of coupling is

$$K = \frac{M}{\sqrt{L_1 L_2}} = \frac{M}{L}$$

or

$$M = KL$$

The loop equations for the transformer are

$$e = (j\omega L)i_1 - (j\omega KL)i_2$$
$$0 = -(j\omega KL)i_1 + (70 + j\omega L)i_2$$

Solving for i_1

$$i_1 = \frac{\begin{vmatrix} e & -j\omega KL \\ 0 & 70 + j\omega L_1 \end{vmatrix}}{\begin{vmatrix} j\omega L & -j\omega KL \\ -j\omega KL & (70 + j\omega L_1) \end{vmatrix}} = \frac{e(70 + j\omega L)}{(70 + j\omega L)(j\omega L) + \omega^2 K^2 L^2}$$

The input admittance to the transformer is

$$Y_T = \frac{i_1}{e} = \frac{70 + j\omega L}{\omega^2 L^2 (K^2 - 1) + j70\omega L}$$

This may be separated into a real and imaginary portion

$$Y_T = \frac{(70 + j\omega L)\,[\omega^2 L^2 (K^2 - 1) - j70\omega L]}{[\omega^2 L^2 (K^2 - 1)]^2 + (70\omega L)^2}$$

$$= \frac{70\omega^2 L^2 K^2}{[\omega^2 L^2 (K^2 - 1)]^2 + (70\omega L)^2} + \frac{j[\omega^3 L^3 (K^2 - 1) - \omega L(70)^2]}{[\omega^2 L^2 (K^2 - 1)]^2 + (70\omega L)^2}$$

The real part is set equal to the source conductance

$$\frac{1}{500} = \frac{70\omega^2 L^2 K^2}{[\omega^2 L^2 (K^2 - 1)]^2 + (70\omega L)^2}$$

But

$$\omega = 2\pi f = 2\pi (10^8/2\pi) = 10^8 \text{ rad/sec}$$

and

$$L = 10^{-6} \text{ henry}$$

or

$$\omega L = 10^8 (10^{-6}) = 10^2 \text{ ohms}$$

so that

$$500(70)\,10^4 K^2 = 10^8 (K^4 - 2K^2 + 1) + 0.49 \times 10^8$$

This may be reduced to

$$K^4 - 5.5K^2 + 1.49 = 0$$

$$K^2 = \frac{5.5 \pm \sqrt{(5.5)^2 - 4(1.49)}}{2} = \frac{1}{2}(5.5 \pm \sqrt{30.2 - 5.96})$$

$$= \frac{1}{2}(5.5 \pm \sqrt{24.24}) = \frac{1}{2}(5.5 \pm 4.92)$$

Since the sum will give a value of K greater than one which is impossible, we take the difference to get

$$K = \sqrt{0.29} = 0.539 \qquad\qquad \text{ANS.}$$

The transformer susceptance is the evaluated imaginary part of the admittance

$$B_T = \frac{j[10^6 (0.29 - 1.00) - 10^2 (4900)]}{[10^4 (0.29 - 1.00)]^2 + 4900(10^4)}$$

$$= -j\frac{1.20 \times 10^6}{0.99 \times 10^8} = -j1.21 \times 10^{-2} \text{ mho}$$

This susceptance is cancelled by a positive (capacitative) susceptance of the same value

$$\omega C = 1.21 \times 10^{-2}$$

$$C = \frac{1.21 \times 10^{-2}}{\omega}$$

$$= \frac{1.21 \times 10^{-2}}{10^8} = 121 \text{ micromicrofarads} \qquad \text{ANS.}$$

2–15

A radio-frequency transformer for power transmission purposes consists of two equal coils, each having an inductance of one millihenry. The mutual inductance between the coils can be adjusted from 100 to 150 microhenries by moving one coil with respect to the other. This transformer is to be used to furnish perfect coupling between a circuit of $1600 - j1000$ ohms and a load of $400 + j500$ ohms at a frequency of 1 Mc, with maximum selectivity.

Calculate the circuit elements required, and show by a diagram how the circuit is connected.

SOLUTION

A load can be matched to a generator using a Tee matching section which is also a form of equivalent circuit for a transformer.

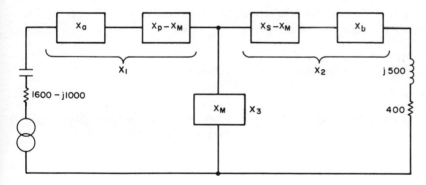

The expressions relating X_1, X_2, and X_3 are

$$X_1 = \pm\sqrt{\frac{R_G}{R_L}(X_3{}^2 - R_G R_L)} - X_3$$

$$X_2 = \pm\sqrt{\frac{R_L}{R_G}(X_3{}^2 - R_G R_L)} - X_3 \qquad *$$

*From John D. Ryder, *Networks, Lines, and Fields*, second edition, copyright 1955. Used by permission of Prentice-Hall, Inc., Englewood Cliffs, N.J.

A requirement is that all three reactances cannot be the same type. The critical value for X_3, which is the mutual reactance, is

$$X_3 = \sqrt{R_G R_L}$$
$$= \sqrt{(400)(1600)} = 800 \text{ ohms inductive} \qquad †$$

At 10^6 cps

$$M = \frac{800}{2\pi(10^6)} = 127.6 \text{ microhenries which is realizable.}$$

Using the critical value for X_3 one obtains that

$$|X_1| = |X_2| = |X_3| ‡$$

If all the three reactances cannot be the same type there are three possibilities if X_3 is inductive

Case 1 X_1 capacitive, X_2 capacitive
Case 2 X_1 capacitive, X_2 inductive
Case 3 X_1 inductive, X_2 capacitive

The values of the added reactances X_a and X_b are found from

$$X_1 = -j1000 + X_a + (X_p - X_M)$$
$$X_2 = j500 + X_b + (X_s - X_M)$$

X_p and X_s are the reactances of the transformer primary and secondary which are equal.

$$X_p = X_s = j\omega L = j2\pi fL$$
$$= j2\pi(10^6)(10^{-3}) = j6280 \text{ ohms}$$

Case 1:

$$X_a = X_1 + j1000 - X_p + X_M = -j800 + j1000 - j6280 + j800 = -j5280$$
$$X_b = X_2 - j500 - X_s + X_M = -j800 - j500 - j6280 + j800 = -j6780$$

Case 2:

$$X_a = -j5280$$
$$X_b = X_2 - j500 - X_s + X_M = +j800 - j500 - j6280 + j800 = -j5180$$

Case 3:
$$X_a = j800 - j500 - j6280 + j800 = -j3680$$
$$X_b = -j6780$$

†*Ibid.*
‡*Ibid.*

The possible capacitor values required are

Case 1 $C_a = 30 \times 10^{-12}$ farads, $C_b = 23.5 \times 10^{-12}$ farads
Case 2 $C_a = 30 \times 10^{-12}$ farads, $C_b = 30.7 \times 10^{-12}$ farads
Case 3 $C_a = 43.3 \times 10^{-12}$ farads, $C_b = 23.5 \times 10^{-12}$ farads ANS.

3-1

A 3-phase, 3-wire, 2200-v. line supplies power to a 3-phase transformer which in turn supplies three 3-phase balanced loads, as follows:

(1) 200 kva, at 208 v. and a power factor of 0.8, to induction motors driving machine tools

(2) 100 kva, at 120 v. and a power factor of 0.95, to lights

(3) 50 kva, at 208 v. and a power factor of 0.90, to induction motors driving pumps.

Calculate the current in the 3-phase, 2200-v. line, neglecting the exciting currents and losses in the transformer.

SOLUTION

This problem can be solved by considering all loads referred to the 2200-v. line (voltage assumed line-to-line).

Loads (1) and (3) are stated as inductive and so have lagging power factors. The lighting load, load (2), should be resistive but may have an inductive line component, hence it also is at a lagging power factor.

Load 1:

$$I_1 = \frac{va_1}{\sqrt{3}E} = \frac{200,000}{\sqrt{3}(2200)} = 52.5\underline{/\theta_1} \text{ amp}$$

$$\theta_1 = \cos^{-1} 0.80 = -36.8°$$

Load 2:

$$I_2 = \frac{va_2}{\sqrt{3}E} = \frac{100,000}{\sqrt{3}(2200)} = 26.25\underline{/\theta_2} \text{ amp}$$

$$\theta_2 = \cos^{-1} 0.95 = -18°$$

Load 3:

$$I_3 = \frac{va_3}{\sqrt{3}E} = \frac{50,000}{\sqrt{3}(2200)} = 13.12\underline{/\theta_3} \text{ amp}$$

$$\theta_3 = \cos^{-1} 0.90 = -25.8°$$

$$I_{\text{line total}} = I_1 + I_2 + I_3 = 52.5\underline{/-36.8} + 26.25\underline{/-18} + 13.15\underline{/-25.8}$$

$$= 42.0 - j31.4 + 25.0 - j8.1 + 11.85 - j5.7$$

$$= 78.85 - j45.2 = 90.5\underline{/-29.8°} \text{ amp}$$

or

$$90.5 \text{ amp at a p.f. of } \cos (29.8°) = 0.87 \text{ lagging} \qquad \text{ANS.}$$

3–2

In the circuit shown, the unbalanced 3-phase generator supplies power to an unbalanced 3-phase load. The circuit data are:

$$\begin{array}{ll}
E_{ga} = E_1 = 120 \underline{/0°} \quad \text{v.} & Z_1 = 10 + j0 \text{ ohms} \\
E_{gb} = E_2 = 115 \underline{/120°} \quad \text{v.} & Z_2 = 3 + j4 \text{ ohms} \\
E_{gc} = E_3 = 125 \underline{/-120°} \text{ v.} & Z_3 = 5 - j5 \text{ ohms}
\end{array}$$

Calculate the voltages V_{oa}, V_{ob}, V_{oc}.

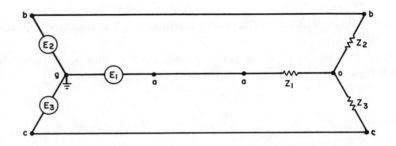

SOLUTION

Write the equation for the summation of the currents at the node "o" in terms of the voltages and admittances and solve for the node voltage, V_o. The desired voltages are determined by taking the difference between V_o and the line voltages.

At node "o"

$$I_{oa} + I_{ob} + I_{oc} = 0$$

But

$$\begin{aligned}
I_{oa} &= \frac{(V_o - V_a)}{Z_1} = (V_o - V_a)Y_1 \\
I_{ob} &= (V_o - V_b)/Z_2 = (V_o - V_b)Y_2 \\
I_{oc} &= (V_o - V_c)/Z_3 = (V_o - V_c)Y_3
\end{aligned}$$

where the voltages are all expressed using point "g" as a reference. Thus

$$V_o Y_1 - V_a Y_1 + V_o Y_2 - V_b Y_2 + V_o Y_3 - V_c Y_3 = 0$$

or

$$V_o = \frac{V_a Y_1 + V_b Y_2 + V_c Y_3}{Y_1 + Y_2 + Y_3}$$

But

$$V_a = 120 \underline{/-180^\circ}$$
$$V_b = 115 \underline{/-60^\circ}$$
$$V_c = 125 \underline{/60^\circ}$$

and

$$Y_1 = 1/Z_1 = 1/(10 \underline{/0^\circ}) = 0.10 \underline{/0}$$

$$Y_2 = 1/Z_2 = \frac{1}{3 + j4} = \frac{1}{5 \underline{/53.2^\circ}} = 0.20 \underline{/-53.2^\circ}$$

$$Y_3 = 1/Z_3 = \frac{1}{5 - j5} = \frac{1}{7.07 \underline{/-45^\circ}} = 0.14 \underline{/45^\circ}$$

Thus

$$V_o = \frac{(120 \underline{/-180})(0.10 \underline{/0}) + (115 \underline{/-60})(0.20 \underline{/-53.2}) + (125 \underline{/60})(0.14 \underline{/45})}{0.10 \underline{/0} + 0.20 \underline{/-53.2} + 0.14 \underline{/45}}$$

$$= \frac{12.0 \underline{/-180} + 23.0 \underline{/-113.2} + 17.8 \underline{/105}}{0.10 + 0.12 - j0.16 + 0.10 + j0.10}$$

$$= \frac{-12.0 - 9.05 - j21.1 - 4.6 + j17.2}{0.32 - j0.06}$$

$$= \frac{-25.46 - j3.9}{0.32 - j0.06} = \frac{25.8 \underline{/-171.3}}{0.325 \underline{/-10.6}}$$

$$79.0 \underline{/-160.7} = -75.4 - j26.1$$

Hence

$$V_{oa} = V_o - V_a = 79.0 \underline{/-160.7} - 120 \underline{/-180}$$
$$= -75.4 - j26.1 + 120 = 44.6 - j26.1 = 51.6 \underline{/-30.3} \quad \text{ANS.}$$

$$V_{ob} = V_o - V_b = 79.0 \underline{/-160.7} - 115 \underline{/-60}$$
$$= -75.4 - j26.1 - 57.5 + j99.5$$
$$= -132.9 + j73.4 = 149.3 \underline{/151.1} \quad \text{ANS.}$$

$$V_{oc} = V_o - V_c = 79.0 \underline{/-160.7} - 125 \underline{/60}$$
$$= -75.4 - j26.1 - 62.5 - j108.2$$
$$= -137.9 - j134.3 = 192 \underline{/-135.8} \quad \text{ANS.}$$

An alternative method of solution for this problem is to determine the line currents and compute the desired voltages as the product of line current and load impedance. The amount of computation required is about the same for either method of solution.

3–3

A 3-phase, wye-connected power system with grounded neutral supplies energy to a 3-phase, wye-connected load shown. The line voltages are:

$$E_{AB} = 2200 \ \underline{/0°}$$
$$E_{BC} = 2200 \ \underline{/120°}$$
$$E_{CA} = 2200 \ \underline{/-120°}$$

Calculate the potential difference between "*O*" and ground when the ground connection at "*O*" is accidentally opened.

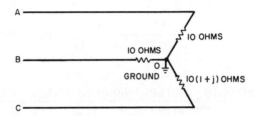

SOLUTION

The vector voltages can be expressed by the following:

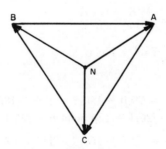

$$E_{AN} = \frac{2200}{\sqrt{3}} = 1270 \ \underline{/30}$$
$$E_{BN} = 1270 \ \underline{/150}$$
$$E_{CN} = 1270 \ \underline{/-90}$$

The vector voltage from N to O when O is ungrounded will be

$$V_{ON} = E_{AN} - V_{AO}$$

But

$$V_{AO} = 10I_{AO}$$

Using a wye to delta transformation at the load

$$I_{AO} = \frac{E_{AB}}{Z_{AB}} + \frac{E_{AC}}{Z_{AC}}$$

$$I_{AO} = \frac{E_{AB}Z_{CO} + E_{AC}Z_{BO}}{Z_{AO}Z_{BO} + Z_{AO}Z_{CO} + Z_{BO}Z_{CO}}$$

$$= \frac{2200\ \underline{/0}(10 + j10) - 2200\ \underline{/-120}(10)}{(10)(10) + 10(10 + j10) + 10(10 + j10)}$$

$$= \frac{22,000 + j22,000 + 11,000 + j19,000}{100 + 100 + j100 + 100 + j100} = \frac{33,000 + j41,000}{300 + j200}$$

$$= \frac{52800\ \underline{/51}}{360\ \underline{/33.6}} = 146\ \underline{/17.4}$$

Thus

$$V_{ON} = 1270\ \underline{/30} - 1460\ \underline{/17.4}$$
$$= +1100 + j635 - 1390 - j438 = -290 + j197$$
$$|V_{ON}| = 350 \text{ v.} \qquad \text{ANS.}$$

3-4

A 3-wire, 3-phase, 60-cycle transmission line has an impedance, per conductor, of $1 + j10$ ohms. The input to this line is at 13,200 v. between conductors. The power taken by the load is 1000 kw at 100 amp and a lagging power factor.

Calculate:

(a) the efficiency of transmission
(b) the voltage at the load
(c) the power factor of the load.

SOLUTION

(a) Efficiency of transmission $= \dfrac{\text{Load Power}}{\text{Load Power} + \text{line power lost}}$

Line impedance $= R + jX = 1 + j10$
Line Power lost $= 3(I_L)^2(R) = 3(100)^2(1) = 30,000$ watts
Efficiency $\dfrac{(1000)100}{(1000 + 30)} = 97\%$ \qquad ANS.

(b) Load voltage is determined from the following vector diagram.

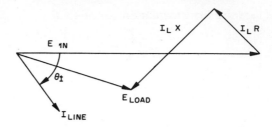

$$E_{\text{in}} = \frac{E}{\sqrt{3}} = \frac{13{,}200}{\sqrt{3}} = 7625 \text{ v.}$$

$$\theta_l = \cos^{-1} \frac{P_{\text{in}}}{\sqrt{3} I_L E} = \cos^{-1} \frac{1{,}030{,}000}{\sqrt{3}(100)(13{,}200)} = \cos^{-1} 0.450 = 63.2°$$

$$\sin \theta_l = 0.891$$

$$\begin{aligned}
E_{\text{load}} &= 7625 - I_L R \cos \theta_l + j I_L R \sin \theta_l - I_L X \sin \theta_l - j I_L X \cos \theta_l \\
&= 7625 - 100(0.45) + j100(0.891) - 1000(0.891) - j1000(0.450) \\
&= 7625 - 45 + j89.1 - 891 - j450 = 6690 - j360 \\
&= 6700 \; \underline{/-3.1°}
\end{aligned}$$

Load voltage line-to-line $= \sqrt{3}(6700) = 11{,}600$ v.   ANS.

(c) Load power factor $= \cos (63.2° - 3.1°) = \cos 60.1° = 0.498.$ ANS.

3–5

A 3-phase, 3-wire transmission line has an impedance per conductor of $60 + j80$ ohms and delivers 1500 kw to a load at 66,000 v. and a power factor of 0.90, lagging.

Calculate the potential difference between line wires at the input end of the line and the power factor at that end.

SOLUTION

The input voltage equals the load voltage plus the line voltage drop. The problem will be solved using a single-phase equivalent.

The line-to-neutral voltage at the load is

$$E_{\text{load}} = \frac{66{,}000}{\sqrt{3}} = 38{,}000 \text{ v.}$$

The line current is

$$\begin{aligned}
I_L &= \frac{P}{3(E_{\text{load}})(pf)} \\
&= \frac{1{,}500{,}000}{(3)(38{,}000)(0.90)} = 14.6 \text{ amp}
\end{aligned}$$

The current lags the load voltage by an angle θ

$$\theta = \cos^{-1} 0.9 = 25.9°$$
$$\sin \theta = 0.436$$

A single phase vector diagram may be drawn

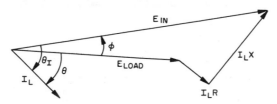

$$E_{in} = E_{load} + I_L R \cos \theta + I_L X \sin \theta + j(I_L X \cos \theta - I_L R \sin \theta)$$

$$I_L R = (14.6)(60) = 876, \quad I_L X = (14.6)(80) = 1170$$

$$\begin{aligned} E_{in} &= 38,000 + (876)(0.9) + (1170)(0.436) + j[(1170)(0.9) - (876)(0.436)] \\ &= 38,000 + 780 + 510 + j[1050 - 380] \\ &= 39,300 + j670 = 39,300 \underline{/1°} \end{aligned}$$

The line-to-line input voltage is

$$E_{l-l} = \sqrt{3}(39,300) = 68,100 \text{ v.} \qquad \text{ANS.}$$

The input power factor is $\cos \theta_I$

$$\begin{aligned} \cos \theta_I &= \cos (\theta + \phi) = \cos (25.9° + 1°) \\ &= \cos (26.9°) = 0.893 \qquad \text{ANS.} \end{aligned}$$

3–6

A transmission line is 100 miles long and delivers 3-phase, 60-cycle power to a load of 24,000 kva at 66,000 v. 0.8 power factor lagging. The series impedance of each line is $0.1901 + j0.740$ ohms/mile; the shunt admittance is $j5.88 \times 10^{-6}$ mhos/mile.

Find the efficiency of the transmission line.

(Note: In the examination when this problem was given the suggestion was made to replace the line by an equivalent pi network.)

SOLUTION

The suggested equivalent circuit can be analyzed to determine the power losses attributable to the transmission line. The efficiency can be determined from the power loss P and the power delivered to the load P_L as

$$\eta = \frac{100 P_L}{P + P_L}$$

The circuit illustrates the transmission line portion of a single-phase equivalent, shown as a pi circuit. The generator is connected to terminals A-A' and the load to terminals B-B'.

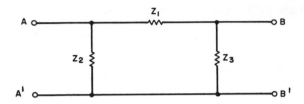

In this equivalent Z_1 represents the total series impedance for the 100-mile line

$$Z_1 = (0.1901 + j0.740)(100)$$
$$= 19.01 + j74.0 \text{ ohms}$$

and Z_2 and Z_3 represent the shunt impedance equally divided between both ends. It is assumed the shunt admittance is from each line to neutral (ground).

$$Z_2 = Z_3 = \frac{1}{j(5.88 \times 10^{-6})(50)}$$
$$= \frac{1}{j2.94 \times 10^{-4}} \text{ ohms}$$

The only line losses occur in the resistance component of Z_1. This component has been computed to be 19.01 ohms. Hence the losses are

$$P = (I_{AB})^2 19.01$$

But

$$I_{AB} = I_{Z_3} + I_L = \frac{E_{BB'}}{Z_3} + \frac{P_L}{E_{BB'}(\cos \theta)}$$

The voltage given is assumed line-to-line at the load. The equivalent line-to-neutral voltage, $E_{BB'}$, is

$$E_{BB'} = \frac{66,000}{\sqrt{3}} = 38,100 \text{ volts}$$

and will be taken as angular reference.

For the single phase equivalent the power is one-third the total load power. The term $P_L/\cos \theta$ is recognized as the load volt-amperes. Thus

$$I_{AB} = (38,100 \underline{/0}) (2.94 \times 10^{-4} \underline{/90}) + \frac{(2.4 \times 10^7) \underline{/-cos^{-1} 0.8}}{(3)(38,100)}$$

$$= 11.2 \underline{/90} + 210 \underline{/-36.9}$$
$$= j11.2 + 168 - j126$$
$$= 168 - j114.8 = 203 \underline{/-34.2}$$

In terms of the power in each of the three phases, the efficiency is

$$\eta = \frac{(100)(2.4 \times 10^7)(0.80)(1/3)}{(203)^2(19.01) + (2.4 \times 10^7)(0.80)(1/3)}$$

$$= \frac{6.4 \times 10^8}{0.784 \times 10^6 + 6.4 \times 10^6} = 89.0\% \qquad \text{ANS.}$$

3–7

A Y-connected generator rated at 220 v. has 0.2 ohm resistance and 2.0 ohm reactance per phase. The generator is connected by lines each having an impedance of 2.06 $\underline{/29.05°}$ ohms to a Y-Y transformer bank. Each transformer has a total equivalent impedance referred to the high side of 100 $\underline{/60°}$ ohms, and the transformer bank is connected through lines each of which has a resistance of 50 ohms and an inductive reactance of 100 ohms. If the ratio of transformation is 6 and the low voltage side is connected to the generator lines, calculate the actual fault current for a three-phase symmetrical short circuit at the load.

SOLUTION

A single phase equivalent circuit may be drawn as shown.

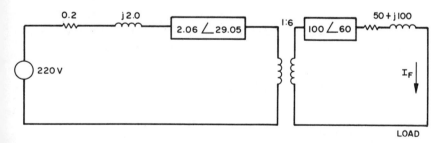

The actual fault is line-to-line. The line current at the fault will be $\sqrt{3}$ times as great as the line-to-neutral current calculated but the actual fault current will be $1/\sqrt{3}$ times as great as the line current. Hence the actual fault current will be the same as the short-circuit

line-to-neutral current in the circuit. If the generator and all impedances are referred to the load side of the circuit, the current is

$$I_F = \frac{a(220)}{100 \,\underline{/60} + 50 + j100 + a^2(2.06 \,\underline{/29.05}) + a^2(0.2) + ja^2(2.0)}$$

But $a = 6$ so that

$$I_F = \frac{1320}{100 \,\underline{/60} + 50 + j100 + 74.1 \,\underline{/29.05} + 7.2 + j72}$$

Thus

$$I_F = \frac{1320}{50 + j86.6 + 50 + j100 + 64.6 + j36 + 7.2 + j72}$$

$$= \frac{1320}{171.8 + j294.6} = \frac{1320}{341 \,\underline{/59.8}} = 3.87 \text{ amp} \qquad \text{ANS.}$$

3–8

A 3-phase transmission line 20 miles long has a resistance of 0.6
ohm/mile of conductor and a reactance of 0.27 ohm/mile of conductor, at 60 cps. The line delivers 1000 kw to an inductive load at a
power factor of 80%. The potential difference between line wires at
the load is 11,000 v.

(a) Calculate the voltage between wires at the input end of the
line.

(b) Calculate the total rating in kva of a bank of capacitors placed
at the input of the line, which will increase the power factor at that
point to 90%, lagging.

SOLUTION

The input voltage is the sum of the load voltage plus the line impedance drops. The single-phase equivalent will be used.

The load voltage is

$$V_L = \frac{11,000}{\sqrt{3}} = 6350 \text{ v. line to neutral}$$

The line current is

$$I_L = \frac{P}{\sqrt{3}V_L \cos \theta}$$

$$= \frac{10^6}{\sqrt{3}(11,000)(0.80)} = 65.5 \text{ amp}$$

The angle between I_L and V_L is

$$\cos^{-1} 0.8 = 36.9°$$

The total line impedance is

$$Z_L = 20(0.6 + j0.27) = 12 + j5.4 \text{ ohms}$$

The input voltage is

$$
\begin{aligned}
V_{in} &= V_L + I_L Z_L \\
&= 6350 + (65.5 \; \underline{/-36.9})(12 + j5.4) \\
&= 6350 + (52.4 - j39.2)(12 + j5.4) \\
&= 6350 + 630 - j470 + j282 + 212 \\
&= 7192 - j188 \\
&= 7195 \; \underline{/-1.5} \text{ line to neutral} \\
&= \sqrt{3}(7195) = 12{,}470 \text{ v. line to line} \qquad \text{ANS.}
\end{aligned}
$$

At the input the current lags the voltage by

$$36.9° - 1.5° = 35.4°$$

The input power factor is

$$\cos 35.4° = 0.815$$

The total input kva is

$$
\begin{aligned}
\text{input kva} &= \sqrt{3} V_{in} I_L \\
&= \frac{\sqrt{3}(12{,}470)(65.5)}{1000} \\
&= 1418 \text{ kva.}
\end{aligned}
$$

The reactive kva at the input kvar is

$$\text{kvar} = 1418 \sin 35.4° = 820 \text{ kva}$$

The reactive kva corresponding to a 0.90 pf is

$$
\begin{aligned}
\text{kvar}' &= 1418 \sin (\cos^{-1} 0.9) \\
&= 1418 \sin 25.9° = 620 \text{ kva.}
\end{aligned}
$$

Thus the total kva rating of the capacitor bank at the input is the difference, or for the capacitor

$$
\begin{aligned}
\text{capacitor kva} &= (820 - 620) \\
&= 200 \text{ kva} \qquad \text{ANS.}
\end{aligned}
$$

3–9

A motor load draws 100 kw at a lagging power factor of 0.8 from a 3-phase, 60-cycle 208/120-v. system. A capacitor bank corrects the power factor of the motor load to 0.9, lagging. In addition, power is supplied to two unity power factor lighting loads, as shown.

Calculate the current in each of the four conductors of this system.

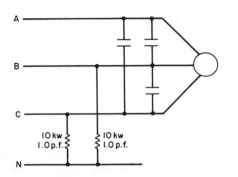
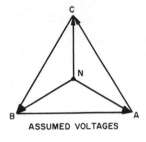

ASSUMED VOLTAGES

SOLUTION

The motor load is balanced, so it contributes nothing to neutral current. Assume the voltages as shown above.

$$E_{AB} = 208\underline{/0} \qquad\qquad E_{AN} = 120\underline{/-30}$$
$$E_{BC} = 208\underline{/-120} \qquad\qquad E_{BN} = 120\underline{/-150}$$
$$E_{CA} = 208\underline{/+120} \qquad\qquad E_{CN} = 120\underline{/90}$$

All currents will be computed with respect to the equivalent line-to-neutral voltages. Subscript "M" will refer to motor loads, subscript "L," to lighting loads.

$$I_{AM} = \frac{P_M/3}{E_{AN}\cos\theta_M}$$
$$= \frac{100,000}{3(120)0.90} = 308 \text{ amp}$$

There is no lighting load in line A so that $I_A = I_{AM}$

$$I_A = 308 \text{ amp} \qquad\qquad \text{ANS.}$$
$$|I_{BM}| = |I_{AM}| = 308 \text{ amp lagging } E_{BN} \text{ by } \theta \text{ degrees}$$

But

$$\theta = \cos^{-1} 0.90 = 25.9$$

Thus

$$I_{BM} = 308\underline{/-175.9}$$

However

$$I_{BL} = \frac{P_{BL}}{E_{BN}} = \frac{10,000}{120} = 83.3 \text{ amp}$$

I_{BL} is in phase with E_{BN} so that $I_{BL} = 83.3\underline{/-150}$
The total line current I_B is given by

$$\begin{aligned}
I_B &= I_{BL} + I_{BM} \\
&= 83.3\underline{/-150} + 308\underline{/-175.9} \\
&= -72 - j41.6 - 307 - j22.0 \\
&= -379 - j63.6 \\
&= 385\underline{/-170.5} \text{ amp} \quad\quad\quad \text{ANS.}
\end{aligned}$$

Also

$$\begin{aligned}
|I_{CM}| &= |I_{BM}| = 308 \text{ amp} \\
&I_{CM} \text{ lags } E_{CN} \text{ by } 25.9° \text{ so that} \\
I_{CM} &= 308\underline{/64.1}
\end{aligned}$$

But

$$|I_{CL}| = |I_{BL}| = 83.3 \text{ amp in phase with } E_{CN}$$

Thus

$$I_{CL} = 83.3\underline{/90}$$

The total line current I_C is given by

$$\begin{aligned}
I_C &= I_{CL} + I_{CM} \\
&= 83.3\underline{/90} + 308\underline{/64.1} \\
&= j83.3 + 134.5 + j277.5 \\
&= 134.5 + j360.8 = 384\underline{/69.5} \text{ amp} \quad\quad\quad \text{ANS.}
\end{aligned}$$

The neutral current I_N is given by

$$\begin{aligned}
I_N &= I_{BL} + I_{CL} \\
&= 83.3\underline{/-150} + 83.3\underline{/90} \\
&= -72 - j41.6 + j83.3 \\
&= -72 + j41.7 \\
&= 83.3\underline{/150} \text{ amp} \quad\quad\quad \text{ANS.}
\end{aligned}$$

3–10

A fully-loaded, 3-phase, 2200-v. circuit supplies 100 kw to a load having a power factor of 70.7%, lagging. The circuit used costs $5000 installed. Additional circuit capacity is required in order to accommodate a greater load at the same power factor. A 3-phase, 150-kva, 2200-v. bank of capacitors is available at $1000.

If this bank were bridged across the line at the load, how many additional kilowatts could the line supply without overloading? Is this method of increasing the transmission capacity of this line economical? Submit calculations substantiating your conclusions.

SOLUTION

Assume a lossless capacitor bank. The line rating is on the basis of maximum current carried or kva delivered.
    The line current is

$$I_L = \frac{P}{\sqrt{3}E \cos \theta}$$

$$= \frac{100,000}{\sqrt{3}(2200)0.707} = 37.0 \text{ amp}$$

This value is the maximum the line can carry. The angle between current and voltage θ may be found from

$$\cos \theta = 0.707 \text{ lagging}$$
$$\theta = -45°$$

Under these load conditions

$$I_L = 37 \cos (45°) - j37 \sin (45°)$$
$$= 26.2 - j26.2 \text{ amp}$$

The capacitor current will be

$$I_C = \frac{va}{\sqrt{3}E}$$

$$= \frac{150,000}{\sqrt{3}(2200)} = +j39.3 \text{ amp}$$

The sum of load and capacitor current is

$$I_C + I_L = 26.2 - j26.2 + j39.2$$
$$= 26.2 + j13.1 \text{ amp}$$

The additional load current will be denoted I_A. The power factor of the added load is the same as the original load; hence the added current will be

$$I_L' = 0.707I_A - j0.707I_A$$

Let the total current be I_T

$$|I_T| = 37 = (26.2 + 0.707I_A) + j(13.1 - 0.707I_A)$$

This may be solved for I_A as

$$(37)^2 = (26.2 + 0.707I_A)^2 + (13.1 - 0.707I_A)^2$$
$$1370 = 686 + 37I_A + 0.5I_A{}^2 + 172 - 18.5I_A + 0.5I_A{}^2$$

The quadratic is

$$I_A{}^2 + 18.5I_A - 512 = 0$$

$$I_A = \frac{-18.5 \pm \sqrt{(18.5)^2 + 4(512)}}{2}$$

Taking only the positive value

$$I_A = 15.6 \text{ amps.}$$

The added power is P_A

$$P_A = \sqrt{3}EI_A \cos \theta$$
$$= \sqrt{3}(2200)(15.6)(0.707) = 42,000 \text{ watts} \qquad \text{ANS.}$$

For this power factor load, the incremental cost of the original line is

$$\text{original cost} = \frac{\$5000}{100 \text{ kw}} = \$50/\text{kw}$$

The incremental cost of increasing the capacity is

$$\text{increased capacity cost} = \frac{\$1000}{42 \text{ kw}} = \$23.8/\text{kw.}$$

This method, then, is more economical than building additional line because the incremental cost of the added capacity is less than one-half the incremental cost of the original line.

4–1

A shunt-wound interpole motor has a field winding on 4 main poles and an armature with a simplex-wave winding located in 45 slots, each with 8 conductors. When 120 v. are impressed on the shunt field, the flux per pole is 760,000 lines. The armature circuit resistance, including brushes and interpole winding, is 0.08 ohm.

Calculate the speed of this motor when it is driven from 120-v. mains and the armature current is 85 amp.

SOLUTION

The speed of the motor may be determined from the expression for generated voltage.

$$E_G = \frac{pZ\phi n}{(60)(10^8)b}$$

where

$$p = 4 \text{ poles}$$
$$Z = (45)(8) = 360 \text{ conductors}$$
$$\phi = 760,000 \text{ lines}$$
$$n = ?$$
$$b = 2 \text{ for simplex wave winding}$$

But

$$E_G = V_T - I_A R$$
$$= 120 - (85)(0.08)$$
$$= 120 - 6.8 = 113.2 \text{ v.}$$

Thus

$$n = \frac{E_G(60)(10^8)b}{pZ\phi}$$
$$= \frac{(113.2)(60)(10^8)(2)}{(4)(360)(760,000)} = 1240 \text{ rpm} \qquad \text{ANS.}$$

4–2

A 4-pole, simplex lap-wound, direct-current armature has 48 slots containing 48 coils, each of two turns. The flux per pole, in the field structure for this armature, is 0.5×10^6 lines. The rated current per coil is 10 amp.

Calculate:

(a) the speed for this machine in order that its generated emf be 220 v.

(b) the generated mechanical horsepower when this machine is operated as a motor under conditions of (a)

SOLUTION

(a) The speed may be determined from the expression for generated voltage

$$E_G = \frac{pZ\phi n}{60b10^8}$$

or

$$n = \frac{60b10^8 E_G}{pZ\phi}$$

where

$$E_G = 220 \text{ v.}$$
$$p = 4 \text{ poles}$$
$$\phi = 0.5 \times 10^6 \text{ lines}$$

$b = 4$ (for simplex lap winding)

$Z = (48 \text{ coils}) (2 \text{ turns/coil}) (2 \text{ conductors/turn}) = 192$

Thus

$$n = \frac{(220)(4)(60)(10^8)}{(4)(192)(0.5)(10^6)} = 13{,}750 \text{ rpm} \qquad \text{ANS.}$$

(b) If it is assumed that the armature coils carry rated current, the mechanical horsepower may be determined from the electrical power delivered to the armature.

A simplex lap-wound armature has four parallel paths, each of which carries 10 amp. Hence the total armature current is 40 amp.

$$P_A = (220)(40) = 8800 \text{ watts}$$

$$\text{HP} = \frac{P_A}{746} = \frac{8800}{746} \quad 11.8 \text{ hp.} \qquad \text{ANS.}$$

4–3

A 220-v., direct-current, shunt motor with interpoles drives a constant-torque load at 1200 rpm while drawing 30 amp through the armature which has a resistance of 0.2 ohm. When a resistance of 0.35 ohm is connected in series with the armature and the field current is suitably reduced, the speed is again 1200 rpm.

(a) Calculate the value of the new armature current.

(b) Calculate the ratio of the field fluxes, with and without series resistance in the armature circuit.

SOLUTION

Assume: 1) constant terminal voltage
        2) resistances are total and include equivalent brush drop
Since the load is constant torque and constant speed, the power delivered to the armature is the same in both cases. The case without added resistance will be denoted by subscript "1" and with the added resistance by subscript "2." Thus if E_G is the armature induced voltage and I_A armature current

$$E_{G_1} I_{A_1} = E_{G_2} I_{A_2}$$

But

$$I_{A_1} = 30 \text{ amp}$$

and

$$E_{G_1} = V_T - I_{A_1} R_{A_1}$$
$$= 220 - 30(0.2) = 220 - 6 = 214 \text{ v.}$$

Also

$$E_{G_2} = V_T - I_{A_2}R_{A_2}$$
$$= 220 - I_{A_2}(0.55)$$

Hence

$$(214)(30) = [220 - I_{A_2}(0.55)]I_{A_2}$$

This may be solved for I_{A_2} as

$$0.55I_{A_2}^2 - 220I_{A_2} + 6420 = 0$$

$$I_{A_2} = \frac{220 \pm \sqrt{(220)^2 - 4(0.55)(6420)}}{2(0.55)}$$
$$= \frac{220 \pm \sqrt{48,400 - 14,120}}{1.10} = 200 \pm \frac{\sqrt{34,280}}{1.10}$$
$$= 200 \pm \frac{185}{1.10} = 200 \pm 168.5$$
$$= 31.5, \ 368.5$$

The desired value is the lower value.
Thus

$$I_{A_2} = 31.5 \text{ amp} \qquad \text{ANS.}$$

(b) In general, the developed torque of a machine is

$$T = K_T \phi I_A$$

Since the developed torque is the same in both cases

$$K_T \phi_1 I_{A_1} = K_T \phi_2 I_{A_2}$$

Or the ratio of field fluxes may be written as

$$\frac{\phi_2}{\phi_1} = \frac{I_{A_1}}{I_{A_2}}$$
$$= \frac{30}{31.5} = 0.953 \qquad \text{ANS.}$$

4-4

A 220-v. shunt motor driving its normal load draws an armature current of 50 amp from 220-v. mains. The armature resistance of this machine, including brushes, is 0.25 ohms and the speed of operation is 1200 rpm.

What armature current will this machine draw from 200-v. mains when driving the same load, with the field adjusted to maintain a speed of 1200 rpm?

SOLUTION

The load and speed remain constant, hence it may be assumed that the power delivered to the armature will be the same in both cases. The values with 220-v. line will be denoted subscript "1" and the values with 200-v. line will be denoted subscript "2." The power delivered to the armature is $E_G I_A$ so that

$$E_{G_1} I_{A_1} = E_{G_2} I_{A_2}$$

But

$$I_{A_1} = 50 \text{ amp}$$

and

$$E_{G_1} = V_{T_1} - I_{A_1} R_A$$
$$= 220 - 50(0.25) = 220 - 12.5 = 207.5 \text{ v.}$$

and

$$E_{G_2} = V_{T_2} - I_{A_2} R_A$$
$$= 200 - I_{A_2}(0.25)$$

Hence

$$(207.5)(50) = [200 - I_{A_2}(0.25)]I_{A_2}$$

This may be solved for I_{A_2} as

$$0.25 I_{A_2}{}^2 - 200 I_{A_2} + 10{,}375 = 0$$
$$I_{A_2} = \frac{200 \pm \sqrt{(200)^2 - 4(0.25)(10{,}375)}}{2(0.25)}$$
$$= 400 \pm 2\sqrt{40{,}000 - 10{,}375} = 400 \pm 2\sqrt{29{,}625}$$
$$= 400 \pm 344.8$$
$$= 55.2, \, 744.8$$

The lower value is the desired value. Thus

$$I_{A_2} = 55.2 \text{ amp} \qquad\qquad \text{ANS.}$$

4–5

A 220-v., d-c motor has an armature resistance of 0.4 ohm, a shunt field of 175 ohms and a series field of 0.4 ohm. This machine is connected as a short-shunt compound machine to 220-v. mains.

Calculate the line current and the total or gross mechanical horsepower generated in the armature when the armature current is 30 amp. Neglect the brush loss.

SOLUTION

cf. [Fitzgerald et al, *Machinery* (2) p. 251]
The equivalent circuit for the machine is shown as follows:

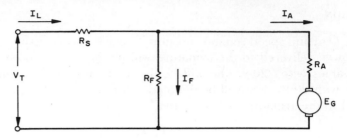

The equations for this circuit may be written

$$V_T = I_L R_S + I_F R_F$$

But

$$I_F = I_L - I_A$$

so that

$$V_T = I_L R_S + I_L R_F - I_A R_F$$

or

$$I_L = \frac{V_T + I_A R_F}{(R_S + R_F)}$$
$$= \frac{220 + 30(175)}{(0.4 + 175)} = \frac{220 + 5250}{175.4} = \frac{5470}{175.4} = 31.2 \text{ amp} \qquad \text{ANS.}$$

The total or gross mechanical horsepower generated in the armature is the horsepower equivalent of the electrical power delivered to the armature.

$$\text{HP} = \frac{E_G I_A}{746}$$

But

$$E_G = V_T - I_L R_S - I_A R_A$$
$$= 220 - 31.2(0.4) - 30(0.4)$$
$$= 220 - 12.5 - 12.0 = 195.5 \text{ v.}$$

Thus

$$\text{HP} = \frac{(195.5)(30)}{746} = 7.85 \text{ hp} \qquad \text{ANS.}$$

4–6

A small traction motor used in street car operation is rated at 50 hp and 760 rpm when its efficiency is 0.89. This motor is constructed with six field poles, and the simplex-wave armature has 240 conductors. The resistances of the armature and series field are 0.30 and 0.15 ohm, respectively. The brush and contact resistances are included in the armature resistance. The terminal voltage is 550 v.

Calculate

(a) the net output torque at rated load

(b) the stray power loss at rated load

(c) the impressed voltage required to drive the motor at 1000 rpm and deliver the same torque as when the machine is operated with rated voltage and at rated speed

(d) the effective air-gap flux per pole under rated conditions.

SOLUTION

The machine is represented by the figure.

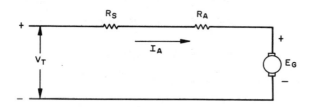

(a) If the output is 50 hp, the torque at 760 rpm is

$$T = \frac{33,000(\mathrm{HP})}{2\pi n}$$

$$= 5250\frac{(50)}{(760)} = 346 \text{ ft-lbs} \qquad \text{ANS.}$$

(b) To determine the stray power loss, it is assumed that the total input power to the machine is the sum of three parts: the power output, the winding resistance loss, and the stray power loss; and that the electrical power delivered to the armature is the sum of the power output and the stray power loss.

The power output in watts P_o is

$$P_o = 50(746) = 37,300$$

The power into the machine P_I using the efficiency η is

$$P_I = \frac{P_o}{\eta} = V_T I_A$$

$$= \frac{37,300}{0.89} = 42,000 \text{ watts}$$

So that

$$I_A = \frac{P_I}{V_T}$$

$$= \frac{42,000}{550} = 76.5 \text{ amp}$$

Hence, the stray power loss P_{sp} is

$$
\begin{aligned}
P_{sp} &= P_I - P_o - I_A{}^2(R_S + R_A) \\
&= 42,000 - 37,300 - (76.5)^2(0.15 + 0.30) \\
&= 42,000 - 37,300 - 2630 \\
&= 2070 \text{ watts} \hspace{3cm} \text{ANS.}
\end{aligned}
$$

(c) Let unprimed quantities designate values at 760 rpm and the primed quantities designate values at 1000 rpm. The impressed voltage at 1000 rpm will be

$$V_T{}' = E_G{}' + I_A{}'(R_A + R_S)$$

But

$$E_G{}' = K_G\phi'n' = 1000K_G\phi'$$

and if T_T is the total developed torque

$$I_A{}' = \frac{T_T{}'}{K_T\phi'}$$

The total torque consists of the delivered torque plus the stray power torque.

$$T_T{}' = T + T_{sp}{}'$$

But if power P is in watts.

$$T = \frac{P}{746}\frac{33,000}{2\pi n} = 7.05\frac{P}{n}$$

or

$$T'_{sp} = 7.05\frac{P_{sp}{}'}{1000}$$

The assumption will be made that the stray-power loss is proportional to the square of the speed [cf. Pender et al, *Handbook* (12), pp. 8–30]. Hence

$$P_{sp}{}' = P_{sp}\left[\frac{1000}{746}\right]^2$$

so that

$$T_{sp}{}' = 7.05\left(\frac{2070}{1000}\right)\left(\frac{1000}{746}\right)^2 = 26.2 \text{ ft-lbs}$$

and

$$T_{sp} = 7.05\left(\frac{2070}{760}\right) = 19.2 \text{ ft-lbs}$$

The resultant torque T_T is

$$T_T' = 346 + 26.2 = 372.2 \text{ ft-lbs}$$

and

$$T_T = 346 + 19.2 = 365.2 \text{ ft-lbs}$$

Another assumption is that the iron is operated in the linear region which makes the flux ϕ directly proportional to the armature current. Or

$$(I_A')^2 = \frac{T_T'}{K_{T_2}}$$

$$I_A' = I_A\sqrt{\frac{T_T'}{T_T}}$$

$$= 76.5\sqrt{\frac{372.2}{365.2}} = 77.1 \text{ amp}$$

But

$$E_G' = K_{G_2}I_A'n'$$

or

$$E_G' = E_G\frac{I_A'n'}{I_An}$$

However

$$E_G = V_T - I_A(R_S + R_A)$$
$$= 550 - 76.5(0.15 + 0.30) = 550 - 34.4 = 515.6 \text{ v.}$$

so that

$$E_G' = 515.6\left(\frac{77.1}{76.5}\right)\left(\frac{1000}{760}\right) = 685 \text{ v.}$$

Finally

$$V_T = 685 + 77.1(0.45) = 685 + 34.7 = 719.7 \text{ v.} \qquad \text{ANS.}$$

(d) The effective flux per pole may be found from the following

$$E_G = \frac{pZ\phi n}{60b10^8}$$

rewritten to become

$$\phi = \frac{E_G 60b10^8}{pZn}$$

Under the stated conditions

$$b = 2$$
$$Z = 240$$

$$p = 6$$
$$E_G = 515.6$$
$$n = 760$$

Hence

$$\phi = \frac{(515.6)\,(60)\,(2)\,(10^8)}{(6)\,(240)\,(760)}$$
$$= 5.65 \times 10^6 \text{ lines} \qquad \text{ANS.}$$

4–7

Two shunt field, d-c generators G_1 and G_2 are rated at 100 and 150 kw at 110 v., respectively. Their external load characteristics may be considered as straight lines without serious error. The drop in the external voltage, from no load to full load, is 10 v. in G_1 and 20 v. in G_2.

Calculate the no-load voltages of these generators when they are operated in parallel to supply a 120-v. load of 2000 amp which is divided between them in proportion to their ratings.

SOLUTION

Each generator may be considered to have an equivalent circuit consisting of a generator or battery whose voltage is equal to the no-load voltage in series with a resistance. It will be assumed that the equivalent resistance is independent of no-load voltage.

The no-load voltage of each generator will be the terminal voltage plus the drop in the series resistance. Thus if subscript "1" refers to the 100-kw generator G_1 and subscript 2 refers to the 150-kw generator G_2,

$$E_{NL_1} = 120 + R_{eq_1}\,(I_1)$$
$$E_{NL_2} = 120 + R_{eq_2}\,(I_2)$$
$$R_{eq_1} = \frac{\Delta V_1}{\Delta I_1} = \frac{\Delta V_1}{P_1/V_1} = \frac{10}{100{,}000/110} = 0.0110 \text{ ohms}$$
$$R_{eq_2} = \frac{\Delta V_2}{\Delta I_2} = \frac{\Delta V_2}{P_2/V_2} = \frac{20}{150{,}000/110} = 0.0147 \text{ ohms}$$

But

$$I_1 + I_2 = 2000 \text{ amp}$$

and

$$\frac{I_1}{100} = \frac{I_2}{150}$$
$$1.5 I_1 = I_2$$

or

$$I_1 = \frac{2000}{1.5 + 1} = 800 \text{ amp}$$

and
$$I_2 = 1.5I_1 = 1200 \text{ amp}$$
Hence
$$E_{NL_1} = 120 + 800(0.0110) = 128.8 \text{ v.}$$
$$E_{NL_2} = 120 + 1200(0.0147) = 137.6 \text{ v.} \qquad \text{ANS.}$$

4–8

The rated armature current of a 230-v., d-c motor is 75 amp. The maximum allowable momentary armature current for this machine is 225 amp. The resistance of the armature is 0.2 ohm and the brush drop is 2 v.

Determine the resistance of each step of the starter for this motor when the armature current during the starting period is limited to the range from 75 to 225 amp.

SOLUTION

If the added starting resistance is denoted R_E, a loop equation for the machine may be written as

$$V_T = I_A(R_E + R_A) + V_B + E_G$$

or with values substituted

$$230 = I_A(R_E + 0.2) + 2 + E_G$$

This may be solved for R_E as

$$R_E = \frac{228 - 0.2I_A - E_G}{I_A}$$

The solution will be carried out in the minimum number of steps, starting at motor standstill.

At standstill, $E_{G_1} = 0$ and I_A is limited to 225 amp. The value of R_E to accomplish this is obtained as

$$R_{E_1} = \frac{228 - 0.2(225) - 0}{225}$$

$$= \frac{228 - 45}{225} = \frac{183}{225} = 0.814 \text{ ohms}$$

This value of R_E is maintained until the motor speeds up to the point where I_A drops to 75 amp. The value of E_{G_2} at this condition is

$$E_{G_2} = 228 - I_A(R_{E_1} + 0.2)$$
$$= 228 - 75(0.814 + 0.20)$$

$$= 228 - 75(1.014)$$
$$= 228 - 76.1 = 151.9 \text{ v.}$$

At this point the resistance may be decreased to allow I_A to increase to 225 amp. The new value of R_E is

$$R_{E_2} = \frac{228 - 0.2(225) - 151.9}{225} = \frac{76.1 - 45.0}{225}$$
$$= \frac{31.1}{225} = 0.138 \text{ ohms}$$

The value of E_G when I_A drops to 75 amp may be found

$$E_{G_3} = 228 - 75(0.338) = 228 - 25.4$$
$$= 202.6 \text{ v.}$$

Again R_E is decreased to allow I_A to increase to 225 amp. This new value may be found as

$$R_{E_3} = \frac{228 - 0.2(225) - 202.6}{225}$$

This expression yields a negative quantity so that the external resistance now becomes zero.

The total resistances required in each step of the starter are

$$0.814 \text{ and } 0.138 \text{ ohms.} \qquad \text{ANS.}$$

If a tapped resistance is to be used, the total resistance is

$$0.814 \text{ ohms and a tap is at } 0.138 \text{ ohms.} \qquad \text{ANS.}$$

5–1

A wye-connected, 200-kva, 440-v., 3-phase, 3-wire alternator yields 150 v. between line terminals on open circuit. With the field excitation unchanged, the short-circuit current is 300 amp. The ohmic resistance of this machine, between line terminals, is 0.10 ohm and the ratio of effective to ohmic resistance for this machine is 1.25.

Calculate the full-load terminal voltage of this machine when the excitation is adjusted to yield a no-load voltage of 500 v. and the power factor of the load is 0.80, lagging.

SOLUTION

Assume full-load refers to full-kva-load.

The single-phase equivalent circuit and vector diagram are as shown.

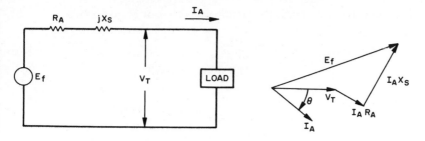

The equation for terminal voltage is

$$V_T = E_f - I_A R_A - jI_A X_S$$

The problem will be solved in one phase of an equivalent wye-connected system. Thus

$$E_f = \frac{500}{\sqrt{3}} = 288.5 \text{ v.}$$

The machine impedance values will be determined using the data from the open-circuit and short-circuit tests.

$$\begin{aligned} Z_S &= R_A + jX_S \\ &= \frac{E_{oc}}{I_{sc}} \\ &= \frac{150/\sqrt{3}}{300} = 0.2885 \text{ ohms/phase} \end{aligned}$$

The ohmic resistance/phase is one half the ohmic resistance between terminals. The effective resistance is 1.25 times the ohmic resistance. Thus

$$R_A = 1.25\left(\frac{0.10}{2}\right) = 0.0625 \text{ ohms}$$

and

$$\begin{aligned} X_S &= \sqrt{(Z_S)^2 - (R_A)^2} \\ &= \sqrt{(0.2885)^2 - (0.0625)^2} \\ &= \sqrt{0.0833 - 0.0039} = \sqrt{0.0794} = 0.280 \text{ ohms} \end{aligned}$$

The terminal voltage equation may be rewritten

$$E_f = (V_T + I_A R_A \cos\theta + I_A X_S \sin\theta) + j(I_A X_S \cos\theta - I_A R_A \sin\theta)$$

$$\theta = \cos^{-1} 0.8 = 36.9$$

$$\sin\theta = 0.6$$

Assuming full kva load, the armature current is given by

$$I_A = \frac{va}{3V_T}$$

$$= \frac{200,000}{3V_T} = \frac{66,670}{V_T}$$

$$I_A R_A = (0.0625)\left(\frac{66,670}{V_T}\right) = \frac{4160}{V_T}$$

$$I_A X_S = (0.280)\left(\frac{66,670}{V_T}\right) = \frac{18,670}{V_T}$$

so that

$$288.5 = \left[V_T + \frac{4160}{V_T}(0.8) + \frac{18,670}{V_T}(0.6)\right] + j\left[\frac{18,670}{V_T}(0.8) - \frac{4160}{V_T}(0.6)\right]$$

$$= \left[V_T + \frac{3330}{V_T} + \frac{11,200}{V_T}\right] + j\left[\frac{14,910}{V_T} - \frac{2500}{V_T}\right]$$

or

$$(288.5)^2 = \left(V_T + \frac{14,530}{V_T}\right)^2 + \left(\frac{12,410}{V_T}\right)^2$$

$$8.33 \times 10^4 = V_T{}^2 + 29,060 + \frac{2.11 \times 10^8}{V_T{}^2} + \frac{1.541 \times 10^8}{V_T{}^2}$$

or

$$V_T{}^4 - 5.42 \times 10^4 V_T{}^2 + 3.65 \times 10^8 = 0$$

solving the quadratic yields

$$V_T{}^2 = \frac{5.42 \times 10^4 \pm \sqrt{(5.42 \times 10^4)^2 - 4(3.65 \times 10^8)}}{2}$$

$$= \frac{10^4}{2}(5.42 \pm \sqrt{29.4 - 14.6}) = \frac{10^4}{2}(5.42 \pm 3.85)$$

$$= 4.635 \times 10^4, 0.785 \times 10^4$$

or

$$V_T = \sqrt{4.635 \times 10^4} = 215 \text{ v.}$$

and

$$V_T = \sqrt{0.785 \times 10^4} = 88.7 \text{ v.}$$

The higher value is the desired value so that

$$V_T = 215 \text{ v. line-to-neutral}$$
$$= \sqrt{3}(215) = 373 \text{ v. line-to-line} \qquad \text{ANS.}$$

(Note: A slightly different solution results if "full-load" is assumed to mean rated armature current corresponding to full load at rated voltage.)

5–2

A 3-phase, 1500-kva, 5500-v., Y-connected alternator has an effective resistance and a synchronous reactance of 0.35 and 6.6 ohms per phase, respectively, and delivers full-load current at a lagging power factor of 0.8. What will be the terminal voltage of this machine if its excitation remains unchanged and full-load current is delivered to a load having a leading power factor of 0.8?

SOLUTION

The problem is solved using the single-phase equivalent circuit shown below.

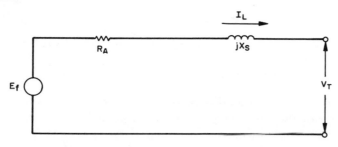

$R_A = 0.35$ ohms
$X_S = 6.6$ ohms
$V_T = $ terminal voltage — equivalent line-to-neutral

The voltage loop equation is

$$V_T + I_L R_A + j I_L X_S = E_f$$

When the machine delivers full load at 0.8 lagging pf, the excitation voltage may be determined and used to solve for terminal voltage when the current is delivered at 0.8 pf leading. The vector diagram is shown below.

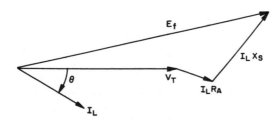

$$E_f = V_T + I_L R_A \cos \theta - j I_L R_A \sin \theta + I_L X_S \sin \theta + j I_L X_S \cos \theta$$

$$V_T = \frac{5500}{\sqrt{3}} = 3180 \text{ v.}$$

At full load

$$I_L = \frac{1,500,000}{3(3180)} = 158 \text{ amp}$$

Hence

$$I_L R_A = 158(0.35) = 55.3$$

and

$$I_L X_S = 158(6.6) = 1040$$

$$\theta = \cos^{-1} 0.8 = 36.8°$$

$$\sin \theta = 0.6$$

so that

$$E_f = 3180 + 55.3(0.8) - j55.3(0.6) + 1040(0.6) + j1040(0.8)$$
$$= 3180 + 44 - j33 + 625 + j833$$
$$= 3849 + j800 = 3930 \ \underline{/11.8}$$

In the case where full load is delivered at 0.8 pf leading, the vector diagram with the same magnitude of E_f as in the previous part of the problem is as shown.

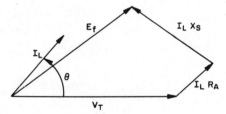

As before

$$E_f = V_T + I_L R_A \cos \theta + j I_L R_A \sin \theta - I_L X_S \sin \theta + j I_L X_S \cos \theta$$

$$\theta = \cos^{-1} 0.8 = 36.8° \qquad \sin \theta = 0.6$$

or

$$3930 = V_T + 44 + j33 - 625 + j833$$
$$= V_T - 581 + j866$$
$$= \sqrt{(V_T - 581)^2 + (866)^2}$$

$$15,400,000 = V_T^2 - 1162 V_T + 339,000 + 750,000$$

or

$$V_T{}^2 - 1162V_T - 14{,}311{,}000 = 0$$

Solving the quadratic

$$V_T = 4410, \; -3250$$

The negative value corresponds to motor action and is disregarded. Hence

$$V_T = 4410 \text{ v. equivalent line-to-neutral} \qquad \text{ANS.}$$

or

$$\sqrt{3}(4410) = 7650 \text{ v. line-to-line} \qquad \text{ANS.}$$

5–3

A 3-phase, 230-v., 6-pole, 60-cycle induction motor is loaded by means of a prony brake, the length and dead weight of which are 2 ft and 2 lbs respectively. The power input is measured by two watt-meters P_1 and P_2 according to the two-wattmeter method. With 230 v. impressed on this motor, the total force delivered by the prony brake is 30 lbs, P_1 and P_2 indicate 3.5 and 7.0 kw, respectively, and the slip is 10%.

Calculate:

(a) the horsepower output of the motor
(b) its efficiency
(c) its power factor.

SOLUTION

(a) HP output $= \dfrac{2\pi Tn}{33{,}000}$

$T =$ torque (in foot-pounds) $= 2(30 - 2) = 2(28) = 56$ ft-lbs

$$n = \text{speed in rpm} = \frac{120f}{P}(1 - S)$$

$$= \frac{120(60)}{6}(1.0 - 0.1) = 1200(0.90) = 1080 \text{ rpm}$$

Thus

$$\text{HP} = \frac{2\pi(56)(1080)}{33{,}000} = 11.5 \text{ hp.} \qquad \text{ANS.}$$

(b) Efficiency $= \dfrac{P_o}{P_{in}}(100) = \eta$

but

$$P_o = 11.5(746) \text{ watts}$$

and

$$P_{\text{in}} = P_1 + P_2 = 10,500 \text{ watts}$$

Thus

$$\eta = \frac{11.5(746)(100)}{10,500} = 81.7\% \qquad \text{ANS.}$$

(c) If $\cos \theta =$ power factor, in two wattmeter method

$$\tan \theta = \frac{\sqrt{3}(P_1 - P_2)}{(P_1 + P_2)}$$
$$= \frac{\sqrt{3}(7.0 - 3.5)}{(7.0 + 3.5)} = \frac{\sqrt{3}(3.5)}{10.5} = 0.578$$

Hence

$$\theta = 30°$$

and

$$\cos \theta = 0.866 \qquad \text{ANS.}$$

5–4

The efficiency and power factor of a 50-hp, 6-pole, 440-v., 60-cycle induction motor are 90% and 92.5%, respectively, at full load. This motor draws 525% of full-load current and develops 175% of full-load torque when started across the line with full voltage. Specify the turns ratio of an autotransformer starter that will permit this motor to be started with a torque equal to 60% of that at full load. What will be the starting current in the line when this starter is used? Neglect the effects of saturation and the losses in the starter.

SOLUTION

The torque developed by an induction motor is proportional to the square of the applied voltage while the line current is directly proportional to the applied voltage. These two statements may be written:

$$T = K_1(E)^2$$

and

$$I = K_2(E)$$

Two torque expressions may be written: one for full voltage and one for reduced voltage E_s. T_{FL} represents full load torque.

$$1.75T_{FL} = K_1(440)^2$$

and

$$0.60T_{FL} = K_1(E_s)^2$$

Hence

$$\frac{0.60T_{FL}}{1.75T_{FL}} = \frac{K_1(E_s)^2}{K_1(440)^2}$$

or

$$E_s = 440\sqrt{\frac{0.60}{1.75}} = 440(0.585) = 259 \text{ v.}$$

The transformer turns ratio is simply the ratio of voltages

$$\text{turns ratio} = \frac{440}{259} = 1.70{:}1 \qquad \text{ANS.}$$

The full-load, full voltage line current I_L is

$$I_L = \frac{746\text{HP}}{\sqrt{3}E\eta \cos\theta}$$
$$= \frac{746(50)}{\sqrt{3}(440)(0.90)(0.925)} = 58.8 \text{ amp}$$

The full-load starting current I_s is

$$I_s = 5.25I_L$$
$$= 5.25(58.8) = 308 \text{ amp}$$

The motor starting current at reduced voltage I_s' is directly proportional to voltage. Thus

$$I_s' = I_s\left(\frac{E_s}{E_{FL}}\right)$$
$$= 308\left(\frac{259}{440}\right) = 181 \text{ amp}$$

The line current at reduced-voltage start I_L' will be the motor starting current transformed by the turns ratio of the autotransformer.

$$I_L' = \frac{I_s'}{\text{turns ratio}}$$
$$= \frac{181}{1.70} = 106.5 \text{ amp} \qquad \text{ANS.}$$

5–5

A 3-phase, 60-cycle, 220-v., 4-pole, squirrel cage induction motor operates at rated voltage and rated frequency with a line current of 71.4 amp, 4.45% slip, and 88% efficiency. The power input is measured by the two-wattmeter method, and the readings are +15,550 watts and +9750 watts. Find:

(a) shaft speed
(b) horsepower output
(c) delivered torque
(d) power factor
(e) total losses (watts)

SOLUTION

(a) Shaft speed is given by

$$n = \frac{120f}{p}(1 - S)$$
$$= \frac{(120)(60)}{4}(1 - 0.0445) = 1800(0.9555)$$
$$= 1720 \text{ rpm} \qquad \text{ANS.}$$

(b) The horsepower output is given by

$$HP = \frac{\eta P_{in}}{746}$$
$$= \frac{(0.88)(15,550 + 9750)}{746} = \frac{(0.88)(25,300)}{746} = 29.8 \text{ hp. ANS.}$$

(c) The delivered torque is given by

$$T = \frac{(33,000)HP}{2\pi n}$$
$$= \frac{5250(29.8)}{1720} = 910 \text{ ft-lbs} \qquad \text{ANS.}$$

(d) The power factor is $\cos \theta$, where in the two-wattmeter method, θ is given by

$$\theta = \tan^{-1} \sqrt{3} \frac{(P_1 - P_2)}{(P_1 + P_2)}$$
$$= \tan^{-1} \sqrt{3} \frac{(15,550 - 9750)}{(15,550 + 9750)} = \tan^{-1} \sqrt{3} \frac{(5800)}{(25,300)} = \tan^{-1} 0.398 = 21.7°$$
$$\cos \theta = \cos (21.7°) = 0.930 \qquad \text{ANS.}$$

(e) The total losses would be

$$\text{Losses} = P_{in}(1 - \eta)$$
$$= (15{,}550 + 9750)(1.0 - 0.88) = (25{,}300)(0.12)$$
$$= 3040 \text{ watts.} \qquad \text{ANS.}$$

5–6

The losses in a 3-phase, 60-cycle, 4-pole induction motor at full load are:

core	3.0%
friction and windage	2.0%
rotor copper	3.0%
stator copper	5.0%

(a) Calculate, as accurately as these data permit, the efficiency and speed of this machine at 75% of full load.
(b) List the assumptions made in your calculations.

SOLUTION

It is more meaningful to answer part (b) first, then answer part (a). The assumptions are:
1. Core, friction, and windage losses remain unchanged in magnitude.
2. Copper losses are proportional to the square of the current.
3. The current is directly proportional to the load.

$$\text{Efficiency} = \eta = \frac{\text{power output}}{\text{power output} + \text{losses}}$$

Power output = 75%	= 0.75 per unit
Losses: core = 3%	= 0.03
friction and windage = 2%	= 0.02
rotor copper = $(0.03)(0.75)^2$	= 0.0169
stator copper = $(0.05)(0.75)^2$	= 0.0281
Total losses	= 0.0950 per unit

Thus

$$\eta = \frac{(0.75)100}{(0.75 + 0.095)} = \frac{(0.75)100}{(0.845)} = 88.8\% \qquad \text{ANS.}$$

The speed n is given by

$$n = \frac{120f}{p}(1.0 - S)$$

The slip S is given by

$$S = \frac{\text{rotor copper loss}}{\text{power transferred across air gap}}$$

$$= \frac{\text{rotor copper loss}}{\text{input} - \text{stator copper loss}}$$

$$= \frac{0.0169}{0.845 - 0.0281}$$

$$= \frac{0.0169}{0.8169} = 0.0207$$

Thus

$$n = \frac{120(60)}{4}(1.0 - 0.0207)$$

$$= 1800(0.9793)$$

$$= 1760 \text{ rpm}$$ ANS.

5–7

A 440-v., 60-cycle, 4-pole, 3-phase, wound-rotor induction motor is directly connected to a pump which delivers 1000 cfm of water against an effective head of 8.7 ft. Under this load, the motor draws 15.62 kw at a power factor of 0.92. When operated without load, the motor draws 803 watts. The stator and rotor resistances, per phase, are 0.202 and 0.022 ohm, respectively. The effective turns ratio between the stator and rotor is 4:1.

Calculate the efficiency of the pump.

SOLUTION

$$\text{The pump efficiency is } \eta_p = \frac{\text{pump output}}{\text{pump input}}$$

$$= \frac{\text{pump output}}{\text{motor input} - \text{motor losses}}$$

$$\text{Pump output} = Qwh$$

$$= 1000(62.4)(8.7) = 542{,}000 \text{ ft-lbs/min}$$

$$= \frac{(542{,}000)(746)}{33{,}000} = 12{,}280 \text{ watts}$$

$$\text{Motor input} = 15{,}620 \text{ watts}$$

$$\text{Motor loss} = \text{rotational losses} + I^2R \text{ losses}.$$

Assume resistances are per phase for equivalent "Y." Total equivalent resistance referred to stator is

$$R_T/\text{phase} = R_{\text{stator}} + a^2 R_{\text{rotor}}$$

$$= 0.202 + (4)^2(0.022) = (0.202) + (0.352) = 0.554 \text{ ohms}$$

$$\text{Full-load stator current/phase} = \frac{15{,}620}{\sqrt{3}(440)(0.92)} = 22.3 \text{ amps}$$

Assuming the same power factor at no-load as at full-load

$$\text{No-load stator current/phase} = \frac{803}{\sqrt{3}(440)(0.92)} = 1.15 \text{ amps}$$

Total full-load resistive loss $= 3(22.3)^2(0.554) = 825$ watts

Total no-load resistive loss $= 3(1.15)^2(0.554) = 2.2$ watts

Rotational losses $= P_{NL} - P_R = 803 - 2 = 801$ watts

Pump input $=$ motor output $= 15,620 - (801 + 825) = 13,994$ watts

Hence

$$\eta_p = \frac{(12,280)(100)}{13,994} = 88.0\% \qquad \text{ANS.}$$

5-8

The data for a 335 hp, 2000-v., three-phase, 6-pole, 50-cycle, Y-connected induction motor are as follows: Ohmic resistance per phase of stator, 0.165 ohm; rotor, 0.0127 ohm; ratio of transformation, 4:1. No-load test: Line voltage, 2000 v.; line current, 15.3 amp; power, 10,000 watts. The friction and windage of the motor are 2000 watts. Blocked test: Line voltage, 440 v.; line current, 170 amp; power, 40,500 watts. When the slip is 0.015, determine:

  (a) the current in the stator and rotor

  (b) motor output

  (c) speed

  (d) torque developed by rotor and torque at pulley

  (e) power factor

  (f) efficiency

SOLUTION

cf. [Puckstein et al, *Machines* (13) Chapter 23].

The various quantities may be determined from an analysis of a single-phase equivalent circuit shown below.

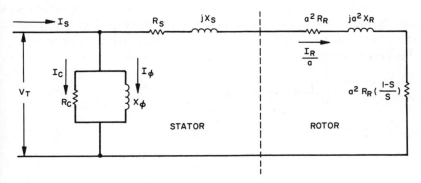

The resistances and reactances are a-c effective values. The effective values of winding resistance and reactance are determined from the blocked test. It is assumed that the current and power drawn by the equivalent core loss resistance R_c and magnetizing reactance X_ϕ can be neglected. It is further assumed that the ratio of a-c to ohmic resistance K is the same in both stator and rotor. The slip is unity. Hence

$$R_S + a^2R_R = \frac{P_B}{3I_B^2}$$

$$= \frac{40,500}{3(170)^2} = 0.466 \text{ ohms}$$

But

$$R_S = K(0.165)$$

and

$$a^2R_R = K(4)^2(0.0127)$$
$$= K(0.2035)$$

Thus

$$K = \frac{0.466}{0.165 + 0.2035} = \frac{0.466}{0.3685} = 1.268$$

so that

$$R_S = 1.268(0.165) = 0.209 \text{ ohms}$$

and

$$a^2R_R = 1.268(0.2035) = 0.258 \text{ ohms}$$

The sum of the reactances may be determined as

$$jX = j(X_S + a^2X_R) = j\sqrt{Z^2 - R^2}$$

$$= j\sqrt{\left(\frac{V}{\sqrt{3}I}\right)^2 - R^2}$$

$$= j\sqrt{\left[\frac{440}{\sqrt{3}(170)}\right]^2 - (0.466)^2} = j\sqrt{(1.49)^2 - (0.466)^2} = j\sqrt{2.22 - 0.21}$$

$$= j\sqrt{2.01} = j1.415 \text{ ohms}$$

In the no-load test, the power consumed by the winding resistances may be neglected. The mechanical power developed in the rotor is the 2000 watts friction and windage loss. The current taken to supply this power, neglecting the winding reactances, is

$$(I_R/a)_{\text{no load}} = \frac{P_R}{3V_T}$$

$$= \frac{P_R}{3V_T/\sqrt{3}}$$

$$= \frac{2000}{\sqrt{3}(2000)} = 0.577 \text{ amp}$$

The no-load power after friction and windage have been subtracted is consumed by the core loss. The values of I_c and I_ϕ determined from this test data will be the same as those when the machine is run under load because the applied voltage is the same in both cases.

$$I_c = \frac{P_c}{3V_T}$$
$$= \frac{10,000 - 2000}{\sqrt{3}(2000)}$$
$$= \frac{8000}{\sqrt{3}(2000)} = 2.31 \text{ amp}$$

The total in-phase current in the no-load test is

$$I_c + \frac{I_R}{a} = 2.31 + 0.577$$
$$= 2.89 \text{ amp}$$

The quadrature current I_ϕ in the no-load test is

$$I_\phi = j\sqrt{(15.3)^2 - (2.89)^2}$$
$$= j\sqrt{234 - 8.35} = j\sqrt{225.6} = j15.05 \text{ amp}$$

(a) When the slip is 0.015, the reflected rotor current I_R/a is

$$\frac{I_R}{a} = \frac{V_T}{R_S + a^2R_R + a^2R_R(1 - S)/S + j(X_S + a^2X_R)}$$
$$= \frac{V_T}{R_S + a^2R_R/S + j(X_S + a^2X_R)}$$
$$= \frac{2000}{\sqrt{3}(0.209 + 0.258/0.015 + j1.415)}$$
$$= \frac{1155}{17.4 + j1.415} = \frac{1155}{17.45/4.66} = 66.2/\underline{-4.66} \text{ amp}$$

Hence the magnitude of the rotor current I_R is

$$I_R = a(66.2)$$
$$= 4(66.2) = 264.8 \text{ amp} \qquad\qquad \text{ANS.}$$

The stator current, including core currents, is

$$I_S = \frac{I_R}{a} + I_c + I_\phi$$
$$= 66.2/\underline{-4.66} + 2.31 - j15.05$$
$$= 66.0 - j5.39 + 2.31 - j15.05$$
$$= 68.3 - j20.4 = 71.2/\underline{-16.7} \text{ amp} \qquad \text{ANS.}$$

(b) The motor output P_o is the mechanical power developed, reduced by the windage and friction.

$$P_o = 3\left(\frac{I_R}{a}\right)^2 a^2 R_R\left(\frac{1-S}{S}\right) - 2000$$

$$= 3(66.2)^2(0.258)\left(\frac{1-0.015}{0.015}\right) - 2000$$

$$= 222,500 - 2000 = 220,500 \text{ watts} \qquad \text{ANS.}$$

or

$$P_o = \frac{220,500}{746} = 296 \text{ hp} \qquad \text{ANS.}$$

(c) The speed n is given

$$n = \frac{120f}{p}(1-S)$$

$$= \frac{120(50)}{6}(1.0 - 0.015) = 1000(0.985)$$

$$= 985 \text{ rpm} \qquad \text{ANS.}$$

(d) If the power P is in watts, the developed torque T is given by

$$T = \frac{33,000P}{2\pi(746)n} = 7.05\frac{P}{n}$$

The rotor developed power has been calculated to be 222,500 watts. The rotor developed torque is

$$T_R = 7.05\frac{(222,500)}{985}$$

$$= 1590 \text{ ft-lbs.} \qquad \text{ANS.}$$

The pulley power is 220,500 watts. The pulley torque is

$$T_P = 7.05\frac{(220,500)}{985}$$

$$= 1575 \text{ ft-lbs} \qquad \text{ANS.}$$

(e) The phase angle of the line current I_S has been calculated to be 16.7°. The power factor is

$$\text{power factor} = \cos(16.7°)$$

$$= 0.959 \qquad \text{ANS.}$$

(f) The power input to the motor is

$$P_{\text{in}} = \sqrt{3}VI_S \cos\theta$$

$$= \sqrt{3}(2000)(71.2)(0.959) = 237,000 \text{ watts}$$

The efficiency η is

$$\eta = \left(\frac{P_o}{P_{\text{in}}}\right)100 = \frac{(220,500)100}{237,000} = 93.1\% \qquad \text{ANS.}$$

5–9

A 450-hp, 3-phase, 2200-v., 60-cycle, 6-pole, wound-rotor, induction motor has the following circuit constants per phase, referred to the stator:

rotor resistance	0.15 ohm
rotor leakage reactance	0.75 ohm
stator resistance	0.32 ohm
stator leakage reactance	1.15 ohms
connection of windings	Y-Y

In addition, the core loss is 2500 watts; the friction and windage losses total 12,000 watts and the magnetizing current is 25 amp.

Calculate the speed and efficiency of this machine at full load.

SOLUTION

An equivalent circuit for one phase is shown below.

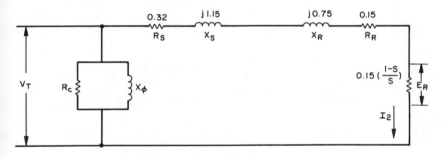

The speed can be found from the slip using the expression

$$n = \frac{120f}{p}(1-S)$$
$$= \frac{120(60)}{6}(1-S) = 1200(1-S)$$

The slip S may be determined from a numerical value of the "power resistor," $(0.15)(1-S)/S$.

If the delivered power is 450 hp, the power delivered to the "power resistor" is

$$P_R = (450)(746) + \text{friction and windage}$$
$$= 336,000 + 12,000 = 348,000 \text{ watts}$$

or per phase

$$P = \frac{348,000}{3} = 116,000 \text{ watts/phase}$$

But the following is also true

$$P_R = 3(I_2)^2(0.15)\left(\frac{1-S}{S}\right)$$

$$= 0.45I_2^2\left(\frac{1-S}{S}\right)$$

so that if I_2 can be determined, the value of S may be computed. If the voltage across the "power resistor" is E_R, the following may be written since I_2 is in phase with E_R.

$$V_T = I_2[(R_S + R_R) + j(X_S + X_R)] + E_R$$

$$\frac{2200}{\sqrt{3}} = I_2[(0.32 + 0.15) + j(1.15 + 0.75)] + E_R$$

$$1270 = 0.47I_2 + j1.90I_2 + E_R$$

But

$$E_R = \frac{116,000}{I_2}$$

so that

$$1270 = \left|\left(\frac{116,000}{I_2} + 0.47I_2\right) + j1.90I_2\right|$$

$$(1270)^2 = \left(\frac{116,000}{I_2} + 0.47I_2\right)^2 + (1.90I_2)^2$$

This may be reduced to the quadratic

$$I_2{}^4 - 3.92 \times 10^5 I_2{}^2 + 3.51 \times 10^9 = 0$$

which has roots

$$I_2{}^2 = \frac{3.92 \times 10^5 \pm \sqrt{15.38 \times 10^{10} - 14.04 \times 10^9}}{2}$$

$$= \frac{10^5}{2}(3.92 \pm \sqrt{13.98})$$

$$= 3.83 \times 10^5,\ 9 \times 10^3$$

or

$$I_2 = 620,\ 95 \text{ amps}$$

The desired value is the lower value of 95 amp. The slip may be determined from

$$\frac{1-S}{S} = \frac{348,000}{0.45I_2{}^2}$$

$$= \frac{348,000}{(0.45)(9 \times 10^3)} = 89$$

Solving for the value of S yields

$$1 - S = 89S$$

$$S = \frac{1}{90} = 0.0111$$

Hence the speed n is

$$n = 1200(1.0 - 0.0111)$$
$$= 1200(0.9889) = 1187 \text{ rpm} \qquad \text{ANS.}$$

The efficiency η is given by

$$\eta = \frac{\text{output}}{\text{output} + \text{losses}}$$

The total winding losses $= 3(I_2)^2(0.32 + 0.15)$
$$= 3(95)^2(0.47) = 12,700 \text{ watts}$$

Thus

$$\eta = \frac{(336,000)(100)}{336,000 + (12,000 + 12,700 + 2500)}$$
$$= \frac{(336,000)100}{363,200} = 92.6\% \qquad \text{ANS.}$$

5–10

A 3-phase, 1000-hp, 12-pole, 2200-v., 25-cycle induction motor operates at full load with a slip of 1.75%. The effective resistance and reactance of the stator are 0.195 ohm and 0.59 ohm, respectively, between terminals. The effective resistance and reactance of the rotor are 0.1433 ohm and 0.29 ohm, respectively, between terminals. The transformation ratio from stator to rotor is 22 to 15. Find the voltage required during starting in order that the starting torque be equal to that developed at rated load.

SOLUTION

This problem may be solved by analysis of the single-phase equivalent circuit shown below by equating starting torque to full-load torque.

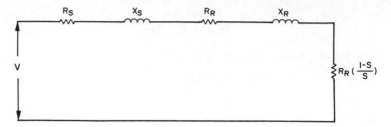

The torque expression may be written as

$$T = 7.05\frac{P}{n}$$

The total power may be written as

$$P = \frac{3V^2 R_R(1-S)/S}{(R_S + R_R/S)^2 + (X_S + X_R)^2}$$

and the speed is

$$n = \frac{120f}{p}(1-S)$$

Hence the torque becomes

$$T = \frac{(7.05)(3)V^2 R_R/S}{(120f/p)[(R_S + R_R/S)^2 + (X_S + X_R)^2]}$$

If 1000 hp is delivered to the load at full load, the full load torque T_{FL} is

$$T_{FL} = 7.05\frac{HP(746)}{n}$$

$$= \frac{7.05(1000)(746)}{[(120)(25)/(12)](1-0.0175)}$$

$$= \frac{7.05(1000)(746)}{(250)(0.9875)} = 21{,}400 \text{ ft-lbs.}$$

The starting torque is determined by evaluating the torque equation at $S = 1.0$. The problem is incomplete since it is not stated whether the windings are wye or delta connected.

Assume wye-connected windings. The single phase equivalent circuit is then the equivalent line-to-neutral connection and the machine impedances are one-half the line-to-line impedances. The rotor impedances must be transformed to the stator circuit by multiplying by the square of the effective stator-to-rotor turns ratio. The equivalent circuit impedances are

$$R_S = \frac{0.195}{2} = 0.0975 \text{ ohms}$$

$$X_S = \frac{0.590}{2} = 0.295$$

$$R_R = \frac{0.1433}{2}\left(\frac{22}{15}\right)^2 = 0.154$$

$$X_R = \frac{0.290}{2}\left(\frac{22}{15}\right)^2 = 0.312$$

and the applied voltage is

$$V = \frac{V_S}{\sqrt{3}}$$

where V_S is the line starting voltage to be determined.
The starting torque T_S is

$$
\begin{aligned}
T_S &= \frac{(7.05)\,(3)\,(V_S/\sqrt{3})^2(0.154)}{(250)\,[\,(0.0975 + 0.154)^2 + (0.295 + 0.312)^2]}\\
&= \frac{1.083V_S^2}{250[\,(0.252)^2 + (0.607)^2]}\\
&= \frac{1.083V_S^2}{250[0.0635 + 0.3685]}\\
&= \frac{1.083V_S^2}{250(0.432)} = 0.010V_S^2
\end{aligned}
$$

Hence

$$0.010V_S^2 = 21{,}400$$

or

$$
\begin{aligned}
V_S &= \sqrt{\frac{21{,}400}{0.010}}\\
&= \sqrt{2.14 \times 10^6} = 1462 \text{ v.} \qquad \text{ANS.}
\end{aligned}
$$

6–1

A full-wave single-phase rectifier consists of two diodes whose internal resistance may be taken as a constant value of 400 ohms. The load resistance is 2500 ohms. The transformer winding is center-tapped with a total voltage of 500 v. rms from end-to-end. Neglect the transformer winding impedance.

Calculate

(a) the d-c load current
(b) the peak voltage across each diode
(c) the d-c output power.

SOLUTION

The circuit diagram is as shown.

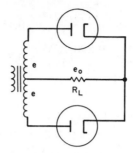

(a) The d-c or average load current is given by

$$I_{av} = \frac{2I_M}{\pi} = (0.637)I_M$$

But

$$I_M = \frac{E_M}{R_L + R_d}$$

where

$$E_M = \frac{(\sqrt{2})500}{2} = 354 \text{ v.}$$

$$R_L = 2500 \text{ ohms}$$

$$R_d = 400 \text{ ohms}$$

so that

$$I_M = \frac{354}{2500 + 400}$$

$$= \frac{354}{2900} = 0.122 \text{ amp}$$

Thus

$$I_{av} = 0.637(0.122) = 0.0777 \text{ amp} \qquad \text{ANS.}$$

(b) The peak voltage across each diode E_{piv} occurs when the voltage across the load has its peak value. At that instant, the transformer voltage is at its peak value and the non-conducting diode experiences a voltage equal to the sum of the peak value of one-half the total transformer voltage and the peak load voltage. Thus

$$E_{piv} = E_M + e_o$$
$$= E_M + I_M R_L$$
$$= 354 + (0.122)2500$$
$$= 354 + 305 = 659 \text{ v.} \qquad \text{ANS.}$$

(c) The d-c output power is P_o, given by

$$P_o = (I_{av})^2 R_L$$
$$= (0.0777)^2 (2500)$$
$$= (0.00603)(2500) = 15.1 \text{ watts} \qquad \text{ANS.}$$

6–2

A selenium half-wave rectifier is rated at 10 amp and a maximum inverse peak voltage of 200 v. This rectifier is used in series with a rheostat to charge batteries from a 120-v., 60-cycle line. The system operates well when five 6-v. batteries are charged in series at 10 amp. When it is attempted to charge ten such batteries in series, the fuse blows before the charging current, as indicated by a d-c ammeter, reaches 10 amp.

State why this happens and give reasons for your answer.

SOLUTION

A simplified schematic is illustrated.

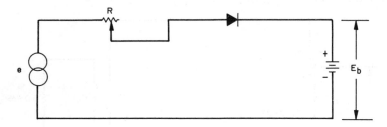

The voltage e is given by

$$e = \sqrt{2}\ 120 \sin (2\pi 60)t$$
$$= 170 \sin 377t$$

The peak inverse voltage E_{piv} applied to the rectifier element will be $(170 + E_b)$ volts if E_b maintains its voltage between cycles in the same manner as a capacitor or storage battery does. For five 6-v. batteries in series

$$E_b = 5(6) = 30 \text{ v.}$$

and

$$E_{piv} = 170 + 30 = 200 \text{ v.}$$

which is just within the rating of the rectifier.
For ten 6-v. batteries in series

$$E_b = 10(6) = 60 \text{ v.}$$

so that

$$E_{piv} = 170 + 60 = 230 \text{ v.}$$

This exceeds the rectifier rating which means that in the reverse
direction the rectifier will conduct heavily while the applied voltage exceeds 200 v. The high conduction averages enough current to
blow the fuse.

6–3

In the amplifier shown, the tube used is a linear triode having a
mu-factor of 8 and a plate resistance of 1800 ohms. The quiescent
current of this tube is 0.050 amp. The output transformer is ideal
and has a turns ratio N_1/N_2 of 25. The reactance of C at the frequency
of the signal is negligible.

Neglecting distortion and its effects, calculate:
(a) the power delivered to the 8-ohm load
(b) the power dissipated in each resistor
(c) the plate dissipation.

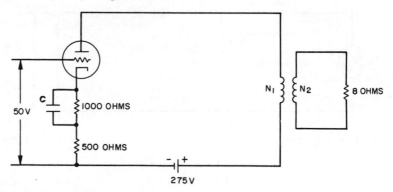

SOLUTION

(a) The power delivered to the 8-ohm load is only signal power,
which may be determined from the linear equivalent circuit.

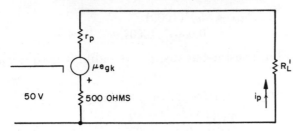

The power delivered to the load P_L is given by

$$P_L = (i_p)^2 R_L'$$

where

$$R_L' = \left(\frac{N_1}{N_2}\right)^2 8$$
$$= (25)^2 8 = 5000 \text{ ohms}$$

But

$$i_p = \frac{\mu e_{gk}}{r_p + R_L' + 500}$$
$$= \frac{8 e_{gk}}{1800 + 5000 + 500} = \frac{8 e_{gk}}{7300} = 1.08 \times 10^{-3} e_{gk}$$

and

$$e_{gk} = 50 - 500 i_p$$

hence

$$i_p = 1.08(10^{-3})(50 - 500 i_p)$$
$$= 0.054 - 0.540 i_p$$

or

$$i_p = \frac{0.054}{1.54} = 0.0351$$

Thus

$$P_L = (0.0351)^2 (5000) = 6.15 \text{ watts} \qquad \text{ANS.}$$

(b) There are three resistors in which power is dissipated: the 8-ohm load, the 500-ohm and the 1000-ohm cathode resistors.

The only power in the 8-ohm load is the signal power which has been calculated to be 6.15 watts.

The 1000-ohm resistor is bypassed to signal and hence has only plate-supply power which is

$$P_{1000} = (I_b)^2(1000)$$
$$= (0.050)^2(1000) = 2.50 \text{ watts} \qquad \text{ANS.}$$

The 500-ohm resistor has dissipated within it both d-c and signal power.

$$P_{500} = (I_b)^2(500) + (i_p)^2(500)$$
$$= 500[(0.050)^2 + (0.0351)^2]$$
$$= 500(0.0025 + 0.00123) = 1.86 \text{ watts} \qquad \text{ANS.}$$

(c) The plate dissipation is the difference between plate supply power and all resistive dissipation (including power output)

$$P_P = (275)(0.050) - (6.15 + 2.50 + 1.86)$$
$$= 13.75 - 10.51 = 3.24 \text{ watts} \qquad \text{ANS.}$$

6–4

A resistance-coupled audio amplifier stage uses a tube having a mu of 30 and a r_p of 25,000 ohms. The plate-circuit load resistor is 100,000 ohms and the grid-leak resistor of the next following tube is 250,000 ohms. The bias is obtained by means of a cathode resistor of 8000 ohms—but the by-pass condenser is defective (a lead has come loose inside the unit) and it acts as an open circuit. Draw the a-c equivalent circuit and compute the voltage gain of the stage.

SOLUTION

The a-c equivalent circuit may be drawn from the description given and the problem solved by analysis of the circuit.

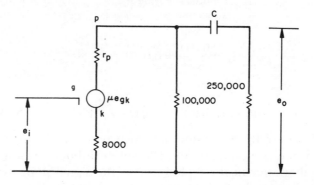

The gain expression is

$$A = \frac{e_o}{e_i} = \frac{\mu R_L}{R_L + r_p + (1 + \mu)R_k}$$

Assume the reactance of the coupling capacitor C to be negligible. The load impedance consists of the parallel combination of the 100,000 and 250,000-ohm resistors.

$$R_L = \frac{(100,000)(250,000)}{100,000 + 250,000} = \frac{250,000}{3.5} = 71,300 \text{ ohms}$$

Thus

$$A = \frac{30(71,300)}{71,300 + 25,000 + (30 + 1)8000}$$

$$= \frac{2.14 \times 10^6}{10^3(71.3 + 25 + 248)}$$

$$= \frac{2.14 \times 10^3}{344.3} = 6.20 \qquad \text{ANS.}$$

6–5

In the circuit shown, the reactances of the capacitors may be neglected, and the vacuum tube may be considered as a linear element with a mutual conductance g_m of 0.001 mho and a plate resistance of one megohm. (10^6 ohms)

   (a) Explain the purpose of this type of circuit.

   (b) Calculate the value of the voltage V_{ab}.

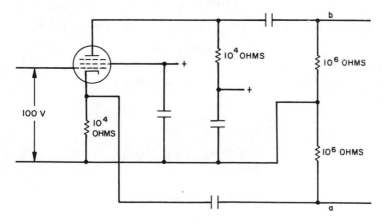

SOLUTION

cf.: [Seely, *Circuits* (21) Chapter 9]

   (a) The use of this circuit is to provide equal-amplitude, out-of-phase signals to drive a push-pull amplifier.

   (b) The circuit may be analyzed using the small-signal equivalent circuit as shown.

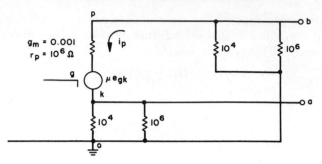

The value of the amplification factor mu is

$$\mu = g_m r_p = (0.001)(10^6) = 1000$$

The voltage V_{ab} is

$$V_{ab} = V_{ao} + V_{ob}$$

But

$$V_{ao} = i_p\left[\frac{(10^4)(10^6)}{10^4 + 10^6}\right]$$

$$= i_p\left[\frac{10^4}{1.01}\right] = 0.99 \times 10^4 i_p$$

and similarly because the load resistance is the same as for V_{ao}

$$V_{ob} = 0.99 \times 10^4 i_p$$

so that

$$V_{ab} = 2(0.99 \times 10^4)i_p = 1.98 \times 10^4 i_p$$

But

$$i_p = \frac{\mu e_{gk}}{10^6 + 1.98 \times 10^4}$$

$$= \frac{1000 e_{gk}}{1.02 \times 10^6} = 9.8 \times 10^{-4} e_{gk}$$

However

$$e_{gk} = 100 - 0.99 \times 10^4 i_p$$

Substituting and solving for i_p yields

$$i_p = 9.8 \times 10^{-4}(100 - 0.99 \times 10^4 i_p)$$
$$= 0.098 - 9.7 i_p$$

or

$$i_p = \frac{0.098}{1 + 9.7}$$

$$= \frac{0.098}{10.7} = 9.16 \times 10^{-3} \text{ amp}$$

so that

$$V_{ab} = (1.98 \times 10^4)(9.16 \times 10^{-3})$$
$$= 181.5 \text{ v}$$

ANS.

6–6

A Class A amplifier consists of a pentode coupled by an R-C network to a power triode. The voltage gain of the pentode stage is to be 100 at mid-frequency, with the upper half-power frequency at 20,000 cps. The μ and g_m of the pentode are 1000 and 0.001 mho, respectively, and its output capacitance is 10 mmf. The input and grid-plate capacitances in the triode are respectively 15 and 10 mmf. All capacitances include the effects of wiring.

Calculate the maximum allowable voltage gain in the triode stage if the upper half-power frequency is to be realized.

SOLUTION

A linear equivalent circuit which neglects the effects of all capacitances except the three mentioned in the problem, is shown below.

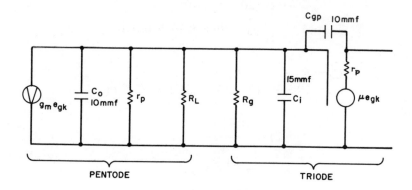

The total load presented to the pentode consists of the three resistances r_p, R_L, R_g and the capacitances C_o, C_i, and the added input capacity due to the triode grid-plate capacity, all in parallel. At midband, the capacitances have negligible admittances so the midband gain may be written as

$$A = g_m\left(\frac{1}{1/r_p + 1/R_L + 1/R_g}\right) = 100$$
$$= g_m R_{eq}$$

or

$$R_{eq} = \frac{100}{g_m}$$
$$= \frac{100}{0.001} = 10^5 \text{ ohms}$$

At the upper half-power (3-db) frequency f

$$f = \frac{1}{2\pi R_{eq} C_T}$$

where C_T is the sum of the three capacitances mentioned. If A_{TR} is the triode gain, the added input capacity C_A for a simple amplifier is

$$C_A = (1 + A_{TR}) C_{gp}$$

But

$$C_T = C_o + C_i + C_A$$
$$= [10 + 15 + 10(1 + A_{TR})] 10^{-12}$$

and

$$C_T = \frac{1}{2\pi f R_{eq}}$$
$$= \frac{1}{2\pi (20{,}000)(10^5)}$$
$$= \frac{10^{-9}}{12.57} = 79.5 \times 10^{-12} \text{ farads}$$

so that

$$C_A = C_T - (C_o + C_i)$$
$$= 79.5 - (10 + 15) = 54.5 \times 10^{-12} \text{ farads}$$

and

$$A_{TR} = \frac{C_A}{C_{gp}} - 1$$
$$= \frac{54.5}{10} - 1$$
$$= 5.45 - 1 = 4.45 \qquad \text{ANS.}$$

6-7

The bypass capacitors C in the circuit shown have negligible reactances. The mutual conductance of the pentode g_m is $1{,}000 \times 10^{-6}$ mho and its plate resistance r_p is 10^6 ohms. The effective capacitances of C_1, C_2, and C_3 are 10, 5, and 10 micromicrofarads.

Calculate the magnitude of the voltage gain of this amplifier when the angular velocity of the signal is 10^6 rad/sec.

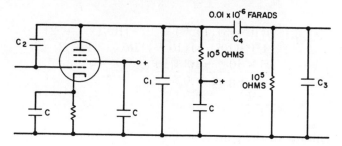

SOLUTION

The gain of this circuit may be computed from

$$A = \frac{(j\omega C_{gp} - g_m)Z_T}{1 + j\omega C_{gp}Z_T}$$

The grid-plate capacity C_{gp} is the same as C_2, Z_T is the total plate-circuit impedance in parallel with the plate resistance of the tube, and the values of ω and g_m are given. The reactances of the various capacitances in the plate circuit are

$$X_{C_1} = \frac{1}{j\omega C_1}$$
$$= \frac{1}{j10^6(10)(10^{-12})} = -j10^5 \text{ ohms}$$
$$X_{C_3} = \frac{1}{j\omega C_3}$$
$$= \frac{1}{j(10^6)(10)(10^{-12})} = -j10^5 \text{ ohms}$$
$$X_{C_4} = \frac{1}{j\omega C_4}$$
$$= \frac{1}{j(10^6)(10^{-8})} = -j10^2 \text{ ohms}$$

Because the reactance of C_4 is negligible compared to the other values, Z_T consists of five elements in parallel: r_p, C_1, C_3 and the two 10^5-ohm resistors. Hence

$$Z_T = \frac{1}{1/r_p + 1/10^5 + 1/10^5 + j\omega C_1 + j\omega C_3}$$
$$= \frac{1}{10^{-6} + 10^{-5} + 10^{-5} + j10^{-5} + j10^{-5}}$$
$$= \frac{10^5}{2.1 + j2}$$

Then

$$A = \frac{[j(10^6)(5)(10^{-12}) - 10^{-3}]10^5/(2.1 + j2)}{1 + j(10^6)(5)(10^{-12})(10^5)/(2.1 + j2)}$$

$$= \frac{[j5 \times 10^{-6} - 10^{-3}]10^5}{2.1 + j2 + j0.5}$$

$$\approx \frac{-10^2}{2.1 + j2.5}$$

The magnitude of the gain is

$$|A| = \frac{100}{|2.1 + j2.5|}$$

$$= \frac{100}{3.26} = 30.7 \qquad \text{ANS.}$$

6–8

A simple $R\text{-}C$ coupled one stage uncompensated vacuum-tube amplifier has a midband gain of $-200 + j0$. The 3-db frequencies are 50 and 50,000 cps. Negative feedback is introduced with a feedback factor of $1/20$ with no other changes.

(a) Find the new magnitude of gain at 50 and 50,000 cps.

(b) Find the new 3-db gain frequencies.

SOLUTION

(a) Assume the feedback is frequency-independent. The modified gain may be written as

$$A = \frac{A_o}{1 + A_o B}$$

$$= \frac{A_o}{1 + A_o/20}$$

At midband the gain A_M is

$$A_M = \frac{-200}{1 + 200/20}$$

$$= \frac{-200}{1 + 10} = -18.18$$

At the 3-db frequencies of 50 and 50,000 cps, the unmodified gain A_o' is

$$A_o' = \frac{A_o}{1 \pm j1}$$

$$= \frac{-200}{1 \pm j1} = -100 \pm j100$$

Taking the minus sign, the modified gain is

$$A = \frac{-100 - j100}{1 + (100 + j100)/20}$$
$$= \frac{-100(1 + j)}{1 + 5 + j5}$$
$$= \frac{-100(1 + j1)(6 - j5)}{(6 + j5)(6 - j5)}$$
$$= \frac{-100(11 + j1)}{36 + 25} = \frac{-100}{61}(11 + j1) = -18.04 + j1.64$$

The gain magnitude is

$$|A| = 18.1 \qquad \text{ANS.}$$

(b) At the new 3-db gain frequencies, the gain is 3-db down from 18.18

or

$$|A'| = (18.18)(0.707) = 12.84$$

The unmodified gain as a function of frequency may be written for higher frequencies as

$$\frac{A_H}{A_o} = \frac{1}{1 + jf/f_H}$$

and for lower frequencies

$$\frac{A_L}{A_o} = \frac{1}{1 - jf_L/f}$$

where f_H and f_L are the upper and lower 3-db frequencies. The high-frequency gain may be written

$$A_H = \frac{A_o}{1 + jK}$$

so that the feedback gain, to evaluate the value of $K = f/f_H$ at the new 3-db frequency, is

$$A = \left| \frac{A_o/(1 + jK)}{1 + A_o/20(1 + jK)} \right| = 12.84$$

This may be written as

$$\frac{A_o}{|1 + jK + A_o/20|} = 12.84$$

Substituting the value of A_o and rewriting, this becomes

$$\frac{200}{12.84} = |1 + 10 + jK|$$

$$15.55 = \sqrt{(11)^2 + (K)^2}$$

From which

$$K^2 = (15.55)^2 - (11)^2 = 242 - 121 = 121$$
$$K = \sqrt{121} = 11$$

Thus the new upper 3-db frequency may be obtained

$$K = \frac{f}{f_H} = 11$$
$$f = 11f_H$$
$$= 11(50,000) = 550,000 \text{ cps} \qquad \text{ANS.}$$

The expression for A_L is

$$A_L = \frac{A_o}{1 - jK'}$$

where

$$K' = \frac{f_L}{f}$$

At the new lower 3-db frequency

$$A = \left| \frac{A_o/(1 - jK')}{1 + A_o/20(1 - jK')} \right| = 12.84$$

or

$$\frac{A_o}{|1 - jK' + A_o/20|} = 12.84$$

or substituting values

$$\frac{200}{12.84} = 15.55 = |11 - jK'|$$
$$= \sqrt{(11)^2 + (K')^2}$$

or

$$K' = 11$$

The new lower 3-db frequency may be obtained

$$f = \frac{f_L}{K} = \frac{50}{11} = 4.54 \text{ cps} \qquad \text{ANS.}$$

6-9

   The amplifier shown is to deliver 1.25 watts to the 2,000-ohm load. Both tubes operate in Class A_1. The reactance of all capacitors may be neglected.

Calculate the minimum value of *e* which will yield the required output

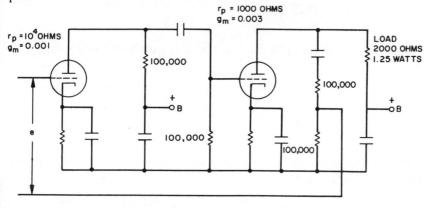

SOLUTION

The voltage across the 2000-ohm load necessary to produce 1.25 watts is

$$P_o = \frac{e_o^2}{R_L}$$
$$e_o = \sqrt{P_o R_L}$$
$$\quad = \sqrt{(1.25)(2000)} = 50 \text{ v.}$$

But if the overall gain of the circuit *A* is

$$A = \frac{e_o}{e}$$

then

$$e = \frac{e_o}{A} = \frac{50}{A}$$

and it is necessary to find the value of *A*. The small-signal equivalent circuit is shown below.

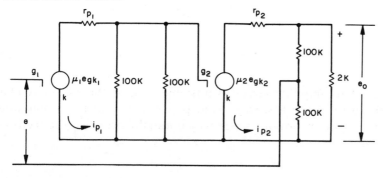

The values of amplification factor are

$$\mu_1 = r_{p_1} g_{m_1} = (10)(10^3)(10^{-3}) = 10$$
$$\mu_2 = r_{p_2} g_{m_2} = (10^3)(3)(10^{-3}) = 3$$

Neglecting the loading of the two $100\ K$ resistors on the $2\ K$ load,

$$e_o = \frac{-\mu_2 e_{gk_2}(2)(10^3)}{r_{p_2} + 2 \times 10^3}$$
$$= \frac{-3(e_{gk_2})(2)(10^3)}{10^3 + 2 \times 10^3} = -2e_{gk_2}$$

The two $100\ K$ resistors in the first tube circuit are in parallel, hence the load is $50\ K$, and

$$e_{gk_2} = \frac{-\mu_1 e_{gk_1}(5)(10^4)}{r_{p_1} + 5 \times 10^4}$$
$$= \frac{-10 e_{gk_1}(5)(10^4)}{10^4 + 5 \times 10^4} = -10\left(\frac{5}{6}\right)e_{gk_1} = -8.33 e_{gk_1}$$
$$e_o = (-2)(-8.33 e_{gk_1}) = 16.66 e_{gk_1}$$

But e_{gk_1} is the sum of the input voltage e and the portion of the output voltage which is fed back to the input. The two $100\ K$ resistors provide a voltage divider such that $e_o/2$ is fed back. Thus

$$e_{gk_1} = e + e_o/2$$

But

$$e_{gk_1} = \frac{e_o}{16.66}$$

Hence

$$e_o = 16.66e + 8.33e_o$$
$$-7.33e_o = 16.66e$$

from which

$$\frac{e_o}{e} = A = \frac{16.66}{-7.33} = -2.27$$

or

$$e = \frac{50}{A} = \frac{50}{-2.27} = -22.0 \text{ v.} \qquad \text{ANS.}$$

(Note: This amplifier circuit is unstable because the voltage fed back to the grid of the first stage is in phase with, and has a magnitude greater than, the input voltage which initially provided the feed-back voltage.)

6–10

A pair of triodes, ideal in that their plate characteristics follow the 3/2 power of the effective grid voltage, are used in the ideal push-pull amplifier shown. The excitation on the grids varies the plate current per tube from cut-off to the maximum allowable value of 0.125 amp at zero effective grid voltage.

Calculate the maximum power that this amplifier delivers to its load under the conditions stated, and the optimum turns ratio $2N_1/N_2$ for the output transformer.

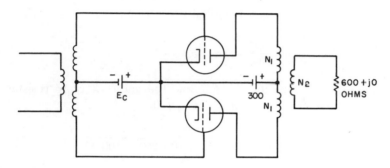

SOLUTION

The plate current may be expressed as

$$i_p = K(\mu e_g + e_b)^{3/2}$$

Optimum power is delivered to the load when the reflected load impedance Z_L', is given by

$$Z_L' = 2r_p$$

But

$$Z_L' = \left(\frac{2N_1}{N_2}\right)^2 Z_L$$
$$= \left(\frac{2N_1}{N_2}\right)^2 600$$

The value of the maximum power is

$$P_{max} = \frac{(\mu e_{gk})^2 Z_L'}{(r_p + Z_L'/2)^2}$$

It is necessary to determine the value of r_p, Z_L', and μe_{gk}. These values may be determined from the plate current expression. The value of the constant K may be evaluated by substituting values. When e_g is zero and e_b is 300 v., the plate current is 0.125 amp. Thus

$$0.125 = K(0 + 300)^{3/2}$$

or

$$K = \frac{0.125}{(300)^{3/2}} = \frac{0.125}{5200} = 24 \times 10^{-6}$$

The value of r_p may be found from

$$r_p = \frac{1}{g_p} = \frac{1}{\partial i_p/\partial e_p}\bigg|_{e_g} = \text{constant}$$

so that

$$\frac{\partial i_p}{\partial e_p} = \frac{3}{2} K (\mu e_g + e_b)^{1/2}$$

Assuming constant tube parameters, the value of plate resistance can be evaluated at the condition of $e_g = 0$.

$$r_p = \frac{1}{\partial i_p/\partial e_p} = \frac{1}{3/2(24 \times 10^{-6})(0 + 300)^{1/2}}$$
$$= \frac{10^6}{1.5(24)(17.3)} = 1600 \text{ ohms}$$

The turns ratio may be written

$$\left(\frac{2N_1}{N_2}\right)^2 = \frac{Z_L'}{Z_L}$$

or

$$\frac{2N_1}{N_2} = \sqrt{\frac{2r_p}{Z_L}}$$
$$= \sqrt{\frac{3200}{600}} = 2.31 \qquad \text{ANS.}$$

or

$$\frac{N_1}{N_2} = \frac{2.31}{2} = 1.155$$

The power output requires the determination of the peak or rms value of e_{gk}. The bias E_c is such that the peak of e_{gk} equals E_c. Hence at cutoff

$$0 = (-2\mu E_c + 300)^{3/2}$$

or

$$\mu E_c = 150$$

or for the rms value

$$\mu e_{gk} = \frac{\mu E_c}{\sqrt{2}}$$

$$= \frac{150}{\sqrt{2}}$$

Hence the maximum power is

$$P_{max} = \frac{(150/\sqrt{2})^2(3200)}{(1600+1600)^2} = \frac{(150)^2}{2(3200)} = 3.52 \text{ watts} \qquad \text{ANS.}$$

7-1

Design a resistance pad having a loss of 10 db and matching a 200 ohm circuit to one having a resistance of 600 ohms.

SOLUTION

Assume a Tee circuit shown below where the generator impedance is 200 ohms and the load is 600 ohms.

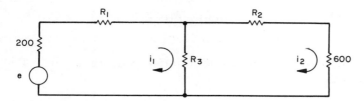

Three equations may be written:

$$200 = R_1 + \frac{(600+R_2)R_3}{600+R_2+R_3} \qquad (1)$$

$$600 = R_2 + \frac{(200+R_1)R_3}{200+R_1+R_3} \qquad (2)$$

$$\frac{i_1}{i_2} = \frac{600+R_2+R_3}{R_3} \qquad (3)$$

If the attenuation is 10 db

$$\frac{P_1}{P_2} = \frac{i_1^2(200)}{i_2^2(600)} = \text{antilog } \frac{10 \text{ db}}{10} = 10$$

$$\frac{i_1}{i_2} = \sqrt{30} = 5.48$$

$$5.48 = \frac{600+R_2+R_3}{R_3}$$

or

$$R_2 = 4.48R_3 - 600 \qquad (4)$$

This may be substituted into Eq. (1)

$$200 = R_1 + \frac{(600 + 4.48R_3 - 600)R_3}{600 + 4.48R_3 - 600 + R_3}$$

$$200 = R_1 + \frac{4.48R_3{}^2}{5.48R_3} = R_1 + 0.818R_3$$

or

$$R_1 = 200 - 0.818R_3 \qquad\qquad (5)$$

If Eqs. (5) and (4) are substituted into (2) then

$$600 = 4.48R_3 - 600 + \frac{(200 + 200 - 0.818R_3)R_3}{200 + 200 - 0.818R_3 + R_3}$$

$$1200 = 4.48R_3 + \frac{400R_3 - 0.818R_3{}^2}{400 + 0.182R_3}$$

$$(1200)(400) + (1200)(0.182R_3) = (4.48R_3)(400) +$$
$$(4.48R_3)(0.182R_3) + 400R_3 - 0.818R_3{}^2$$
$$1200 + 0.546R_3 = 4.48R_3 + R_3$$

$$R_3 = \frac{1200}{4.934} = 243.5 \text{ ohms} \qquad\qquad \text{ANS.}$$

$$R_1 = 200 - (0.818)(243.5) = 1 \text{ ohm} \qquad\qquad \text{ANS.}$$

$$R_2 = (4.48)(243.5) - 600 = 490 \text{ ohms} \qquad\qquad \text{ANS.}$$

Note: Check that the input and output impedances are truly 200 and 600 ohms.

7–2

The circuit shown is that of a filter section. Determine the band of frequencies over which the attenuation of signals is zero.

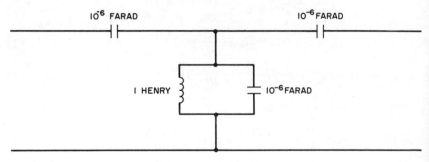

SOLUTION

The band of frequencies where the attenuation is zero is the pass band defined by the following

$$-1 \leq \frac{Z_1}{4Z_2} \leq 0$$

where in this Tee configuration the two series elements each represent an impedance $Z_1/2$ and the shunt branch has an impedance Z_2. Thus

$$\frac{Z_1}{2} = \frac{1}{j\omega C}$$

or

$$Z_1 = \frac{2}{j\omega(10^{-6})}$$

and

$$Z_2 = \frac{j\omega L(1/j\omega C)}{j\omega L + 1/j\omega C}$$

$$= \frac{j\omega L}{1 - \omega^2 LC}$$

because $L = 1$ henry

$$Z_2 = \frac{j\omega}{1 - \omega^2(10^{-6})}$$

Hence

$$\frac{Z_1}{4Z_2} = \frac{2/j\omega(10^{-6})}{4j\omega/[1 - \omega^2(10^{-6})]} = \frac{1 - \omega^2(10^{-6})}{-2\omega^2(10^{-6})}$$

The pass band is defined by the extremes of the range of $Z_1/4Z_2$. One extreme ω_1 is given by

$$\frac{Z_1}{4Z_2} = 0$$

or

$$1 - \omega_1^2(10^{-6}) = 0$$

$$\omega_1^2 = \frac{1}{10^{-6}}$$

and

$$\omega_1 = 10^3 \text{ rad/sec}$$

or

$$f_1 = \frac{\omega_1}{2\pi} = 159 \text{ cps.}$$

The other extreme ω_2 is given by

$$\frac{Z_1}{4Z_2} = -1$$

or

$$1 - \omega_2{}^2(10^{-6}) = 2\omega_2{}^2(10^{-6})$$

so that

$$\omega_2{}^2 = \frac{1}{3(10^{-6})}$$

or

$$\omega_2 = 576 \text{ rad/sec.}$$

or

$$f_2 = \frac{\omega_2}{2\pi} = 91.9 \text{ cps.}$$

Thus the pass band is

$$91.9 \text{ to } 159 \text{ cps.} \qquad \text{ANS.}$$

or

$$576 \text{ to } 1000 \text{ rad/sec.} \qquad \text{ANS.}$$

7–3

Calculate the cut-off frequencies and the minimum image resistance in the pass band for the filter section shown.

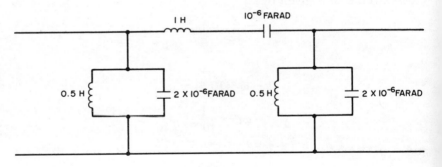

SOLUTION

cf.: [Ryder, *Networks*, (19), Chap. 4.]
The cut-off frequencies are given by the following

$$\frac{Z_1}{4Z_2} = -1, \frac{Z_1}{4Z_2} = 0$$

where Z_1 is the impedance of the series branch and $2Z_2$ is the impedance of either shunt branch. For this constant-K filter section, the
minimum image resistance is the value of image resistance R_K given by

$$R_K = \sqrt{\frac{L_2}{C_1}}$$

where L_2 is one-half the inductance of the shunt branch and C_1 is
the capacitance of the series branch.

The calculation of R_K is

$$R_K = \sqrt{\frac{0.5/2}{10^{-6}}}$$

$$= \sqrt{0.25 \times 10^6} = 500 \text{ ohms} \qquad \text{ANS.}$$

The calculation of the cut-off frequencies is

$$Z_1 = j\omega L_1 + \frac{1}{j\omega C} = j\left(\omega - \frac{1}{\omega(10^{-6})}\right)$$

$$2Z_2 = \frac{(j\omega L_2)(1/j\omega C_2)}{j\omega L_2 + 1/j\omega C_2}$$

$$= \frac{j\omega L_2}{1 - \omega^2 L_2 C_2} = \frac{j0.5\omega}{1 - \omega^2(10^{-6})}$$

Thus

$$\frac{Z_1}{4Z_2} = \frac{Z_1}{2(2Z_2)} = \frac{j[\omega - 1/\omega(10^{-6})]}{j\omega/[1 - \omega^2(10^{-6})]}$$

$$= \left(1 - \frac{1}{10^{-6}\omega^2}\right)(1 - 10^{-6}\omega^2)$$

$$= 2 - 10^{-6}\omega^2 - \frac{1}{10^{-6}\omega^2}$$

If $Z_1/4Z_2 = -1$, then

$$-1 = 2 - 10^{-6}\omega^2 - \frac{1}{10^{-6}\omega^2}$$

The resulting quadratic is

$$\omega^4 - 3(10^6)\omega^2 + 10^{12} = 0$$

From which

$$\omega^2 = \frac{3(10^6) \pm \sqrt{9(10^{12}) - 4(10^{12})}}{2}$$

$$= \frac{10^6}{2}(3 \pm \sqrt{5}) = \frac{10^6}{2}(3 \pm 2.236)$$

$$= 2.618 \times 10^6, \, 0.382 \times 10^6$$

This, in turn, gives the two values of ω:

$$\omega_1 = \sqrt{2.618 \times 10^6} = 1620 \text{ rad/sec} \qquad \text{ANS.}$$

or

$$f_1 = \frac{\omega_1}{2\pi} = \frac{1620}{2\pi} = 258 \text{ cps}$$

and

$$\omega_2 = \sqrt{0.382 \times 10^6} = 619 \text{ rad/sec} \qquad \text{ANS.}$$

or

$$f_2 = \frac{\omega_2}{2\pi} = \frac{619}{2\pi} = 98.5 \text{ cps}$$

If $Z_1/4Z_2 = 0$, then

$$2 - 10^{-6}\omega^2 - \frac{1}{10^{-6}\omega^2} = 0$$

The resulting quadratic is

$$\omega^4 - 2(10^6)\omega^2 + 10^{12} = 0$$

which is a perfect square

$$(\omega^2 - 10^6)^2 = 0$$

or

$$\omega^2 = 10^6$$

and

$$\omega = 1000 \text{ rad/sec.}$$

This value is not a cut-off frequency. It is the geometric mean of the cut-off frequencies and hence is the mid-frequency of the response.

7-4

The network shown is a T-section of an *m*-derived low-pass filter. Determine:

(a) the cut-off frequency
(b) the frequency of infinite attenuation
(c) the attenuation at $\omega = 10,000$ rad/sec.

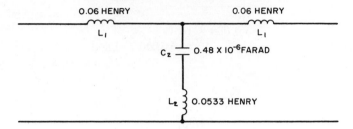

SOLUTION

cf.: [*Data* (17), pp. 165, 166, 1112.]

(a) The cut-off frequencies are defined by the limits of the pass-band which is given by

$$-1 \le \frac{Z_1}{4Z_2} \le 0$$

For this filter, the impedance of the series arm is $Z_1/2$ and the impedance of the shunt arm is Z_2. Using symbols

$$Z_1 = j2\omega L_1$$
$$Z_2 = j\left(\omega L_2 - \frac{1}{\omega C_2}\right)$$

so that

$$\frac{Z_1}{4Z_2} = \frac{j2\omega L_1}{j4(\omega L_2 - 1/\omega C_2)}$$
$$= \frac{\omega L_1}{2(\omega L_2 - 1/\omega C_2)}$$

The condition of $Z_1/4Z_2 = 0$ yields $\omega_c = 0$ as a cut-off condition. The condition of $Z_1/4Z_2 = -1$ yields

$$\frac{\omega_c L_1}{2(\omega_c L_2 - 1/\omega_c C_2)} = -1$$

$$\omega_c L_1 = -2\,\omega_c L_2 + \frac{2}{\omega_c C_2}$$

or

$$\omega_c = \sqrt{\frac{2}{C_2(L_1 + 2L_2)}}$$
$$= \sqrt{\frac{2}{0.48 \times 10^{-6}[0.06 + 2(0.0533)]}}$$

$$= \sqrt{\frac{2}{0.080 \times 10^{-6}}}$$
$$= \sqrt{25 \times 10^{-6}} = 5000 \text{ rad/sec}$$

or

$$f_c = \frac{\omega_c}{2\pi}$$
$$= \frac{5000}{2\pi} = 795 \text{ cps} \qquad\qquad \text{ANS.}$$

(b) The frequency of infinite attenuation f_i is the frequency at which the shunt branch is resonant. Thus at ω_i,

$$\omega_i L_2 - \frac{1}{\omega_i C_2} = 0$$

$$\omega_i = \frac{1}{\sqrt{L_2 C_2}}$$
$$= \frac{1}{\sqrt{0.0533(0.48 \times 10^{-6})}}$$
$$= \frac{1}{\sqrt{0.0256 \times 10^{-6}}} = 6250 \text{ rad/sec}$$

or

$$f_i = \frac{\omega_i}{2\pi} = \frac{6250}{2\pi} = 995 \text{ cps} \qquad\qquad \text{ANS.}$$

(c) The attenuation at $\omega = 10{,}000$ rad/sec is found from the relationship [*Data* (17)]:

$$\alpha = \cosh^{-1}\left[1 - 2\frac{1/(\omega_i^2) - 1/(\omega_c^2)}{1/(\omega_i^2) - 1/(\omega^2)}\right]$$
$$= \cosh^{-1}\left[1 - 2\frac{1/(6250)^2 - 1/(5000)^2}{1/(6250)^2 - 1/(10{,}000)^2}\right]$$
$$= \cosh^{-1}\left[1 - 2\frac{10^{-6}[(0.0256) - (0.040)]}{10^{-6}[(0.0256) - (0.010)]}\right]$$
$$= \cosh^{-1}\left[1 - 2\left(\frac{-0.0144}{0.0156}\right)\right]$$
$$= \cosh^{-1}[1 + 1.848]$$
$$= \cosh^{-1}(2.848)$$

Using the table of hyperbolic cosines [*Data* (17) p. 1112]:

$$\alpha = 1.707 \text{ nepers}$$
$$= (1.707)(8.68) = 14.8 \text{ db} \qquad\qquad \text{ANS.}$$

8–1

A 100-mile telephone line has the following parameters per mile of line: $R = 10$ ohms; $L = 0.004$ henry; $C = 0.008 \times 10^{-6}$ farad; and $G = 10^{-6}$ mho.

(a) Calculate the impedance of the termination which will match this line at a frequency, $f = 5000/2\pi$

(b) If this line included no repeaters, what would be the ratio, at this frequency, of the voltage at the input to that at the termination?

SOLUTION

(a) The value of the characteristic impedance is

$$Z_o = \sqrt{\frac{Z}{Y}}$$

$$Z = R + j\omega L = 10 + j(5000)(0.004)$$
$$= 10 + j20$$
$$= 22.4 \,/63.5 \text{ ohms/mile}$$

$$Y = G + j\omega C = 10^{-6} + j(5000)(0.008)(10^{-6})$$
$$= 10^{-6}(1 + j40)$$
$$= 40(10^{-6}) \,/88.6 \text{ mhos/mile}$$

$$Z_o = \sqrt{\frac{22.4 \,/63.5}{40(10^{-6}) \,/88.6}} = 750 \,/\!-12.55 \qquad \text{ANS.}$$

(b) With the line terminated at both ends in Z_o given above, the input-output voltage ratio is

$$\frac{V_{\text{in}}}{V_{\text{out}}} = \epsilon^{\gamma l} = \epsilon^{\alpha l}\epsilon^{j\beta l}$$

$$\gamma = \sqrt{ZY} = \sqrt{(22.4 \,/63.5)(40)(10^{-6}) \,/88.6}$$
$$= 0.030 \,/76$$

$$\alpha + j\beta = 0.030 \cos{(76°)} + j0.030 \sin{(76°)} = 0.00723 + j0.0290$$

The magnitude of the voltage ratio is simply $\epsilon^{\alpha l}$

$$\epsilon^{\alpha l} = \epsilon^{(0.00723)(100)} = \epsilon^{0.723}$$
$$= 2.06 \qquad \text{ANS.}$$

8–2

Each conductor of a 3-phase, 60-cycle transmission line has the following parameters per mile with respect to ground: $R = 0.3$ ohm; $\omega L = 1.2$ ohms; $\omega C = 3 \times 10^{-6}$ mho. The leakage may be neglected.

Calculate the input impedance of a 100-mile length of this conductor, to ground, when the distant end is open-circuited.

SOLUTION

The general expression for the input impedance Z_{in} of a length of transmission line is

$$Z_{in} = Z_o\left(\frac{\epsilon^{\gamma l} + K\epsilon^{-\gamma l}}{\epsilon^{\gamma l} - K\epsilon^{-\gamma l}}\right)$$

where

$$Z_o = \sqrt{\frac{Z}{Y}}$$

and

$$\gamma = \sqrt{ZY}$$

and

$$K \equiv \frac{Z_L - Z_o}{Z_L + Z_o}$$

but

$$Z = R + j\omega L$$
$$= 0.3 + j1.2 \text{ ohms/mile}$$

and

$$Y = G + j\omega C$$
$$= j3 \times 10^{-6} \text{ mhos/mile}$$

so that

$$Z_o = \sqrt{\frac{0.3 + j1.2}{j3 \times 10^{-6}}}$$
$$= \sqrt{-j0.1 \times 10^6 + 0.4 \times 10^6}$$
$$= 10^3\sqrt{0.414\underline{/-14.0}}$$
$$= 644\underline{/-7.0} \text{ ohms}$$

Also

$$\gamma = \sqrt{(0.3 + j1.2)(j3 \times 10^{-6})}$$
$$= 10^{-3}\sqrt{j0.9 - 3.6}$$
$$= 10^{-3}\sqrt{3.72\underline{/166}}$$
$$= 1.93 \times 10^{-3}\underline{/83}$$

The propagation constant γ may also be expressed in the form

$$\gamma = \alpha + j\beta$$

where
$$\alpha = 1.93 \times 10^{-3} \cos 83° = 0.235 \times 10^{-3} \text{ nepers/mile}$$
and
$$\beta = 1.93 \times 10^{-3} \sin 83° = 1.915 \times 10^{-3} \text{ rad/mile}$$

and finally, with an open circuit load, Z_L is infinite
$$K = \frac{\infty - Z_o}{\infty + Z_o} = +1$$

For a 100-mile length of this cable
$$\alpha l = 0.235 \times 10^{-3}(100) = 0.0235 \text{ nepers}$$
$$\beta l = 1.915 \times 10^{-3}(100) = 0.1915 \text{ radians}$$
$$= 10.95 \text{ degrees}$$
so that
$$\epsilon^{\gamma l} = \epsilon^{0.0235}\underline{/10.95}$$
$$= 1.0237\underline{/10.95}$$
and
$$\epsilon^{-\gamma l} = \epsilon^{-0.0235}\underline{/-10.95}$$
$$= 0.9769\underline{/-10.95}$$
Hence
$$Z_{in} = 644\underline{/-7.0}\left[\frac{1.0237\underline{/10.95} + 0.9769\underline{/-10.95}}{1.0237\underline{/10.95} - 0.9769\underline{/-10.95}}\right]$$
$$= 644\underline{/-7.0}\left[\frac{1.005 + j0.195 + 0.959 - j0.1855}{1.005 + j0.195 - 0.959 + j0.1855}\right]$$
$$= 644\underline{/-7.0}\left[\frac{1.964 + j0.0095}{0.046 + j0.3805}\right]$$
$$= 644\underline{/-7.0}\left[\frac{1.964\underline{/0.3}}{0.383\underline{/83.1}}\right]$$
$$= 3300\underline{/-89.8} \text{ ohms} \qquad \text{ANS.}$$

An alternative method of solution of this problem is shown below. The input impedance of an open-circuited transmission line is
$$Z_{in} = Z_o \coth \gamma l$$

This may be expanded as
$$Z_{in} = Z_o \coth (\alpha l + j\beta l)$$
$$= Z_o \frac{\cosh (\alpha l + j\beta l)}{\sinh (\alpha l + j\beta l)}$$
$$= Z_o\left[\frac{\cosh \alpha l \cos \beta l + j \sinh \alpha l \sin \beta l}{\sinh \alpha l \cos \beta l + j \cosh \alpha l \sin \beta l}\right]$$

$$Z_o = 644\underline{/-7.0}$$
$$\alpha l = 0.0235 \text{ nepers}$$
$$\beta l = 0.1915 \text{ radians}$$
$$= 10.95 \text{ degrees}$$

Using tables

$$\cosh (0.0235) = 1.00$$
$$\sinh (0.0235) = 0.0235$$
$$\cos (10.95°) = 0.9818$$
$$\sin (10.95°) = 0.1899$$

so that

$$Z_{\text{in}} = 644\underline{/-7.0}\left[\frac{(1.000)(0.9818) + j(0.0235)(0.1899)}{(0.0235)(0.9818) + j(1.000)(0.1899)}\right]$$

$$= 644\underline{/-7.0}\left[\frac{0.9818 + j0.00446}{0.0231 + j0.1899}\right]$$

$$= 644\underline{/-7.0}\left(\frac{0.982\underline{/0.26}}{0.191\underline{/83.05}}\right) = 3305\underline{/-89.8} \text{ ohms} \qquad \text{ANS.}$$

8–3

A standing-wave line is used to measure the input impedance of, and RF power flowing into, an antenna. The characteristic impedance of the line is 50 ohms. The voltage standing-wave ratio is 2.0. The first voltage minimum occurs at a distance 0.4 wavelengths from the antenna input terminals. The value of the voltage at the first minimum is 120 v. rms.

What is the value of the power delivered to the antenna and what is its input impedance?

SOLUTION

The power delivered to the load P_L is the difference between incident power and reflected power. If E_1 represents the rms value of incident voltage and E_2 represents the rms value of the reflected voltage, in a 50-ohm system

$$P_L = \frac{E_1{}^2 - E_2{}^2}{50}$$

But the voltage standing-wave ratio (*VSWR*) is defined by

$$VSWR = \frac{E_1 + E_2}{E_1 - E_2}$$

The minimum voltage is $E_1 - E_2$ so that

$$E_1 - E_2 = 120 \text{ v.}$$

and

$$E_1 + E_2 = VSWR(E_1 - E_2)$$
$$= 2.0(120) = 240 \text{ v.}$$

From these two equations

$$E_1 = \frac{(E_1 - E_2) + (E_1 + E_2)}{2} = \frac{120 + 240}{2} = 60 + 120 = 180 \text{ v.}$$

and

$$E_2 = 60 \text{ v.}$$

so that

$$P_L = \frac{(180)^2 - (60)^2}{50}$$
$$= 649 - 72 = 577 \text{ watts} \qquad \text{ANS.}$$

The antenna impedance may be found using the equation

$$Z = Z_o \left[\frac{1 - [(VSWR - 1)/(VSWR + 1)]/2\beta l}{1 + [(VSWR - 1)/(VSWR + 1)]/2\beta l} \right]$$

where βl has been given as 0.4 wavelengths. The distance in wavelengths is converted to radians or degrees.

$$\beta l = 0.4(2\pi) = 0.8\pi \text{ radians}$$
$$= 0.8\pi\left(\frac{360}{2\pi}\right) = 144 \text{ degrees}$$

The antenna impedance is

$$Z = 50\left[\frac{1 - [(2-1)/(2+1)]/2(144°)}{1 + [(2-1)/(2+1)]/2(144°)} \right]$$
$$= 50\left[\frac{1 - 0.333/288}{1 + 0.333/288} \right]$$
$$= 50\left[\frac{1.000 - 0.103 + j0.316}{1.000 + 0.103 - j0.316} \right]$$
$$= 50\left[\frac{0.897 + j0.316}{1.103 - j0.316} \right]$$
$$= 50\left[\frac{0.952/19.4}{1.146/{-16.0}} \right]$$
$$= 41.5/35.4 \text{ ohms} \qquad \text{ANS.}$$
$$= 33.8 + j24 \text{ ohms} \qquad \text{ANS.}$$

8–4

An open-wire, dissipationless transmission line has a characteristic resistance of 200 ohms. When a certain load is connected to this line and power is supplied at 600 Mc, a voltage minimum results at a point 22.5 cm from the load and the voltage standing-wave-ratio is 2.16.

(a) Calculate the impedance of the load.

(b) If a short-circuited stub is used to match the load to the line, calculate the length of the shortest stub and its nearest position to the load.

SOLUTION

(a) The impedance at a point on a mismatched line toward the load from a voltage minimum is

$$Z = Z_o\left[\frac{1 - |K|/2\beta l}{1 + |K|/2\beta l}\right]$$

where

$$Z_o = 200 \text{ ohms}$$

and

$$|K| = \frac{VSWR - 1}{VSWR + 1}$$
$$= \frac{2.16 - 1}{2.16 + 1} = \frac{1.16}{3.16} = 0.367$$

and

$$\beta = \frac{2\pi}{\lambda}$$

For an open wire line $v = c$ so that

$$\lambda = \frac{c}{f}$$
$$= \frac{3 \times 10^{10} \text{ cm/sec}}{600 \times 10^6 \text{ cps}} = 50 \text{ cm}.$$

then

$$2\beta l = 2\left(\frac{2\pi}{50}\right)22.5 = 1.8\pi \text{ radians}$$
$$= 324° \text{ or } -36°$$

Then

$$Z = 200\left[\frac{1 - 0.367/\underline{-36°}}{1 + 0.367/\underline{-36°}}\right]$$
$$= 200\left[\frac{1 - 0.297 + j0.216}{1 + 0.297 - j0.216}\right]$$

$$= 200 \left[\frac{0.703 + j0.216}{1.297 - j0.216} \right]$$

$$= 200 \left[\frac{0.735/17.0}{1.31/-9.5} \right]$$

$$= 112/26.5 \text{ ohms} \qquad \text{ANS.}$$

$$= Z_L$$

(b) The position and length of a stub may be found using the derived equations. The distance from the load to the stub is βl given by

$$\tan \beta l = \frac{b \pm \sqrt{g[(g-1)^2 + b^2]}}{(g^2 - g + b^2)}$$

$$g + jb = \frac{1}{(Z_L/Z_o)} = \frac{Z_o}{Z_L} = \frac{200}{112/26.5}$$

$$= 1.788/-26.5 = 1.60 - j0.80$$

$$\tan \beta l = \frac{-0.80 \pm \sqrt{1.60[(0.60)^2 + (0.80)^2]}}{(1.60)^2 - 1.60 + (0.80)^2}$$

$$= \frac{-0.80 \pm \sqrt{1.60[0.36 + 0.64]}}{2.56 - 1.60 + 0.64}$$

$$= \frac{-0.80 \pm 1.267}{1.60} = 0.292$$

$$\beta l = 16.3° = 0.0905\pi \text{ radians}$$

Thus

$$l = \frac{0.0905\pi}{\beta}$$

and

$$\beta = \frac{2\pi}{\lambda}$$

so that

$$l = \frac{0.0905\pi\lambda}{2\pi} = 0.0453 \text{ wavelength}$$

But if $f = 600 \times 10^6$ cps the wavelength λ is

$$\lambda = \frac{c}{f} = \frac{3 \times 10^{10}}{6 \times 10^8} = 50 \text{ cm}$$

Thus

$$l = 0.0453(50) = 2.265 \text{ cm} \qquad \text{ANS.}$$

The susceptance at the stub point is found by evaluating the following

$$b' = \frac{b + (1 - g^2 - b^2) \tan \beta l - b \tan^2 \beta l}{1 - 2b \tan \beta l + (g^2 + b^2) \tan^2 \beta l}$$

$$= \frac{-0.80 + [1 - (1.60)^2 - (0.80)^2]0.292 + 0.80(0.292)^2}{1 + 2(0.80)(0.292) + [(1.60)^2 + (0.80)^2](0.292)^2}$$

$$= \frac{-0.80 - 0.643 + 0.068}{1.0 + 0.467 + 0.272} = \frac{-1.375}{1.739} = -0.79$$

Hence this short-circuited stub must add a normalized susceptance of +0.79 mhos. For such a stub

$$\frac{Y_{sc}}{Y_o} = -j \cot \beta l = +j0.79$$

$$\cot \beta l = -0.79$$

$$\beta l = 128.2° = 0.713\pi \text{ radians}$$

$$l = \frac{0.713\pi}{\beta} = \frac{0.713\pi\lambda}{2\pi} = 0.356 \text{ wavelengths}$$

$$= 0.356(50) = 17.8 \text{ cm.} \qquad \text{ANS.}$$

Summary:

(a) The load impedance is 112/26.5 ohms.

(b) A short-circuited stub 17.8 cm long is located 2.265 cm from the load to result in an impedance-matched transmission line.

Alternate Solution: Use Smith Chart

1. The position of a voltage minimum is represented by the points on the zero reactance line between 0.0 and 1.0 normalized resistance component. This particular point is plotted at 1 where the normalized resistive component r is

$$r = \frac{1}{VSWR} = \frac{1}{2.16} = 0.463$$

2. The actual load impedance is obtained by traversing the $VSWR = 2.16$ circle from point 1 in a direction toward the load a distance of 22.5 cm. The wave length λ is

$$\lambda = \frac{c}{f} = \frac{3 \times 10^{10}}{6 \times 10^8} = 50 \text{ cm.}$$

so that the distance is

$$\text{distance between minimum and load} = \frac{22.5}{50} = 0.45 \text{ wave lengths}$$

The actual load impedance is plotted as point 2 and is read as $0.5 + j0.25$ ohms (normalized).

$$Z_L = 200(0.5 + j0.25)$$
$$= 100 + j50$$
$$= 112/26.5 \text{ ohms} \qquad \text{ANS.}$$

3. The matching stub is found by first inverting the load impedance

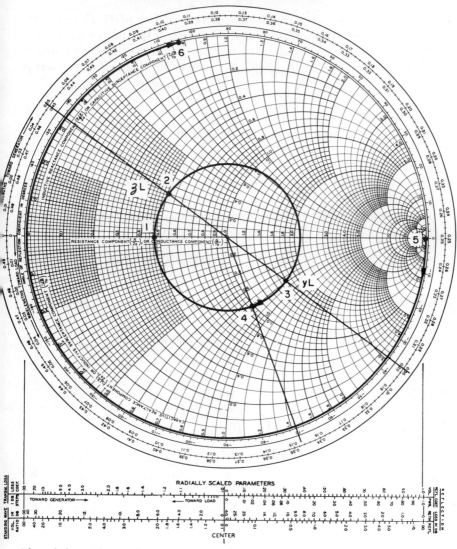

Adapted from Electronics, *Vol. 17, No. 1, pp. 130–133, 318–325, Jan. 1944.*
Copyright 1949 by Kay Electric Co., Pine Brook, N.J.

to its admittance shown as point 3 and read as $1.6 - j0.8$ mhos
(normalized).

4. The 2.16-*VSWR* circle is traversed toward the generator until the
normalized conductance is unity, shown as point 4, where the admittance is $1.0 - j0.77$ mhos. The distance travelled is

$$0.20 - 0.155 = 0.045 \text{ wavelengths} = 50(0.045) = 2.25 \text{ cm} \qquad \text{ANS.}$$

from the load to the stub location.

5. The required stub is one having a susceptance of +0.77 mhos. Its length is found by starting at a short circuit (point 5) and traversing the outside of the chart toward the generator to point 6 where the susceptance is the required value. The distance traversed is

$$0.25 + 0.105 = 0.355 \text{ wave lengths}$$
$$= 50(0.355) = 17.75 \text{ cm.}$$ ANS.

which is the length of the required stub.

8–5

When an unknown circuit element is connected as a load to one end of a transmission line having a characteristic resistance of 200 ohms and operated at 500 Mc, a voltage minimum of 4 v. results at a point 20 cm from the load. The voltage maximum adjacent to this minimum has a value of 20 v.

Calculate the effective impedance of the load at 500 Mc.

SOLUTION

The impedance of the load may be calculated using the formula

$$Z = Z_o \left[\frac{1 - |K|/2\beta l}{1 + |K|/2\beta l} \right]$$

where

$$|K| = \frac{VSWR - 1}{VSWR + 1}$$

$$VSWR = \frac{V_{\max}}{V_{\min}} = \frac{20}{4} = 5.0$$

so that

$$|K| = \frac{5 - 1}{5 + 1} = \frac{4}{6} = 0.667$$

and

$$Z_o = 200 \text{ ohms}$$

and

$$2\beta l = 2\left(\frac{2\pi}{\lambda}\right) l$$

$$= 2\left(\frac{2\pi f l}{c}\right)$$

$$= \frac{4\pi (500 \times 10^6)(20)}{3 \times 10^{10}}$$

$$= 4.19 \text{ radians} = 240 \text{ degrees}$$

Thus

$$Z = 200 \left[\frac{1 - 0.667/240}{1 + 0.667/240} \right]$$

$$= 200 \left[\frac{1 + 0.333 + j0.577}{1 - 0.333 - j0.577} \right]$$

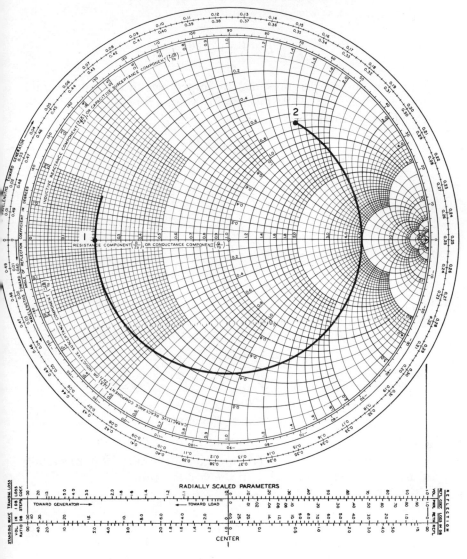

Adapted from Electronics, *Vol. 17, No. 1, pp. 130–133, 318–325, Jan. 1944.*
Copyright 1949 by Kay Electric Co., Pine Brook, N.J.

$$= 200 \left[\frac{1.333 + j0.577}{0.667 - j0.577} \right]$$

$$= 200 \left[\frac{1.455/\underline{23.4}}{0.882/\underline{-40.9}} \right]$$

$$= 330/\underline{64.3} \text{ ohms}$$

$$= 143 + j297 \text{ ohms} \qquad\qquad \text{ANS.}$$

Alternate Solution Using the Smith Chart:

The *VSWR* is

$$VSWR = \frac{V_{max}}{V_{min}} = \frac{20}{4} = 5.0$$

Point 1 on the chart represents the impedance at the voltage minimum with a 5.0:1 *VSWR*. The load is located 20 cm away. This distance in wavelengths is

$$\text{distance} = \frac{l}{\lambda}$$

$$= \frac{20}{\lambda}$$

But

$$\lambda = \frac{c}{f}$$

Hence

$$\text{distance} = \frac{fl}{c} = \frac{5(10^8)(20)}{3(10^{10})} = \frac{1}{3} \text{ wavelength}$$

Point 2 represents a travel along the line of one-third wavelength toward the load at a constant 5.0:1 *VSWR*.

The normalized impedance at point 2 is read to be
$$z_L = 0.71 + j1.49$$
or
$$Z_L = Z_0 z_L$$
$$= 200(0.71 + j1.49)$$
$$= 142 + j298 \text{ ohms} \qquad \text{ANS.}$$

9–1

A time of 10 milliseconds is required for the current to reach 90% of its final (steady state) value in the circuit below.

$E = 10$ v.

$R = 5$ ohms

Switch S_1 was closed at time $t = 0$ with no current flow in the circuit.

(a) What is the time constant in seconds for the circuit?

(b) If $R = 10$ ohms, what is the value of L?

(c) What value of capacitance should be inserted in series with the resistance and inductance of part (b) in order that the frequency of oscillation of resulting current flow be 10^4 cps?

SOLUTION

(a) The expression for current in the circuit after the switch is closed is

$$i = \frac{E}{R}(1 - \epsilon^{-t/\tau})$$

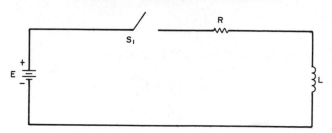

for

$$i = 0.9\frac{E}{R}$$

$$0.9\frac{E}{R} = \frac{E}{R}(1 - \epsilon^{-t/\tau})$$

$$\epsilon^{-t/\tau} = 0.1$$

$$\frac{t}{\tau} = 2.3$$

$$\tau = \frac{10 \times 10^{-3} \text{ sec}}{2.3} = 4.34 \text{ milliseconds} \qquad \text{ANS.}$$

(b) The value of the time constant τ is

$$\tau = \frac{L}{R}$$

$$L = \tau R = (0.00434)(10) = 0.0434 \text{ henrys} \qquad \text{ANS.}$$

(c) The frequency of osciallation is

$$f_o = \frac{1}{2\pi\sqrt{LC}}$$

Thus

$$C = \frac{1}{4\pi^2 f_o^2 L} = \frac{1}{4\pi^2 (10^4)^2 (0.0434)} = 0.00584 \text{ microfarad} \qquad \text{ANS.}$$

9–2

For the circuit shown develop a functional relationship between current and time at $t = 0$ and $t > 0$. The switch closes at $t = 0$ after having been opened for a long time.

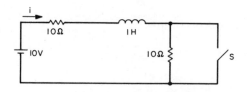

SOLUTION

The differential equation for the circuit is

$$E = Ri + L\frac{di}{dt}$$
$$= (R + LD)i$$

The total solution consists of a steady-state and a transient solution

$$i = i_S + i_T$$
$$= B_1 + B_2\epsilon^{rt}$$

But after the switch has been closed, from the auxiliary equation

$$R + LD = 0$$

or

$$R + Lr = 0$$

or

$$r = -\frac{R}{L}$$
$$= -\frac{10}{1} = -10$$

and

$$B_1 = \frac{E}{R}$$
$$= \frac{10}{10} = 1$$

Hence

$$i = 1 + B_2\epsilon^{-10t}$$

At $t = 0^+$ the current i is the same as at $t = 0^-$. But

$$i(t = 0^-) = \frac{E}{R} = \frac{10}{20} = \frac{1}{2}$$

Hence at $t = 0^+$

$$\frac{1}{2} = 1 + B_2$$

or

$$B_2 = -\frac{1}{2}$$

The total solution becomes

$$i = 1 - \frac{1}{2}\epsilon^{-10t}$$ ANS.

9–3

The ideal switch S is closed until steady-state conditions are established. Then, at an instant of time designated as $t = 0$, the switch is
instantaneously opened. Find the value of $i(t)$ at a time 5.1 sec after
the switch is opened.

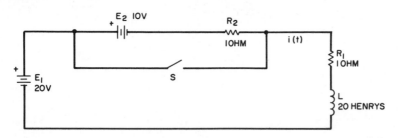

SOLUTION

Solve the differential equation starting at $t = 0$. The loop equation is

$$E = v_{R_1} + v_{R_2} + v_L$$
$$20 - 10 = i(t)[1 + 1] + 20\frac{di(t)}{dt}$$
$$10 = [2 + 20D]i(t)$$

The total solution consists of a steady-state current i_S and a trans-
ient current, i_T.
$$i(t) = i_S + i_T$$
The forms of solution are
$$i_S = B_1$$
and
$$i_T = B_2\epsilon^{rt}$$
But
$$r = -\frac{2}{20} = -\frac{1}{10}$$
Hence
$$i(t) = B_1 + B_2\epsilon^{-t/10}$$

The steady-state solution is determined by substituting i_S into the
differential equation and solving. This yields.
$$10 = 2B_1 + 0$$
Hence
$$B_1 = \frac{10}{2} = 5$$

so that

$$i(t) = 5 + B_2 \epsilon^{-t/10}$$

At time $t = 0^+$, just after switching, the inductor current is the same as it was at $t = 0^-$. But

$$i(t = 0^-) = \frac{E_1}{R_1}$$

$$= \frac{20}{1} = 20 \text{ amp}$$

Hence

$$20 = 5 + B_2$$

or

$$B_2 = 15$$

so that

$$i(t) = 5 + 15\epsilon^{-t/10}$$

At $t = 5.1$ sec

$$\begin{aligned} i(5.1 \text{ sec}) &= 5 + 15\epsilon^{-5.1/10} \\ &= 5 + 15\epsilon^{-0.51} \\ &= 5 + 15(0.601) \\ &= 5 + 9.01 = 14.01 \text{ amp} \end{aligned} \qquad \text{ANS.}$$

9–4

The ideal switch S is initially open. After steady-state conditions are established, the switch is closed at a given instant of time. Compute the value of the current $i_C(t)$ at 4.5 sec after the switch is closed. Assume E is an ideal battery.

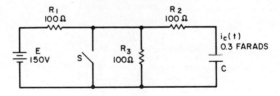

SOLUTION

After the switch is closed the differential equation for the loop containing C is

$$v_C + v_{R_2} = 0$$

$$\frac{1}{C} \int i_C(t) \, dt + R_2 i_C(t) = 0$$

This may be differentiated to obtain

$$\frac{1}{C}i_C + R_2\frac{di_C}{dt} = 0$$

$$\left[\frac{1}{C} + R_2D\right]i_C = 0$$

the solution of which is

$$i_C = B\epsilon^{rt}$$

where from the auxiliary equation $1/C + R_2r = 0$

$$r = -\frac{1}{R_2C}$$

$$= \frac{-1}{100(0.3)} = -\frac{1}{30}$$

At the instant after switching $t = 0^+$ the current will be the capacitor voltage divided by the resistance

$$i_C(t = 0^+) = B = \frac{v_C}{R_2}$$

But the voltage at $t = 0^+$ is the same as at $t = 0^-$. At $t = 0^-$ no current flows in the capacitor hence the voltage across R_3 is the voltage on the capacitor.

$$v_{R_3} = \frac{ER_3}{R_1 + R_3}$$

$$= \frac{150(100)}{100 + 100}$$

$$= 150\left(\frac{1}{2}\right) = 75 \text{ v.}$$

Thus

$$B = \frac{75}{100} = 0.75$$

and

$$i_C = 0.75\epsilon^{-t/30}$$

Hence at $t = 4.5$ sec

$$i_C = 0.75\epsilon^{-4.5/30}$$
$$= 0.75\epsilon^{-0.15}$$
$$= 0.75(0.861)$$
$$= 0.646 \text{ amp} \qquad \text{ANS.}$$

9–5

Determine the current as a function of time $i(t)$ in the following circuit. The ideal switch is closed at $t = 0$. Determine the peak value and the time after switching at which it occurs.

$$e(t) = 10\epsilon^{-5t}$$

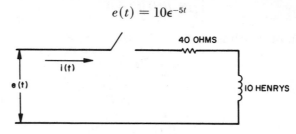

SOLUTION

The current may be determined as the solution to the loop differential equation.

The loop equation is

$$e(t) = v_R + v_L$$

$$10\epsilon^{-5t} = 40i(t) + 10\frac{di(t)}{dt}$$

In operator form the loop equation is

$$10\epsilon^{-5t} = (40 + 10D)i(t)$$

The transient solution i_T is of the form

$$i_T = B_1\epsilon^{rt}$$

The value of r is determined from the auxiliary equation $40 + 10r = 0$

$$r = -\frac{40}{10} = -4$$

Hence

$$i_T = B_1\epsilon^{-4t}$$

The form of the steady-state solution i_S is

$$i_S = B_2\epsilon^{-5t}$$

This is substituted into the differential equation to obtain

$$10\epsilon^{-5t} = 40B_2\epsilon^{-5t} + 10(-5)B_2\epsilon^{-5t}$$
$$= (40 - 50)B_2\epsilon^{-5t}$$

from which

$$10 = -10B_2$$

or

$$B_2 = -1$$

The total general solution is

$$i(t) = i_S + i_T$$
$$= -\epsilon^{-5t} + B_1\epsilon^{-4t}$$

The current in the inductor cannot change instantaneously so that at the instant after switching $t = 0^+$ the current is the same as at the instant before switching $t = 0^-$. So

$$i(t = 0^+) = i(t = 0^-) = 0$$

This requires that

$$0 = -1 + B_1$$

or

$$B_1 = 1$$

The complete solution is

$$i(t) = -\epsilon^{-5t} + \epsilon^{-4t} \qquad \text{ANS.}$$

The time at which the peak current occurs may be found by setting the time derivative of the current equal to zero and solving for the time. The peak current is determined by evaluating $i(t)$ at the time determined

$$\frac{di(t)}{dt} = 5\epsilon^{-5t} - 4\epsilon^{-4t} = 0$$

The time is determined as follows

$$5\epsilon^{-5t} = 4\epsilon^{-4t}$$

$$(5\epsilon^{-5t})(\epsilon^{5t}) = (4\epsilon^{-4t})(\epsilon^{5t})$$

$$5 = 4\epsilon^t$$

$$\epsilon^t = \frac{5}{4} = 1.25$$

$$t = 0.223 \text{ sec} \qquad \text{ANS.}$$

The peak current i_p is

$$i_p = -\epsilon^{-5(0.223)} + \epsilon^{-4(0.223)}$$
$$= -\epsilon^{-1.115} + \epsilon^{-0.892}$$
$$= -0.328 + 0.410$$
$$= 0.082 \text{ amp} \qquad\qquad \text{ANS.}$$

9–6

Certain electric welders have a basic circuit as shown below where S is a switch, operated by an automatic timer, which closes the circuit at any desired point on the 60-cycle, sinusoidal wave of e.

(a) Calculate the magnitude of the transient current resulting when S closes as e is passing through its peak of 100 v.

(b) Calculate the angle at which S should close in order that the transient be zero.

SOLUTION

The current $i(t)$ may be determined as the solution of a differential equation.

The loop equation, after closing the switch, for the circuit is

$$e = v_R + v_L$$
$$= i(t)R + L\frac{di(t)}{dt}$$
$$= [R + LD]i(t)$$

The transient solution i_T is of the form

$$i_T = B_1\epsilon^{rt}$$

But from the auxiliary equation in D, $R + Lr = 0$

$$r = -\frac{R}{L}$$

so that

$$i_T = B_1\epsilon^{-Rt/L}$$

Let the driving function be written with an arbitrary phase angle ϕ as

$$e = 100 \sin (2\pi ft + \phi)$$

$$= 100 \sin (377t + \phi)$$
$$= 100 \sin (\omega t + \phi)$$

The steady-state solution i_S is of the form

$$i_S = B_2 \sin (\omega t + \phi + \psi)$$

If this is substituted into the differential equation, the result is

$$100 \sin (\omega t + \phi) = RB_2 \sin (\omega t + \phi + \psi) + \omega LB_2 \cos (\omega t + \phi + \psi)$$
$$= (R + j\omega L)B_2 \sin (\omega t + \phi + \psi)$$

From which

$$B_2 = \frac{100}{R + j\omega L}$$

and

$$\psi = -\tan^{-1} \frac{\omega L}{R}$$

Hence,

$$i(t) = i_S + i_T$$
$$= \frac{100}{|R + j\omega L|} \sin (\omega t + \phi - \tan^{-1} \omega L/R) + B_1 \epsilon^{-Rt/L}$$

But at $t = 0^+$, $i(t) = 0$ so that

$$B_1 = \frac{100}{|R + j\omega L|} \sin (\phi - \tan^{-1} \omega L/R)$$

This expression for B_1 gives the magnitude of the transient current.

$$B_1 = \frac{100}{|0.1 + j(377)(0.001)|} \sin \left[\phi - \tan^{-1} \frac{(377)(0.001)}{0.1} \right]$$
$$= \frac{100}{|0.1 + j0.377|} \sin \left[\phi - \tan^{-1} \frac{(0.377)}{(0.1)} \right]$$
$$= \frac{100}{0.391} \sin (\phi - 75.15°) = 256 \sin (\phi - 75.15°)$$

(a) In order that the voltage e passes through its peak value at the instant of closing the switch $t = 0$, the angle ϕ must be either 90° or 270°. In either case the magnitude of B_1 is

$$B_1 = 256 \sin (90 - 75.15)$$
$$= 256 \sin (14.85°)$$
$$= 65.6 \text{ amp} \qquad \text{ANS.}$$

(b) For the transient to be zero

$$\phi - 75.15 = 0$$

or

$$\phi = 75.15° \qquad \text{ANS.}$$

9–7

The circuit shown is that of a simple integrator. For a given repetitive input voltage e_1 the output voltage e_2 is also shown.

Draw the exact waveforms of i and e_1 and calculate the significant values in these waves.

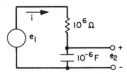

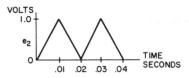

SOLUTION

The current may be found from the output voltage waveform. The input voltage is the sum of the output voltage plus the resistor voltage. The voltage across a capacitor is the ratio of charge to capacity or

$$v_C = \frac{q(t)}{C}$$

but

$$q(t) = \int i(t)\,dt$$

In the range $0 \le t \le 0.01$ sec

$$v_C = \frac{1.0t}{0.01} = 100t$$

so that

$$q(t) = Cv_C$$
$$= 10^{-6}(100t)$$

or

$$i(t) = \frac{dq(t)}{dt}$$
$$= 100 \times 10^{-6} \text{ amp}$$

In the range $0.01 \le t \le 0.02$ sec
$$v_C = -100t$$
$$q(t) = -100 \times 10^{-6}t$$
$$i(t) = -100 \times 10^{-6} \text{ amp}$$

In the range $0.02 \le t \le 0.03$ sec, $i(t)$ is the same as in the range $0 \le t \le 0.01$ sec; in the range $0.03 \le t \le 0.04$ sec, $i(t)$ is the same as in the range $0.01 \leq t \leq 0.02$ sec. Successive complete cycles are the same as the first complete cycle.

The input voltage e_1 is given by

$$e_1 = e_2(t) + i(t)R$$

The desired quantities are plotted as shown.

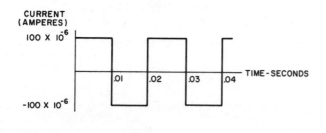

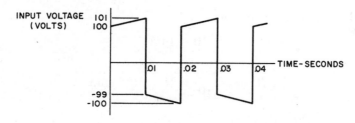

9–8

The voltage e impressed on the circuit shown, varies as indicated. Calculate the value of the steady-state or forced current i.

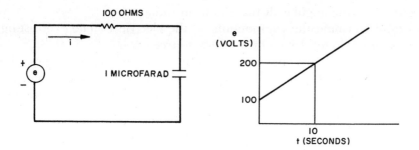

SOLUTION

The solution may be found by assuming a solution and evaluating its constants by substituting the solution in the differential equation.

The loop equation is

$$e(t) = v_R + v_C$$
$$= iR + \frac{1}{C} \int i\,dt$$

The actual values are

$$100 + 10t = 100i + 10^6 \int i\,dt$$

This equation may be differentiated to yield

$$10 = 100\frac{di}{dt} + 10^6 i$$

The steady-state solution is of the form

$$i_S = B$$

which is evaluated as follows

$$10 = 10^6 B$$

or

$$B = i_S = \frac{10}{10^6} = 10 \times 10^{-6} \text{ amp} \qquad\qquad \text{ANS.}$$

9–9

A torque $T = 5{,}000$ dyne-cm is applied to a certain mechanical system which has a response given by the relation

$$T = 5\frac{d^2\theta}{dt^2} + 20{,}000\frac{d\theta}{dt} + 0.2 \times 10^8 \theta$$

where θ is the angular displacement in radians.

(a) Determine the components of the electrical analog consisting of a series circuit driven by a 100-v. source.

(b) Show how the angular velocity of the mechanical system may be determined in the analog circuit by means of a voltage measurement.

(c) Determine whether the mechanical system is over-damped, critically-damped, or under-damped.

SOLUTION

Let the voltage be the analog of the torque and charge be the analog of the angular displacement.

The analog consists of a series R-L-C circuit driven by a battery as shown.

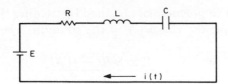

The equation for this circuit is

$$E = Ri(t) + L\frac{di(t)}{dt} + \frac{1}{C}\int i(t)\,dt$$

$$= R\frac{dq}{dt} + L\frac{d^2q}{dt^2} + \frac{q}{C}$$

The equation for the mechanical system is

$$5000 = 5\frac{d^2\theta}{dt^2} + 20{,}000\frac{d\theta}{dt} + 0.2 \times 10^8\theta$$

and for the electrical system with a 100-v. battery the equation is

$$100 = L\frac{d^2q}{dt^2} + R\frac{dq}{dt} + \frac{1}{C}q$$

If the charge in coulombs is to be the analog of angular displacement in radians, the mechanical equation must be scaled to the electrical equation by dividing all coefficients by 50. The scaled mechanical equation becomes

$$100 = 0.10\frac{d^2\theta}{dt^2} + 400\frac{d\theta}{dt} + 0.4 \times 10^6\theta$$

Hence the values of the electrical analog are

$$L = 0.10 \text{ henry}$$
$$R = 400 \text{ ohms}$$
$$C = \frac{1}{0.4 \times 10^6} = 2.5 \times 10^{-6} \text{ farads} \qquad \text{ANS.}$$

(b) The angular velocity of the mechanical system is $d\theta/dt$. Its analog in the electrical system is dq/dt which is the current. Hence, the current is determined by measuring the voltage across the resistor. Division of this voltage by the value of the resistance yields the current and its analog, the mechanical angular velocity.

(c) The differential equation, written in operator form is

$$100 = \left(LD^2 + RD + \frac{1}{C}\right)q(t)$$

The roots of the polynomial obtained by treating the operator as a variable determine the character of the solution. The roots are

$$r = \frac{-R \pm \sqrt{R^2 - 4L/C}}{2L}$$

The character of the solution is contained in the radical

$$\sqrt{R^2 - \frac{4L}{C}}$$
$$= \sqrt{(400)^2 - \frac{4(0.10)}{2.5 \times 10^{-6}}}$$
$$= \sqrt{160,000 - 160,000} = 0 \qquad \text{ANS.}$$

Hence, the system is critically damped.

9–10

One turn of bar copper is produced by cutting a copper washer along a radius and spreading the ends. The washer is cut from soft-drawn copper having a resistivity at 20° C of 1.724×10^{-6} ohm-cm. The washer is 0.125 in thick and has inside and outside diameters of 1 and 9 in, respectively.

Calculate the exact resistance between the ends of the turn, to direct current, taking into account the non-uniform current distribution. Assume the contact at the ends of the turn to be perfect over the entire cross section.

SOLUTION

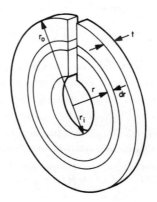

The resistance of a conductor may be calculated from

$$\text{Resistance} = R = \frac{\rho l}{A}$$

or the conductance G is

$$G = \frac{1}{R} = \frac{A}{\rho l}$$

In the incremental ring shown having a conductance dG

$$A = tdr$$

and

$$l = 2\pi r$$

or

$$dG = \frac{tdr}{\rho 2\pi r}$$

The total conductance between the ends is

$$G = \int_{r_i}^{r_o} \frac{tdr}{\rho 2\pi r}$$
$$= \frac{t}{2\pi\rho} \int_{r_i}^{r_o} \frac{dr}{r}$$
$$= \frac{t}{2\pi\rho} \Big[ln\ r \Big]_{r_i}^{r_o}$$
$$= \frac{t}{2\pi\rho} \Big(ln\ \frac{r_o}{r_i} \Big)$$
$$= \frac{0.125(2.54)}{2\pi(1.724 \times 10^{-6})}\ ln\ 9 = 64{,}500 \text{ mhos.}$$

The total resistance is

$$R = \frac{1}{G} = \frac{1}{64{,}500} = 15.6 \times 10^{-6} \text{ ohms} \qquad \text{ANS.}$$

9–11

A capacitor consists of two parallel, plane electrodes each of which has an area of 100 sq cm. The dielectric which separates these electrodes is 0.1 cm thick and has a dielectric constant which varies linearly from 2 at one electrode to 8 at the other.

Calculate the capacitance of this capacitor when fringing is neglected.

SOLUTION

cf: [*Measurements* (15)]
The capacitance of a capacitor is given by

$$C = 0.0885K \frac{S}{\delta} \text{ micromicrofarad}$$

The total capacitance is made up of a large number of incremental capacitors, each of thickness $d\delta$. For N capacitors in series, the inverse total capacitance equals the sum of the inverse capacitances of the various capacitors. Thus

$$\frac{1}{C_T} = \sum_{n=1}^{N} \frac{1}{C_n}$$

But

$$\frac{1}{C_n} = \frac{d\delta}{0.0885K(\delta)S}$$

where

$$K(\delta) = 2 + 60\delta$$

The series may be converted to an integration by letting N go to infinity. Hence

$$\frac{1}{C_T} = \int_0^{0.1} \frac{d\delta}{0.0885S(2 + 60\delta)}$$
$$= \frac{1}{0.0885(100)} \int_0^{0.1} \frac{d\delta}{2 + 60\delta}$$

This may be evaluated using an integral table. The form used is

$$\int \frac{dx}{a + bx} = \frac{1}{b} \ln(a + bx)$$

so that

$$\frac{1}{C_T} = \frac{1}{8.85} \left[\frac{1}{60} \ln(2 + 60\delta) \right]_0^{0.1}$$
$$= \frac{1}{60(8.85)} \left[\ln 8 - \ln 2 \right]$$
$$= \frac{1}{60(8.85)} \ln \frac{8}{2}$$
$$= \frac{1.388}{60(8.85)}$$

Hence

$$C_T = \frac{60(8.85)}{1.388} = 383 \text{ micromicrofarads} \qquad \text{ANS.}$$

9–12

The armature winding of a 4-pole, d-c shunt dynamo has a simplex lap winding arranged in two layers and located in the 58 slots on the armature. Each slot contains 8 conductors. When this machine is operated at 720 rpm with a shunt field current of 10 amp, the open-circuit voltage across the armature is 226 v. The number of turns on each shunt pole is 280.

Calculate the total inductance of the shunt field circuit under these conditions.

SOLUTION

The relationship for inductance is

$$L = \frac{N\phi}{10^8 I} p \text{ henrys}$$

where

$$N = \text{turns/pole} = 280$$
$$\phi = \text{flux/pole} = ?$$
$$I = \text{current} = 10 \text{ amp}$$
$$p = \text{number of poles} = 4$$

But

$$E_G = \frac{pZ\phi n}{10^8 b 60} \text{ volts}$$

where

$E_G = $ open-circuit voltage $= 226$ v.
$Z = $ total number of armature conductors $= 58(8) = 464$
$\phi = $ flux/pole
$n = $ armature speed $= 720$ rpm
$b = $ number of paths $= p$

so that

$$\phi = \frac{E_G 10^8 b 60}{pZn}$$

Thus

$$L = \frac{NpE_G 10^8 b 60}{10^8 IpZn}$$

or

$$L = \frac{280(4)(226)(10^8)(4)(60)}{10^8(10)(4)(464)(720)} = 4.55 \text{ henrys}$$ ANS.

9–13

A closed iron-cored reactor has a winding of 250 turns and a cross-sectional area of iron of 4 sq in. This reactor is to be changed by the insertion of an air gap in the core so that its reactance will be 30 ohms at 5 amp and 60 cps. The saturation curve for the iron may be taken as a straight line passing through the point $B = 45,000$ lines/sq in and $NI = 700$ ampere-turns.

Calculate the length of the necessary air gap, neglecting the effects of fringing.

SOLUTION

This is a magnetic circuit problem in which the total reluctance must be adjusted to provide the proper core flux to result in the desired inductance and hence inductive reactance.

The required inductance is

$$L = \frac{\text{reactance}}{\text{angular frequency}}$$
$$= \frac{30}{2\pi 60} = \frac{30}{377} = 0.0795 \text{ henry}$$

But

$$L = \frac{N\phi}{10^8 I} = \frac{NBA}{10^8 I}$$

or

$$B = \frac{10^8 LI}{NA} = \frac{10^8(0.0795)(5)}{250(4)} = 3.975 \times 10^4 \text{ lines/sq in}$$

(Because the iron is linear, one can use rms current and rms flux density.)

The reluctance of the magnetic circuit is defined as the ratio of magnetomotive force to flux

$$\mathfrak{R} = \frac{F}{\phi}$$
$$= \frac{NI}{BA}$$
$$= \frac{250(5)}{3.975 \times 10^4(4)}$$
$$= 7.86 \times 10^{-3}$$

From the given data for the iron core at a flux density of 45,000 lines/sq in, a *MMF* of 700 ampere-turns is required. Hence, at the operating flux density of 39,750 lines/sq in, the iron *MMF*, MMF_I is

$$MMF_I = \frac{700}{45,000}(39,750) = 618 \text{ ampere-turns}$$

However, the total available *MMF* is 1250 ampere-turns. The *MMF* left to magnetize the air gap MMF_A is

$$MMF_A = 1250 - MMF_I$$
$$= 1250 - 618$$
$$= 632 \text{ ampere turns}$$

The reluctance of the air gap neglecting fringing is

$$\Re_A = \frac{l''}{\mu_o A}$$

But

$$\Re_A = \frac{MMF_A}{\phi_A}$$
$$= \frac{632}{(39,750)(4)} = 3.975 \times 10^{-3}$$

and

$$l'' = \mu_o A \Re_A$$

But for air

$$\mu_o = 3.192$$

Hence

$$l'' = (3.192)(4)(3.975 \times 10^{-3})$$
$$= 50.7 \times 10^{-3} \text{ in} \qquad \text{ANS.}$$

9–14

A given series motor has 2 poles with 95 turns per pole, and with the two coils connected in series. The total resistance of the field coils is 3.02 ohms. With a 60-cycle current of 3.55 amp, the voltage drop across the field coils is 62 v.

Assuming sinusoidal flux and current, find:
(a) the field reactance
(b) the field flux per pole.

SOLUTION

(a) The field reactance X is part of the total impedance which is

$$|R + jX| = \frac{V}{I}$$

$$= \frac{62}{3.55} = 17.45 \text{ ohms}$$

$$|R + jX| = \sqrt{R^2 + X^2}$$
$$= \sqrt{(3.02)^2 + X^2} = 17.45$$

From which

$$X = \sqrt{(17.45)^2 - (3.02)^2}$$
$$= \sqrt{305 - 9}$$
$$= \sqrt{296} = 17.21 \text{ ohms} \qquad \text{ANS.}$$

(b) The inductance of the field circuit is

$$L = \frac{N\phi}{10^8 I}$$

and the reactance is

$$2\pi fL = \frac{2\pi fN\phi}{10^8 I} = 17.21$$

To obtain peak flux, peak current is required. Since the two coils are in series the flux is due to the total ampere turns and is the same under each pole.

$$\phi = \frac{10^8 I(17.21)}{2\pi fN(2)} = \frac{10^8(\sqrt{2})(3.55)(17.21)}{2\pi(60)(2)(95)}$$
$$= 121,000 \text{ lines (peak)} \qquad \text{ANS.}$$

9–15

Three straight long circular buses are mounted as shown.

(a) Calculate the magnitudes of the forces per foot of each conductor when the currents in conductors *A*, *B*, and *C* are 30,000, 15,000, and 15,000 amps, respectively, and are directed as shown.

(b) Indicate the direction of these forces.

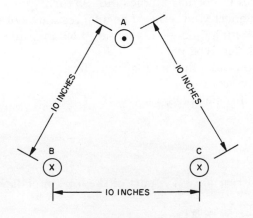

SOLUTION

The expression for the force between parallel current-carrying conductors is

$$\text{Force (pounds)} = \frac{[5.4 \times 10^{-7}][I_1][I_2][\text{length (feet)}]}{\text{Spacing (Inches)}}$$

attractive for I_1 and I_2 in same direction.
Thus for each one-foot length:

$$F_{AB} = \frac{(5.4 \times 10^{-7})(3 \times 10^4)(1.5 \times 10^4)}{10} = 24.3 \text{ lbs repulsion}$$

$$F_{AC} = \frac{(5.4 \times 10^{-7})(3 \times 10^4)(1.5 \times 10^4)}{10} = 24.3 \text{ lbs repulsion}$$

$$F_{BC} = \frac{(5.4 \times 10^{-7})(1.5 \times 10^4)(1.5 \times 10^4)}{10} = 12.15 \text{ lbs attraction}$$

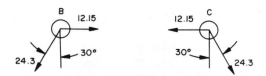

Resultant $A = 2(24.3) \cos 30°$
$\qquad\qquad = 42.1$ lbs vertical (up) ANS.

Resultant B
$\quad F_{\text{Horiz.}} = 12.15 - 24.3 \cos 60°$
$\qquad\quad = 0$
$\quad F_{\text{Vert.}} = 24.3 \sin 60° = 21.05$ lbs downward ANS.

Resultant C
$\quad F_{\text{Horiz.}} = -12.15 + 24.3 \cos 60°$
$\qquad\quad = 0$
$\quad F_{\text{Vert.}} = 24.3 \sin 60°$
$\qquad\quad = 21.05$ lbs downward ANS.

9–16

An ammeter A, a voltmeter V, and wattmeter W, are connected as shown. The wattmeter is uncompensated, and the impedances of its coils may be considered as purely resistive with values of 0.4 and 8000 ohms for the current and voltage coils, respectively. The impedances of the ammeter and voltmeter may also be considered as resistive and their values are 0.1 and 10,000 ohms, respectively.

Calculate the true power delivered to the load when the ammeter, voltmeter, and wattmeter indicate 2.0 amp, 220 v., and 150 watts, respectively.

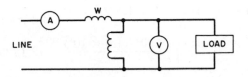

SOLUTION

The power delivered to the load will be the power indicated by the wattmeter less the power consumed by the voltmeter and wattmeter.

The power consumed by the voltmeter is

$$P_V = \frac{(E_V)^2}{R_V}$$
$$= \frac{(220)^2}{10,000}$$
$$= \frac{48,400}{10,000} = 4.84 \text{ watts}$$

The power consumed by the voltage coil of the wattmeter is

$$P_W = \frac{(E_W)^2}{R_W}$$
$$= \frac{(220)^2}{8000}$$
$$= \frac{48,400}{8000} = 6.05 \text{ watts}$$

Hence, the true load power is

$$P_L = 150 - 6.05 - 4.84$$
$$= 139.11 \text{ watts}$$

ANS.

9–17

A 10-ohm resistor carries the output current of a perfect half-wave rectifier. The peak value of each half-wave is 10 amp. The voltage across the resistor is measured by three voltmeters as follows:

(a) A conventional d-c voltmeter with a D'Arsonval movement and a scale indicating volts

(b) A peak-to-peak voltmeter with a scale indicating rms-volts of the equivalent sine wave

(c) A dynamometer voltmeter with a scale indicating rms-values.

Calculate the voltage indicated by each meter, assuming each meter to be perfect.

SOLUTION

The output voltage waveform is as shown. The angular frequency is ω radians per second. The value of E_p the peak voltage is the peak current multiplied by the resistance.

$$E_p = I_M R_L$$
$$= (10)(10) = 100 \text{ v.}$$

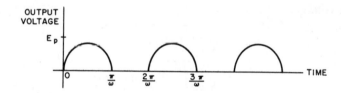

Each segment of the voltage waveform is one-half of a sine wave.

(a) The D'Arsonval meter responds to the average of the waveform. The average voltage E_{av} is

$$E_{av} = \frac{1}{T} \int_0^T e(t)\,dt$$
$$= \frac{\omega}{2\pi} \int_0^{\pi/\omega} E_p \sin \omega t\,dt$$
$$= \frac{\omega}{2\pi} \left[-\frac{E_p}{\omega} \cos \omega t \right]_0^{\pi/\omega}$$
$$= \frac{E_p}{2\pi} \left[-\cos \omega \left(\frac{\pi}{\omega}\right) + \cos 0 \right]$$
$$= \frac{E_p}{2\pi} [1 + 1] = \frac{E_p}{\pi}$$

Hence, the voltmeter reading will be

$$E_{\text{voltmeter}} = \frac{E_p}{\pi}$$

$$= \frac{100}{\pi} = 31.8 \text{ v.} \qquad \text{ANS.}$$

(b) The peak-to-peak voltage E_{pp} of a sine wave in terms of the rms-value of the sinusoid is

$$E_{pp} = 2\sqrt{2}E_{\text{rms}}$$

or

$$E_{\text{rms}} = \frac{E_{pp}}{2\sqrt{2}} = \frac{E_{pp}}{2.828}$$

In this situation, the peak-to-peak voltage is 100 v. so the voltmeter reading will be

$$E_{\text{voltmeter}} = \frac{E_{pp}}{2.828}$$

$$= \frac{100}{2.828} = 35.3 \text{ v.} \qquad \text{ANS.}$$

(c) A dynamometer voltmeter responds to the rms-value of the applied voltage

$$E_{\text{rms}} = \sqrt{\frac{1}{T}\int_o^T [e(t)]^2 dt}$$

$$= \sqrt{\frac{\omega}{2\pi}\int_o^{\pi/\omega} E_p^2 \sin^2 \omega t dt}$$

Using tables of integrals, this is evaluated as

$$E_{\text{rms}} = \sqrt{\frac{\omega}{2\pi}\left(\frac{E_p^2}{2\omega}\right)\left[\omega t - \sin \omega t \cos \omega t\right]_o^{\pi/\omega}}$$

$$= \sqrt{\frac{E_p^2}{4\pi}\left[\omega\left(\frac{\pi}{\omega}\right) - \sin \frac{\omega\pi}{\omega} \cos \frac{\omega\pi}{\omega} + \sin 0 \cos 0\right]}$$

$$= \sqrt{\frac{E_p^2}{4\pi}[\pi - 0 - 0]} = \frac{E_p}{2}$$

Hence the voltmeter reading will be

$$E_{\text{voltmeter}} = \frac{E_p}{2}$$

$$= \frac{100}{2} = 50 \text{ v.} \qquad \text{ANS.}$$

9–18

A motor load on one phase of a 208/120-v., 3-phase, 60-cycle system is measured with these three instruments:

INSTRUMENT	FULL SCALE	% ACCURACY
Ammeter	10 amp	0.5
Voltmeter	250 v.	0.5
Wattmeter	2500 watts	0.25

The measurements are as follows:

Amperes	8.7
Volts	210
Watts	135

(a) With what percentages can the power factor be guaranteed?
(b) How much of the error can be assigned to each instrument?
(c) How much error is possible in the phase angle?

SOLUTION

(a) The power factor is

$$pf = \frac{\text{Power}}{\text{Volt-amperes}}$$

The uncertainty of each reading based on full-scale accuracy is:

$$\text{Wattmeter Error} = (0.0025)(2500) = 6.25 \text{ watts}$$
$$\text{Voltmeter Error} = (0.0050)(250) = 1.25 \text{ v.}$$
$$\text{Ammeter Error} = (0.0050)(10) = 0.05 \text{ amp}$$

Thus the power factor is

$$pf = \frac{135 \pm 6.25}{(210 \pm 1.25)(8.7 \pm .05)}$$

The middle value is

$$pf = \frac{135}{(210)(8.7)} = 0.0738$$

The maximum value is

$$pf = \frac{141.25}{(208.75)(8.65)} = 0.0781$$

The minimum value is

$$pf = \frac{128.75}{(211.25)(8.75)} = 0.0696$$

The power factor then is

$$pf = 0.0738 \pm 0.0043$$

and the percentage error is

$$pf \text{ error} = \frac{(\pm 0.0043)(100)}{0.0738} = \pm 5.83\% \qquad \text{ANS.}$$

(b) The possible error in each instrument is

$$\text{Wattmeter Error} = \frac{(\pm 6.25)(100)}{135} = \pm 4.63\%$$

$$\text{Voltmeter Error} = \frac{(\pm 1.25)(100)}{210} = \pm 0.595\%$$

$$\text{Ammeter Error} = \frac{(\pm 0.05)(100)}{8.7} = \pm 0.575\%$$

Hence the possible error contribution by each instrument is

$$\text{Wattmeter Error} = \frac{(4.65)(100)}{5.83} = 80\% \qquad \text{ANS.}$$

$$\text{Voltmeter Error} = \frac{(0.595)(100)}{5.83} = 10.2\% \qquad \text{ANS.}$$

$$\text{Ammeter Error} = \frac{(0.575)(100)}{5.83} = 9.85\% \qquad \text{ANS.}$$

(c) The power factor angles associated with the possible values are

$$\text{max. angle} = \cos^{-1}(0.0696) = 86.00°$$
$$\text{middle angle} = \cos^{-1}(0.0738) = 85.76°$$
$$\text{minimum angle} = \cos^{-1}(0.0781) = 85.52°$$

The angle error is $\pm 0.24°$ ANS.

or

$$\frac{(\pm 0.24)(100)}{85.76} = \pm 0.280\% \qquad \text{ANS.}$$

9–19

Two types of 100-watt lamps, A and B, are available. Lamp A costs $0.25 each, delivers 18 lumens per watt and has a life of 800 hrs. Lamp B costs $0.20 each, delivers 15 lumens per watt and has a life of 1200 hrs.

Calculate, for each type, the cost of the lamps and power for 10^6 lumen-hours of service when the cost of power is $0.04 per kw.-hr.

SOLUTION

Lamp A: delivers (18 lumens/watt)(100 watts) = 1800 lumens
   life is 800 hrs so output is
$$(1800 \text{ lumens})(800 \text{ hrs}) = 1.44 \times 10^6 \text{ lumen-hrs}$$
   hence one lamp is necessary at cost of \$0.25
   Total hours required for 10^6 lumen-hrs is
$$\frac{10^6 \text{ lumen-hrs}}{1800 \text{ lumens}} = 555 \text{ hrs}$$

   Total energy is
$$\frac{(555)(100)}{1000} = 55.5 \text{ kw-hr}$$

   Cost of energy is
$$(55.5)(\$0.04) = \$2.22$$
   Total cost = \$2.47   ANS.

Lamp B: Delivers (15 lumens/watt)(100 watts) = 1500 lumens
   life is 1200 hrs so output is
$$(1500 \text{ lumens})(1200 \text{ hrs}) = 1.8 \times 10^6 \text{ lumen-hrs}$$
   hence one lamp is necessary at cost of \$0.20
   Total hours for 10^6 lumen-hrs
$$= \frac{10^6}{1500} = 667 \text{ hrs}$$

   Total energy is
$$\frac{(667)(100)}{(1000)} = 66.7 \text{ kw-hr}$$

   Cost of energy is
$$(66.7)(\$0.04) \doteq \$2.67$$
   Total cost = \$2.87   ANS.

Literature Cited

1. *C. R. C. Standard Mathematical Tables.* 12th ed. Formerly "Mathematical Tables" from the *Handbook of Physics and Chemistry.* Cleveland: Chemical Rubber Publishing Company, 1959.
2. Fitzgerald, A. E. and Kingsley, C., *Electric Machinery.* New York: McGraw-Hill Book Company, Inc., 1952.
3. Gardner, M. F. and Barnes, J. L., *Transients in Linear Systems,* Vol. I. New York: John Wiley & Sons, Inc., 1942.
4. Kraus, A. D., *Studying to Pass the Professional Engineers' Licensing Examination.* New York: The Macmillan Company, 1962.
5. Landee, R. W., Davis, D. C., and Albrecht, A. P., *Electronic Designer's Handbook.* New York: McGraw-Hill Book Company, Inc., 1957.

6. Langford-Smith, F., *Radiotron Designer's Handbook*. 4th ed. Harrison, N. J.: Radio Corporation of America, RCA Victor Division, 1953.

7. Liwschitz-Garik, M. and Whipple, C. C., *A-C Machines* (*Electric Machinery*, Vol. II) New York: D. Van Nostrand Co., 1946.

8. M. I. T. Electrical Engineering Staff, *Electric Circuits*. New York: John Wiley & Sons, Inc., 1943.

9. ———, *Magnetic Circuits and Transformers*. New York: John Wiley & Sons, Inc., 1943.

10. Millman, J. and Seely, S., *Electronics*. New York: McGraw-Hill Book Company, Inc., 1941.

11. Moreno, T., *Microwave Transmission Design Data*. New York: Dover Publications, Inc., 1958.

12. Pender, H. and Del Mar, W. A., *Electrical Engineers' Handbook, Electric Power*. 4th ed. New York: John Wiley & Sons, Inc., 1949.

13. Puckstein, A. F. and Lloyd, T. C., *Alternating-Current Machines*. 2nd ed. New York: John Wiley & Sons, Inc., 1942.

14. Ragan, G. L., *Microwave Transmission Circuits* (*M. I. T. Radiation Laboratory Series*, Vol. 9) New York: McGraw-Hill Book Company, Inc., 1948.

15. *Radio Instruments and Measurements*. (National Bureau of Standards Circular C 74). Washington, D. C.: US Government Printing Office, 1937.

16. Reddick, H. W. and Miller, F. H., *Advanced Mathematics for Engineers*. 2nd ed. New York: John Wiley & Sons, Inc., 1947.

17. *Reference Data for Radio Engineers*. 4th ed. New York: International Telephone and Telegraph Corporation, 1956.

18. Ryder, J. D., *Electronic Fundamentals and Applications*. New York: Prentice-Hall, Inc., 1950.

19. ———, *Networks, Lines and Fields*. 2nd ed. New York: Prentice-Hall, Inc., 1955.

20. Sah, A. P., *Fundamentals of Alternating-Current Machines*. New York: McGraw-Hill Book Company, Inc., 1946.

21. Seely, S., *Electron-Tube Circuits*. New York: McGraw-Hill Book Company, Inc., 1950.

22. Siskind, C. S., *Electrical Machines, Direct and Alternating Current*. 2nd ed. McGraw-Hill Book Company, Inc., 1959.

23. Terman, F. E., *Radio Engineering*. 3rd ed. New York: McGraw-Hill Book Company, Inc., 1947.

24. ———, *Radio Engineers Handbook*. New York: McGraw-Hill Book Company, Inc., 1943.

25. Timbie, W. A. and Bush, V., *Principles of Electrical Engineering*. 4th ed. New York: John Wiley & Sons, Inc., 1951.

26. Van Valkenburg, M. E., *Network Analysis*. New York: Prentice-Hall, Inc., 1955.

27. Zobel, O. J., "Theory and design of uniform and composite electric wave filters." Bell System Technical Journal. Vol. 2, p. 1 (1923).

INDEX

383